A Handbook Series on
Electromagnetic Interference and
Compatibility

Volume 7

Electromagnetic Compatibility in Telecommunications

William G. Duff

Interference Control Technologies, Inc.
Gainesville, Virginia

Interference Control Technologies, Inc.
Route 625, Gainesville, VA 22065
TEL: (703) 347-0030   FAX: (703) 347-5813

Library of Congress Catalog Card Number: 88-80525
ISBN: 0-944916-07-4

Dedication

This book is dedicated to two of the most
wonderful people in the world, my parents,

Johnnie Douglas Duff
and
Annetta Rind Duff

Thank you for the love and support you've
given me all these many years.

Other Books in the 12-Volume Series

Table of Contents

Preface

Almost every aspect of modern life is significantly influenced by and depends on the use of the electromagnetic spectrum. This permits production and transmission of electrical power, communications, navigation, radar and the like. Without the use of this valuable and essential natural resource, the basic nature of our society would be completely different.

Electromagnetic compatibility (EMC) is a necessary condition for effective communication-electronic (CE) system performance. EMC is the ability of equipments and systems to function as designed in their intended operational environment without adversely affecting the operation of, or being affected adversely by, other equipments or systems. Thus, the manner and efficiency in which modern life is conducted depends on the ability to achieve and maintain EMC.

In order to permit efficient use of the frequency spectrum, engineers, technicians and users responsible for the planning, design, development, installation and operation of telecommunications systems must have a methodology for achieving EMC. Techniques which permit them to identify, localize and define electromagnetic interference (EMI) problem areas before rather than after they waste time, effort and dollars must be available. More timely and economical corrective measures may then be taken.

The control or reduction of EMI (or its predecessor names, radio noise, electrical noise or radio-frequency-interference [RFI]) is a rapidly expanding technology. It covers the frequency spectrum from dc to about 40 GHz. EMI is the culprit which does not allow radio, TV, radar, navigation and the myriad of electrical, electro-mechanical and electronic and communication devices, apparatus and systems to operate compatibly in a common frequency spectrum environment. EMI can result in a jammed radio, heart-pacer failures, navigation errors and many other nuisance or catastrophic events. Therefore, it follows that this spectrum pollution problem has reached international levels of concern and must be dealt with in proportion to the safety and economic impact involved.

The basic EMC requirement is to plan, specify and design telecommunication systems that can be installed in their operational environment without creating or being susceptible to interference. In order to help satisfy this requirement, careful consideration must be given to a number of factors that influence EMC. It is particularly necessary to consider major sources of EMI, modes of coupling and points or conditions of susceptibility.

There is much written material on EMI which is generally available in trade journals, symposium records and the like. With certain exceptions, in total this material represents an anthology of miscellaneous subjects and topics which do not interrelate very well. Certainly, to either a newcomer to the EMI or electromagnetic compatibility (EMC) disciplines or to others already in these disciplines seeking tutorial or how-to-do-it knowledge, it is very frustating.

The primary purpose of this volume is to provide a methodology for using EMC prediction and analysis techniques and tools for planning, designing, installing and operating telecommunication systems which are free from EMI problems. Careful application of these techniques at appropriate stages in the telecommunication system life cycle will ensure EMC without the wasteful expense of overengineering or the uncertainties of underengineering.

Acknowledgement

Electromagnetic compatibility (EMC) is a difficult subject involving many areas of technology. Over the years that electromagnetic interference (EMI) has been a concern, many individuals have contributed to our knowledge on this subject. I would like to acknowledge that the material presented in this handbook represents the contributions of these many individuals, and I would especially like to express my appreciation to those individuals who have furnished some of the material presented in this handbook. In addition, I would like to thank all of those individuals who have worked in the field of EMC.

For the 29 years that I have been working in the field of EMC, I have been employed by Atlantic Research Corporation, and I am grateful to Atlantic Research for providing me with the opportunity to engage in many challenging assignments in the field of EMC. I would like to acknowledge that I am currently in the ORI Group of Atlantic Research and thank my employer for permitting me to participate in this endeavor.

Throughout the period of time that I have been involved in working on the various papers and reports that formed the basis for this handbook, I have been assisted by Janet Agee, and I am especially grateful to her for this assistance.

On a personal note, I would like to thank my wife Sandi for her love, encouragement and support during the period of time that I was preparing this handbook.

William G. Duff

Common Terms and Abbreviations in EMC Literature

Prefixes for Decimal Multiples

10^{12}	tera	T
10^9	giga	G
10^6	mega	M
10^3	kilo	k
10^2	hecto	h
10	deka	da
10^{-1}	deci	d
10^{-2}	centi	c
10^{-3}	milli	m
10^{-6}	micro	μ
10^{-9}	nano	n
10^{-12}	pico	p

Technical Terms

absolute	abs
alternating current	ac
American wire gage	AWG
ampere	A
ampere per meter	A/m
ampere-hour	Ah
amplitude modulation	AM
amplitude probability distribution	APD
analog to digital	A/D
analog-to-digital converter	ADC or A/D converter
anti-jamming	AJ
arithmetic logic unit	ALU
audio frequency	AF
automatic data processing	ADP
automatic frequency control	AFC
automatic gain control	AGC

average	avg
bandwidth	BW
binary coded decimal	BCD
bit	b
bit-error rate	BER
bits per second	bps
British thermal unit	Btu
broadband	BB
byte	B
bytes per second	Bps
centimeter-gram-second	cgs
central processing unit	CPU
characters per second	cps
common-mode coupling	CMC
common-mode rejection ratio	CMRR
complementary metal-oxide semiconductor	CMOS
continuous wave	CW
coulomb	C
cubic centimeter	cm^3
decibel	dB
decibel above 1 milliwatt	dBm
decibel above 1 volt	dBV
decibel above 1 watt	dBW
degree Celsius	°C
degree Fahrenheit	°F
degree Kelvin	°K
diameter	dia
differential-mode coupling	DMC
digital multimeter	DMM
digital to analog	D/A
digital voltmeter	DVM
digital-to-analog converter	DAC or D/A conv.

Common Terms and Abbreviations in EMC Literature

diode-transistor logic	DTL	instantaneous automatic gain control	IAGC
direct current	dc	insulated-gate field-effect transistor	IGFET
double pole double throw	DPDT	integrated circuit	IC
double sideband	DSB	interference-to-noise ratio	I/N
double sideband suppressed carrier	DSB-SC	intermediate frequency	IF
dual in-line package	DIP	joule	J
electric field	E-field	junction field-effect transistor	JFET
electromagnetic compatibility	EMC	kilogram	kg
electromagnetic interference	EMI	kilohertz	kH
electromagnetic pulse	EMP	kilovolt	kV
electromotive force	EMF	kilowatt	kW
electron volt	eV	kilowatt-hour	kWh
electronic countermeasures	ECM	lambert	L
electrostatic discharge	ESD	large-scale integration	LSI
emitter-coupled logic	ECL	least significant bit	LSB
extremely high frequency	EHF	length	l
extremely low frequency	ELF	length (of cable)	l_c
farad	F	line impedance stabilization network	LISN
fast Fourier transform	FFT	line of sight	LOS
field intensity	FI	liter	l
field intensity meter	FIM	local oscillator	LO
field-effect transistor	FET	low frequency	LF
foot	ft or	lower sideband	LSB
frequency	freq	lumen	lm
frequency division multiplex	FDM	lux	lx
frequency modulation	FM	magnetic field	H-field
frequency shift keying	FSK	master oscillator power amplifier	MOPA
gauss	G	maximum	max
gram	g	maxwell	Mx
ground	gnd	mean time between failure	MTBF
ground loop coupling	GLC	mean time to failure	MTTF
ground support equipment	GSE	mean time to repair	MTTR
hazards of electromagnetic radiation to ordnance	HERO	medium frequency (300 kHz to 3 MHz)	MF
henry	H	metal-oxide semiconductor	MOS
hertz (cycles per second)	Hz	metal-oxide semiconductor field-effect transistor	MOSFET
high frequency	HF	metal-oxide varistor	MOV
high-power transistor-to-transistor logic	HTTL	meter	m
high-speed complementary metal-oxide semiconductor	HCMOS	microfarad	μF
high-threshold logic	HTL	microhenry	μH
hour	hr	micron (10^{-6} meter)	μ
inch	in or "	micro-ohm	$\mu\Omega$
inch per second	ips	microwave	MW
industrial, scientific and medical	ISM	mile	mi
infrared	IR	military specification	MIL-SPEC
input/output	I/O	military standard	MIL-STD
inside dimension	ID	milliamp	mA

million instructions per second	MIPS	pulse position modulation	PPM
millisecond	ms	pulse repetition frequency	PRF
millivolt	mV	pulse-amplitude modulation	PAM
milliwatt	mW	pulse-code modulation	PCM
minimum	min	pulse-duration modulation	PDM
minimum discernable signal	MDS	pulse-width modulation	PWM
minute	min	quasipeak	QP
modulator-demodulator	modem	radiation hazard	RADHAZ
most significant bit	MSB	radio frequency	RF
multilayer board	MLB	radio interference and field intensity	RI-FI
multiplex, multiplexer	mux	radio-frequency interference	RFI
nanofarad	nF	random access memory	RAM
nanohenry	nH	receiver	RX
nanosecond	ns	reference	ref
narrowband	NB	relative humidity	RH
negative	neg	resistance-inductance-capacitance	RLC
negative-positive-negative (transistor)	npn	return to zero	RTZ
negative-to-positive (junction)	n-p	revolutions per minute	rpm
newton	N	roentgen	R
noise equivalent power	NEP or P_n	root-mean-square	rms
		second	s
non-return to zero	NRZ	sensitivity time control	STC
N-type metal-oxide semiconductor	NMOS	shielding effectiveness	SE
		sideband	SB
nuclear electromagnetic pulse	NEMP	siemens	S
		signal-to-interference (ratio)	S/I
oersted	Oe	signal-to-noise (ratio)	S/N
ohm	Ω	silicon controlled rectifier	SCR
ohm-centimeter	Ωcm	single sideband	SSB
ohms per square	Ω/sq	square meter	m^2
ounce	oz	standing-wave ratio	SWR
outside dimension	OD	super high frequency	SHF
peak	pk	super low frequency	SLF
peak-to-peak	p-p	surface acoustic wave	SAW
phase lock loop	PLL	surface-mount technology	SMT
phase modulation	PM	surface-mounted component	SMC
positive	pos	surface-mounted device	SMD
positive-negative-positive (transistor)	pnp	television	TV
		temperature coefficient	TC
positive-to-negative (junction)	p-n	tesla	T
		time division multiplex	TDM
pound (sterling)	£	transistor-to-transistor logic	TTL
pound per square centimeter	p/cm^2	ultra high frequency (360 MHz to 3 GHz)	UHF
pound per square inch	psi	ultraviolet	UV
power factor	PF	very high frequency (30 MHz to 300 MHz)	VHF
printed circuit board	PCB		
private branch exchange	PBX	very high-speed integrated circuit	VHSIC
P-type metal-oxide semiconductor	PMOS	very large-scale integration	VLSI
pulse per second	pps	very low frequency (3 kHz to 30 kHz)	VLF

volt	V	length (coil turn, ground loop, etc.)	l
volt meter	VM	length in millimeters	l_{mm}
voltage standing wave ratio	VSWR	magnetic susceptibility	χ
voltage-to-frequency converter	VFC	magnetizing force	H
voltampere	VA	parasitic capacitance	C_p
volt-ohm meter	VOM	permeability of free space	μ_o
watt	W	permeability of medium relative to μ_o	μ_r
waveguide beyond cuttoff	WGBCO	phase constant	β
weber	Wb	radius	r
words per minute	wpm	relative permittivity	ϵ_r
yard	yd	resistance (in ohms)	R
		rise time	τ_r
		shield thickness	d
		time	t
		time constant, transmission factor	τ
		velocity, volume	V
		wavelength	λ

Mathematical Functions and Operators

absolute value	abs
approximately equal	$\approx$
argument	arg
cosine	cos
cosine (hyperbolic)	cosh
cotangent	cot
cotangent (hyperbolic)	coth
determinant	det
dimension	dim
exponential	exp
imaginary	im
inferior	inf
limit	lim
logarithm, common (base$_{10}$)	log
logarithm, Napierian (base$_e$)	ln
sine	sin
tangent	tan
tangent (hyperbolic)	tanh

Common Variables in EMC Equations

attenuation constant, absorption factor	α
Boltzmann's constant	K
capacitance (in farads)	C
charge	Q
coefficient of self-inductance	L
conductance in mho	G
conductivity, propagation constant, leakage coefficient, deviation	σ
current	I
dielectric constant, permittivity	ϵ
frequency (in Hz)	f
impedance	Z
induced voltage	E
inductance (in henrys)	L
infinity	∞

Chapter 1

An Introduction to EMC Design of Telecommunication Systems

Almost every aspect of modern life is significantly influenced by and depends on the use of the electromagnetic spectrum. This permits production and transmission of electrical power, communications, navigation, radar and the like. Without the use of this valuable and essential natural resource, the basic nature of our society would be completely different.

Electromagnetic compatibility (EMC) is a necessary condition for effective communication-electronic (CE) system performance. EMC is the ability of equipments and systems to function as designed in their intended operational environment without adversely affecting the operation of, or being affected adversely by, other equipments or systems. Thus, the manner and efficiency in which modern life is conducted depends on the ability to achieve and maintain EMC.

For many years, the standard approach to achieving EMC was to wait until problems appeared and then attempt to fix or suppress incompatible emissions or responses in order to eliminate or remove system performance degradation. Actually, the pragmatic approach worked quite well for the time. However, as the number of electronic systems and devices increased, it became obvious that this seat-of-the-pants, after-the-fact approach was not economical; it resulted in a significant reduction in system effectiveness.

Another approach that has been used to achieve EMC is to impose rigid specifications and standards on equipments and systems during their planning and design stages. This approach often results in the wasteful expense of overengineering, and it still provides no guarantee that EMC will be obtained under all operational conditions. Thus, each requirement of an EMC specification or standard should be both necessary and sufficient to ensure compatibility as well as practical to achieve.

In order to permit efficient use of the frequency spectrum, engineers, technicians and users must be responsible for the planning, design, development, installation and operation of telecommunications systems and have a methodology for achieving EMC. Techniques which permit them to identify, localize and define Electromagnetic Interference (EMI) problem areas before rather than after they waste time, effort and dollars must be available. More timely and economical corrective measures may then be taken.

The primary purpose of this volume is to provide a methodology for using EMC prediction and analysis techniques and tools for planning, designing, installing and operating telecommunications systems which are free from EMI problems. Careful application of these techniques at appropriate stages in the telecommunication system life cycle will ensure EMC without either the wasteful expense of overengineering or the uncertainties of underengineering.

This chapter discusses basic EMI problems and describes the role and importance of prediction and analysis in achieving EMC. It introduces the reader to the basic EMC techniques described in the handbook. It also provides him with a brief description on how he may best use this volume for finding solutions to his particular EMC design and analysis problems.

1.1 The EMC Requirement for Telecommunication Systems

The basic EMC requirement is to plan, specify and design telecommunication systems that can be installed in their operational environment without creating or being susceptible to interference. In order to help satisfy this requirement, careful consideration must be given to a number of factors that influence EMC. It is particularly necessary to consider major sources of EMI, modes of coupling and points or conditions of susceptibility. The EMC technician should be familiar with the basic tools (including prediction, analysis, measurement, control, suppression, specifications and standards) that are used to achieve EMC.

Some of the important aspects of the problem are illustrated in Fig. 1.1 which shows a shipboard situation with co-located radar and communication equipments. A similar type of situation may be found at a military air defense site or at a civil airport or air traffic control center. In the situation illustrated, EMI could be coupled between the various elements of the system by different combinations of conduction and radiation via antennas, signal leads and power lines.

This volume is primarily concerned with presenting a methodology for EMC design of telecommunications systems, and illustrating prediction and analysis techniques that are used to identify and define potential EMI problems. The techniques are specifically oriented toward EMI signals that are propagated and received via antennas associated with telecommunications systems. The basic techniques, however, are general and may be used to predict EMI coupled into a system via any combination of conducted and radiated paths. The principal requirement for applying the techniques to a general situation is that the input functions must

Figure 1.1—Shipboard Environment Provides Challenges for the EMC Designer

be specified so that they are consistent with the techniques. Figure 1.2 presents examples of the three basic elements (EMI source, transmission or coupling media and susceptible device) that must be considered in EMI prediction and analysis.

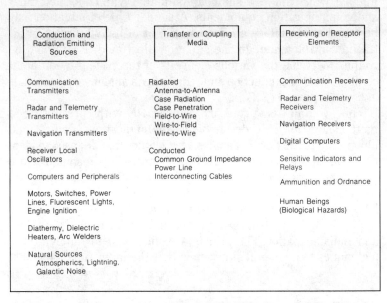

Conduction and Radiation Emitting Sources	Transfer or Coupling Media	Receiving or Receptor Elements
Communication Transmitters	Radiated Antenna-to-Antenna Case Radiation	Communication Receivers
Radar and Telemetry Transmitters	Case Penetration Field-to-Wire Wire-to-Field	Radar and Telemetry Receivers
Navigation Transmitters	Wire-to-Wire	Navigation Receivers
Receiver Local Oscillators	Conducted Common Ground Impedance	Digital Computers
	Power Line	Sensitive Indicators and Relays
Computers and Peripherals	Interconnecting Cables	
Motors, Switches, Power Lines, Fluorescent Lights, Engine Ignition		Ammunition and Ordnance
		Human Beings (Biological Hazards)
Diathermy, Dielectric Heaters, Arc Welders		
Natural Sources Atmospherics, Lightning, Galactic Noise		

Figure 1.2—Three Basic Elements of an Emitting-Susceptibility Situation

1.1.1   Effects of EMI

EMI may directly influence the performance of any CE equipment or system, and it can indirectly affect the overall accomplishment of an operation or mission. Examples of direct influences of EMI on system performance are: false targets and missed targets in a radar display system, wrong navigation data or landing system errors in an aircraft, lost or garbled messages in a communications system, false commands to a missile or electro-explosive device or triggering a heart pacemaker demand-mode of operation. Some resulting indirect effects corresponding to the above include: false alerts in an air-defense system as a result of false targets, surprise enemy attacks as a result of missed targets, aircraft mid-air collisions as a result of navigation errors, aircraft crashes while landing because of altitude or glide-slope errors, ineffective control of riots or fires because of lost or garbled emergency fire or police communications, accidental launching of missiles or detonation of explosives because of wrong electrical commands and the fainting, collapse or even death of the person having a heart pacemaker.

All of these effects, both direct and indirect, have happened as a result of EMI. They can recur, and with the increase of EMI sources and receptors every year the situations will probably become more frequent.

1.1.2   Sources of EMI

Any electrical, electromechanical or electronic device is a potential source of EMI. In general, EMI sources can be classified either as transmitters (equipment whose primary function is to intentionally generate or radiate electromagnetic signals) or incidental sources (equipments that generate electromagnetic energy as an unintended byproduct in the process of performing their primary function). Sometimes sources of EMI are divided into natural and man-made sources. Figure 1.3 shows such an organization.

Transmitters generate electromagnetic energy not only in the basic or intended frequency range, but also over a wide range of other frequencies on both sides of the fundamental carrier, harmonics of the fundamental and other undesired or spurious frequencies. These undesired emissions result from carrier spreading by the baseband transmitter modulation spectrum, production of broadband noise in the output stages and generation of harmonics of the fundamental as a result of nonlinearities in the equipment output stages.

Because of transmitter nonlinearities, signals from two or more transmitters can heterodyne in the output stages of one to produce additional signals at totally different frequencies. This is called "transmitter intermodulation." In designing a telecommunication system, all of these transmitter outputs must be carefully considered. They are explained in detail in Chapter 3 of this volume.

All electrical equipments can be potential sources of incidental radiation. Although the levels associated with these sources are usually relatively low, they often are the cause of interference because of their broadband characteristics. Here, significant emissions occupy several octaves or more of the frequency spectrum. Some of the more important sources include: power lines, automobile engine ignition systems, fluorescent lamps, electrical motors, switches and relays. Because the limitations on system per-

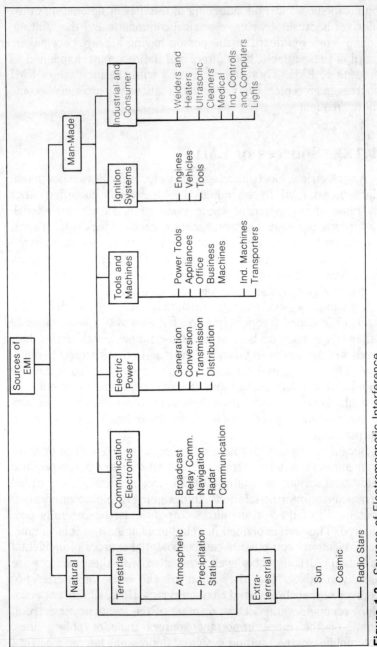

Figure 1.3—Sources of Electromagnetic Interference

formance may be determined by the environmental signals and ambient noise levels present in the vicinity of a potentially susceptible device, it is important to consider these sources of EMI in planning and designing systems. Important categories of environmental noise that must be considered by the systems engineer are natural noise, including atmospheric and cosmic noise, and manmade urban and rural noise.

Table 1.1, which amplifies Fig. 1.3, lists many specific EMI sources. The incidental radio-noise environment of a metropolitan area is produced by distributions of individual noise sources. Composite metropolitan area noise has been the subject of several investigations during the past 20 years. Motivation for experimental investigations and the more recently undertaken theoretical studies has been provided by radio communication and information-handling system requirements. This is primarily because performance of all urban radio telephone, aircraft navigation, radio broadcast and television systems is adversely affected by excessive surface incidental radio-noise levels.

Wide geographic and short-term time variations in man-made radio noise, apparent from limited observations, make it difficult to suggest specific interference levels for different times and geographic locations. Although specific levels are unknown, it is possible to express typical levels of unintended radiation. One convention that has been adopted is the practice of segregating the levels of unintended man-made radiation into categories based on the level of urbanization in the area of measurement or by contour mapping of noise levels. It is recognized that this categorization may ultimately be replaced by classifications based on local industrial or commercial activity as more data becomes available and improved data correlation methods are introduced. Effort has been made in the collation of data to include only incidental noise and to exclude signals that emanate coherently from CE radiators.

Figure 1.4 shows typical levels of unintended man-made radio noise to be found at three arbitrarily chosen types of locations: urban (typically 0 to 16 km from the city center), suburban (16 to 48 km) and rural (beyond 48 km). Since sources contributing most to general levels of man-made radio noise apparently change in the neighborhood of 10 to 20 MHz, and since no measurements used to obtain Fig. 1.4 were made between these frequencies, all values

Table 1.1—Examples of Sources of Electromagnetic Interference

I. Natural Sources
  A. Terrestrial Sources
    1. Atmospherics (thunder-
      storms around the world)
    2. Lightning Discharges (local
      storms)
    3. Precipitation Static
    4. Whistlers
  B. Extraterrestrial Sources
    1. Cosmic Noise
    2. Radio Stars
    3. Sun:
      Disturbed
      Quiet
II. Man-Made Sources
  A. Electric Power
    1. Conversion (Step Up/Down)
      Faulty/Dirty Insulators
      Faulty Transformers
    2. Distribution
      Faulty/Dirty Insulators
      Faulty Transformers
      Faulty Wiring
      Pickup and Reradiation
      Poor Grounding
    3. Generators
    4. Transmission Lines
      Faulty/Dirty Insulators
      Pickup and Reradiation
  B. Communication Electronics
  (CE)
    1. Broadcast
      MF Amplitude Modulation
      VHF/FM
      VHF/UHF TV
    2. Communications (non-relay)
      Aeronautical Mobile
      Amateurs (hams)
      Citizens Radio
      Facsimile
      HF Telegraphy
      HF Telephony
      Land Mobile
      Maritime Mobile
      Radio-Control Devices
      Telemetry
      Telephone Circuits
    3. Navigation (non-radar)
      Aircraft Beacons
      Instrument Landing Sys.
      Loran

      Marker Beacons
      Omega
      VOR/TACAN/VORTAC
    4. Radar
      Air Search
      Air Surface Detection
      Air Traffic Control
      Harbor
      Mapping
      Police Speed Monitor
      Surface Search
      Tracking/Fire Control
      Weather
    5. Relay Communications
      Ionospheric Scatter
      Microwave Relay Links
      Satellite Relay
      Tropospheric Scatter
  C. Tools and Machines
    1. Appliances
      Air Conditioners
      Blenders
      Deep Freezers
      Fans
      Lawn Mowers, Electric
      Mix Masters
      Ovens, Electric
      Ovens, Microwave
      Refrigerators
      Sewing Machines
      Vacuum Cleaners
      Water Pumps
    2. Industrial Machines
      Electric Cranes
      Fork-Lift Trucks
      Lathes
      Milling Machines
      Printing Presses
      Punch Presses
      Rotary Punches
      Screw Machines
    3. Office/Business Machines
      Adding Machines
      Calculators
      Cash Registers
      Electric Typewriters
      Reproduction Equipment
    4. Power Tools
      Band Saws
      Drill Presses
      Electric Drills

Table 1.1—(continued)

Electric Hand Saws	E. Industrial & Consumer
Electric Grinders	(non-motor/engines)
Electric Sanders	1. Heaters and Gluers
Hobby Tools	Dielectric Heaters
Routers/Joiners	Plastic Preheaters
Table Saws	Wood Gluers
5. Transporters	2. Industrial Controls &
Conveyor Belts	Computers
Elevators	Card Punches
Escalators	Card Readers
Moving Sidewalks	Computers
D. Ignition Systems	Machine Controllers
1. Engines	Peripheral Equipment
2. Tools	Process Controllers
Auxiliary Generators	Silicon-Controlled
Lawn Mowers	Rectifiers
Portable Saws	Teletypewriters
3. Vehicles	3. Lights
Aircraft	Faulty Incandescent
Automobiles	Fluorescent Lamps
Farm Machinery	Light Dimmers
Inboard Motors	Neon Lights
Minibikes	4. Medical Equipment
Motorcycles	Diathermy
Outboard Motors	X-Ray Machines
Tanks	5. Ultrasonic Cleaners
Tractors	6. Welders & Heaters
Trucks	Arc Welders
	Heliarc Welders
	Induction Heaters
	Plastic Welders
	RF Stabilized Welders

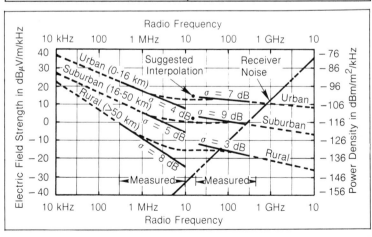

Figure 1.4—Math Models of Median Incidental Man-Made Noise Based on Lossless Omnidirectional Antenna Near Surface

measured at 10 MHz and below were considered separately from those at 20 MHz and above. For frequencies 20 MHz and above, curves were obtained from data given by Young, Simpson, Hamer, Ellis, FCC ACLMRS and the results of some recent measurements by ITSA/ESSA. At frequencies of 10 MHz and below, the curves were derived from data supplied by ITSA/ESSA. The reason for the disparity of data across the 10 to 20 MHz interface is not clear other than below 10 MHz all data were measured with a vertically polarized whip or rod antenna and most data above 20 MHz (especially above 100 MHz) were measured using a tuned dipole, horizontally polarized. Yet polarization, per se, does not explain the disparity since measurements which were made with both polarizations of the same antenna evidenced an average of only 2 dB difference. Accordingly, Fig. 1.4 suggests an interpolation model from about 1 to 200 MHz.

The division of areas, where measurements were taken into urban, suburban and rural areas, were made primarily on the basis of types of locations such as the business areas of New York City, New York; Baltimore, Maryland; Washington, D.C.; Denver, Colorado; Melbourne, Australia; Tel Aviv, Haifa and Jerusalem, Israel.

The "suburban" curve was obtained from data taken at Boulder, Colorado; near Washington, D.C.; Melbourne, Australia; Tel Aviv, Haifa and in suburban areas of England. Those measurements which were considered rural were made at locations chosen to be as free as possible of man-made noise (the stations given in CCIR Report 322 and experimental radio facilities near Boulder, Colorado).

Since measurements at 20 MHz and above were made at only two or three frequencies at each location, frequencies used at other locations generally did not correspond to measurements at the upper end of the spectrum which usually were not made near 20 MHz, and vice versa. In order to eliminate a frequency location bias, the best fit for each set of observations was taken, and equal frequency points were then used from these curves to obtain a best fit to all data.

To indicate the variability of the average noise power, the rms deviation of the median values used to obtain each segment of the curves is indicated as a σ in units of dB. Note that this deviation is found from the average power values for each location and frequency and is not the instantaneous (peak) variation, which is considerably larger than the σ values shown.

In estimating noise level at the receiver due to external sources, the gain, polarization and orientation of the receiving antenna should be considered. Figure 1.4 shows the median operating field intensities and equivalent power densities from various noise sources. These values are the levels expected from an omnidirectional, short, lossless vertical antenna near the surface of the earth. For convenient reference, typical receiver noise is shown in the figure based on a noise figure rising from 10 dB at 1 MHz to 15 dB at 1 GHz to 20 dB at 10 GHz. Many government and commercial receivers would be better than this, and many consumer receivers would be poorer.

Illustrative Example 1.1

TV reception in fringe areas is always a problem for millions of viewers. Typical modern VHF log-periodic TV antennas exhibit gains of about 12 dB. To Channel 9 (186 to 192 MHz), for example, this antenna exhibits an effective area of 2.8 m^2, and the receiver sensitivity (S = N) for a 6 MHz bandwidth is about −93 dBm. This corresponds to an arriving power density of −93 dBm −5 dB m^2 = −98 dBm/m^2 per 6 MHz bandwidth or −132 dBm/m^2/kHz. Determine the effect of incidental man-made noise on reception.

Figure 1.4 indicates that man-made noise in a typical suburban/rural area at 200 MHz may average between −117 and −133 dBm/m^2/kHz. If the emphasis is on the rural side, the I/N ratio is −133 dBm/m^2/kHz − (−132 dBm/m^2/kHz) = −1 dB. On the other hand, if emphasis is more on suburban areas, typical I/N ratios would be more like −117 dBm/m^2 − (−132 dBm/m^2) or 15 dB, thereby compromising reception. Note that if the TV transmitter were in the center of the city, the signal level would be reduced by 6 dB in doubling the location distance from, say, 24 to 48 km. Since the man-made noise would be reduced by 15 dB, and the signal by 6 dB, the S/I ratio actually improves in the rural area. This explains why reception is sometimes better in rural areas than in the closer suburban areas, especially those located near highways or industrial centers.

1.1.3 Modes of Coupling

Emissions may be coupled (see Fig. 1.2) by one or more paths from the interference source to the susceptible receiving device(s). Basically, these paths are classified as either (1) conduction paths, which include all forms of direct hardline, wire or cable coupling, or (2) radiation paths, which involve propagation through the environment or induction (near-field) therein.

Conducted interference may enter a receptor or receiver as a result of directly coupled wiring leads between the receptor and some source of electrical disturbances. Typical conducted paths include interconnecting cables, power leads and control and signal cables.

Radiating interference includes situations in which emissions (1) enter via a receiving system antenna, if applicable, (2) penetrate a shielded housing at the openings and couple into low-level circuitry and (3) couple into various signal, control or power leads of a receptor via radiated paths. EMC design and analysis techniques presented in this volume emphasize those emission that are coupled into receiving systems via the antenna. The techniques may be applied to other interference conditions for which the required input functions are described.

1.1.4 Susceptible Equipments

Any device capable of responding to electrical, electromechanical or electronic emissions or to the fields associated with these emissions is vulnerable to EMI. Susceptibility of all such devices may be divided into two categories: (1) devices susceptible to interfering emissions over a broad band of frequencies and (2) devices that are frequency selective. Typical devices that may be considered vulnerable to interfering emissions over a few or many octaves include remote-control switches, relays, indicator lights, electroexplosive squibs, recording devices, logic circuits and meters. Frequency-selective devices primarily include equipments or systems such as communication, radar and navigation receivers.

1.1.5 Achieving EMC

EMI is an interdisciplinary problem that can be solved by careful consideration and attention during all phases in the life cycle of an equipment or system. In order to achieve EMC economically and effectively, it is necessary to use a combination of: interference prediction and analysis techniques to identify and define the problems; EMC specifications and standards to ensure comprehensiveness during equipment design and development stages; EMI control devices and techniques during equipment or system design, development and production to ensure that specifications and standards are met; EMC system design to ensure that equipments and subsystems do not have adverse EMI interactions; measurements to provide prediction inputs and ensure compliance with EMC specifications and standards and suppression techniques during installation and operation to solve specific problems that arise as a result of severe or unusual operating conditions.

During each phase of the equipment or system life cycle, responsible management and engineering personnel must give appropriate attention to the particular EMC considerations applicable to their areas of responsibility if EMI-free operation is to be assured.

1.2   Stages of EMC Analysis

The scope of this volume of the EMI/EMC handbook series may be made clearer by discussing the various phases in the life cycle of an equipment or system and the EMC design and analysis considerations that apply to each phase. Figure 1.5 illustrates the interrelationship between the levels of EMC design and analysis and system life cycle phases.

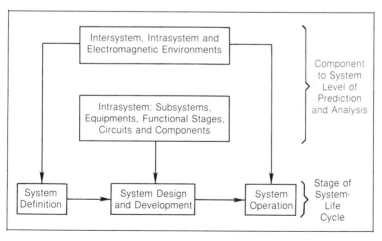

Figure 1.5—Interrelationship between System Life Cycle and Level of EMI Prediction and Analysis

Techniques used for EMC design and analysis of systems are significantly different from techniques used for EMC design and analysis of equipments. In system design, the analyst is interested in determining interactions among various systems. It is necessary to define the output characteristics of EMI sources and the susceptibility of receiving equipments. Consequently, it is not necessary to know detailed internal characteristics of equipments. Thus, in system EMI analysis, the individual elements can be regarded as black boxes with defined input/output characteristics. On the other hand, in analyzing equipments to determine their EMI properties, the analyst must consider the detailed characteristics of components and circuits that the equipment comprises.

A brief discussion of the major design and analysis considerations at each phase in the system life cycle is presented in the following sections.

1.2.1   System Definition Phase

The first step in the life cycle of a system is the definition phase. During this phase, the system progresses from missions or applications to its most basic form, which could be either an idea that originated at a research laboratory or the operational requirement of potential users. It then moves to the definition and specifications of the major system characteristics such as size, weight, type of modulation, data rate, information bandwidth, transmitter power, receiver sensitivity, antenna gains, spurious rejection, etc. It is essential that careful consideration be given to EMC during this definition phase because the major characteristics of equipments and systems are defined and specified at this point.

During the definition phase, the system planner must predict and analyze EMI problems that are likely to be encountered: (1) within or between elements of the system (intrasystem), (2) between elements of the system and elements of other systems that are likely to be operating in the same general area (intersystem) and (3) between elements of the system and the electromagnetic environment in which it is to be operated.

The intrasystem EMI problem is shown in Fig. 1.6. Here, interference is developing because noise spikes on both nearby power cables and wiring harnesses are coupled into low-level, sensitive circuits by magnetic and electric-field coupling. Common ground current impedance coupling and direct radiation from box-to-box, box-to-cables or cables-to-box are other causes of EMI. These EMI problems are discussed in Volume 8 of this handbook series.

In the case of intersystem EMI, primary problems usually result from signals that are coupled from the transmitting antenna of one system to the receiving antenna of another system. This inter-system EMI problem is particularly serious when many systems are required to simultaneously operate in a limited physical area such as a ship, an airplane, a vehicle, a building, a military base, an industrial site, a hospital or a city. This type of problem is il-

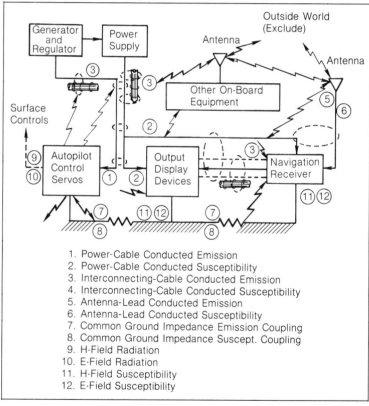

1. Power-Cable Conducted Emission
2. Power-Cable Conducted Susceptibility
3. Interconnecting-Cable Conducted Emission
4. Interconnecting-Cable Conducted Susceptibility
5. Antenna-Lead Conducted Emission
6. Antenna-Lead Conducted Susceptibility
7. Common Ground Impedance Emission Coupling
8. Common Ground Impedance Suscept. Coupling
9. H-Field Radiation
10. E-Field Radiation
11. H-Field Susceptibility
12. E-Field Susceptibility

Figure 1.6—Examples of Intrasystem EMI

lustrated in Fig. 1.7 which shows a microwave communication system attempting to receive signals from distant locations while operating in the immediate vicinity of transmitters associated with other systems. This book presents techniques for achieving EMC in the design of communication systems.

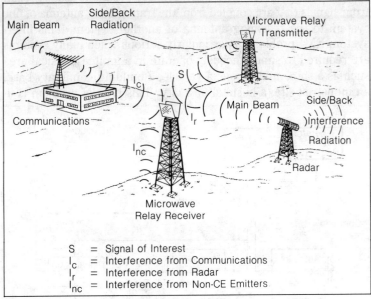

Figure 1.7—The Intersystem EMI Problem

The type of analysis that is performed at the system definition stage must rely on assumed or typical EMI characteristics for the individual elements of the system. Concentration is directed to the manner in which these elements interact in the total system from an EMI standpoint. EMC analysis during definition will assist the engineer in his selection of frequency bands; allocation of system parameters such as transmitter power, antenna gains, receiver sensitivity, type of modulation, rise time and information bandwidth; determination of system EMI specifications and identification of potential deficiencies and problem areas.

1.2.2 System Design and Development

Design and development is the second phase in the life cycle of a system. During this phase, the system progresses from the previously established specifications to the final hardware item.

In the process of designing a system, there are a number of decisions that must be made. In general, an equipment may be considered to consist of combinations of functional stages such as amplifiers, mixers, frequency converters, filters, modulators, detectors, display or readout devices, power supplies, etc. For each equipment, there are a number of important factors including EMC that must be considered. For example, in the case of receivers, it is necessary to define the number of amplifier and converter stages that will be used, and to establish the allocation of gain, selectivity and sensitivity between these stages. More importantly, it is necessary to develop an overall block diagram for the receiver with a complete description of the gains, frequency responses, input and output impedances, dynamic ranges, and susceptibility levels for each stage.

Personnel responsible for the design and development of a system must be concerned with EMI problems resulting from signals externally coupled between antennas of different elements of the system and other transmitters and receivers in the environment, as well as internal EMI problems resulting from cable coupling, case radiation, case penetration and the like. Figure 1.8 suggests a few of these considerations.

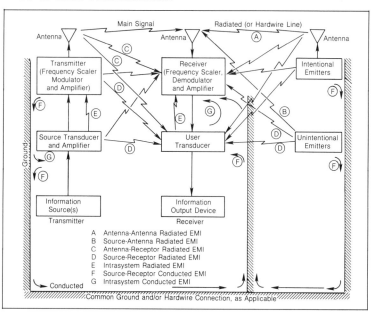

Figure 1.8—Example of Both Intrasystem and Intersystem Interference

1.2.3 System Operation

The final phase in the life cycle of the system shown in Fig. 1.5 is the operational phase. During this phase, a system that has been designed and developed is placed into operation. It is necessary to consider EMC from various operational aspects such as siting effects, frequency assignment, effective radiated power limits and antenna coverage.

This is more generally illustrated in Fig. 1.9 as operational EMI control tools under the four main headings: frequency, time, location and direction management. Each is further illustrated by a number of individual EMC devices and techniques. Figure 1.9 also contains EMI-control techniques useful in the system definition stage. This especially applies for the frequency management heading.

Overall, the types of analysis that are useful at the operational level are similar to those performed at the system definition level. Usually, personnel responsible for compatible system operation are more concerned about the interaction of the elements of the system, both with each other and with elements of other systems, than they are in the internal characteristics of the elements.

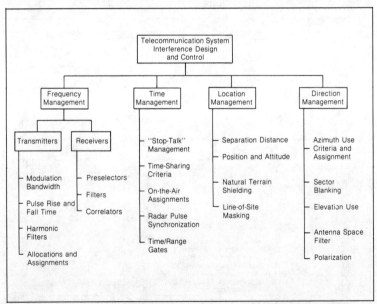

Figure 1.9—Telecommunication System Electromagnetic Interference Control Techniques

1.3   Use of EMC Analysis Techniques

Many different applications for EMC analysis and many different types of applicable techniques exist. In general, the particular type of EMC analysis technique to be selected depends on the specific application, the type and quality of input information available and the cost of performing the analysis. For example, the time required to perform an EMC analysis between a single transmitter-receiver pair may range from a few minutes to about one day. This approximate 100:1 time ratio suggests a cost figure ranging from about $10 to $1,000 per pair. The justifiable cost trade-off, however, is based on both the number of transmitter-receiver pairs involved as well as the impact of a serious EMI problem.

Cost is certainly one of the most important factors that must be considered when deciding on the specific analysis techniques to be selected and applied in a particular problem. The costs of developing an EMC analysis process and of performing that analysis can also vary greatly depending on the specific type of problem, the number of equipments involved, information available for these equipments and the extent to which it is necessary to evaluate the impact of EMI on operational performance. If one is professionally involved in EMC analysis on a more or less regular basis, he has already assembled many of the necessary mathematical models and analysis processes. Most of the time is then spent in collecting data on the transmitters, receivers, antennas and terrain profiles involved.

Where EMC analysis is performed frequently, the process should be automated for economic reasons. For example, automation is a powerful tool for CE equipment operating in a defined frequency band or for frequency assignment of VHF/UHF broadcast or land-mobile radio. This especially applies where either the EMC characteristics of the equipment are known or generalized close representations may be used. A computer analysis process can be developed for specific problems for about $5,000 to $10,000. This process can be used with manual performance data available through the Federal Communications Commission (FCC) in Washington, D.C., the Electromagnetic Compatibility Analysis Center (ECAC) in Annapolis, Md. and other sources to provide useful results at a minimum cost. Thus, when an EMC analysis process and a data base have been established, a prediction or frequency assignment can be performed for about $1,000 per equipment pair or frequency.

1.3.1 Applications for EMC Analysis

EMC analysis provides an engineering tool that is a valuable asset in various phases of CE equipment as well as system design and development such as: (1) the preliminary equipment or system planning and design, (2) the preparation of equipment or system requirements and specifications, (3) the preparation of specification compliance test plans, (4) the evaluation of test results, (5) the revision of either specifications or equipments for conditions of noncompliance and (6) the evaluation of systems in a specific operational environment.

Typical EMC design problems that may be handled by analysis include the following:

1. Examine the EMC situation for a complex of equipments and identify problem areas.
2. Examine the impact of changing the operating frequency of one or more equipments in the complex.
3. Examine the impact of adding an emitter to an existing system or complex of equipments.
4. Examine the interference produced in a susceptible device when added to a system or an existing complex.
5. Determine which one of several possible locations for an emitter or receptor provides the least probable interference.
6. Determine the source and cause of a known interference problem.
7. Determine the type and degree of suppression required to correct a specified interference situation.
8. Obtain site survey or EMC environment information for a given location.
9. Obtain susceptibility information for a given receptor or group of receptors.
10. Determine coupling loss over a specified path.
11. Assist in the selection of system parameters such as power, sensitivity and selectivity.
12. Provide information regarding the adequacy of given specifications for an equipment.
13. Provide information as to the best frequency band to use for a system which is being defined.
14. Provide information on frequency distance separation requirements for co-site equipments.

15. Perform frequency assignments for compatible operation.
16. Evaluate system effectiveness in an operational environment.

For each of the applications listed above, the analysis requirements, input information available and output results desired may be significantly different. For this reason, considerable attention is devoted to specific user requirements in this volume.

1.3.2 Types of EMC Analysis

There are a variety of different types of EMC analysis that may be performed. The type that is best for a particular EMC design problem will depend on the specific application desired, the information available, the extent and depth of analysis required, the output results desired and cost considerations. Some specific types of analysis that are performed using the techniques described in this volume include:

1. A preliminary analysis at the system definition stage to identify potential EMI problem areas and to define equipment EMC specification requirements.
2. An analysis based on statistical summaries of data to identify potential EMI problems between classes of equipments.
3. An analysis based on specification limits to determine their adequacy for assumed operational configurations of systems.
4. An analysis of system performance or operational effectiveness to define the effect of EMI on the overall ability of a system to accomplish its objectives or missions.

Each of these analyses differs in terms of the system life cycle phase at which it may be applied; the type and amount of information required; the time, manpower and cost required to perform the analysis and the results obtained.

1.4 Users of the Spectrum

In order to perform an EMC analysis, a knowledge of the users of the spectrum that may be operating in the environment is essential. The spectrum chart shown in Fig. 1.10 defines various uses and users and identifies specific frequency ranges in which they

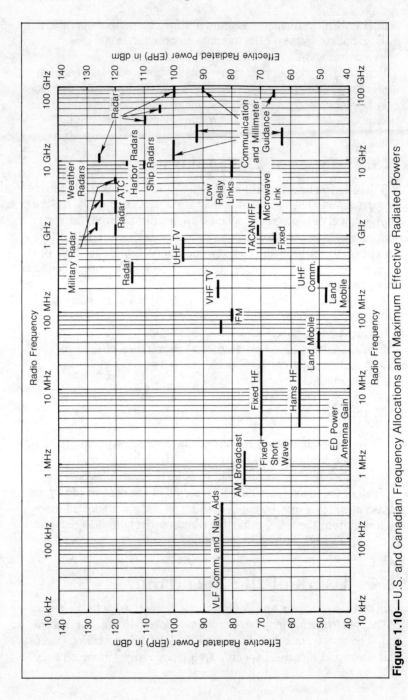

Figure 1.10—U.S. and Canadian Frequency Allocations and Maximum Effective Radiated Powers

operate. This spectrum chart should be studied at the start of any EMC analysis problem so that all potential interference sources may be identified first and included. EMC analysis techniques will not identify problems that are overlooked in preparing input data. Because it is important to be familiar with all principal users of the spectrum and each user's particular problem, brief discussions of the major problems by user category are presented below.

1.4.1 The Military

The military is the largest single user of the electromagnetic spectrum.[1] Military uses include command, control and guidance of friendly forces and weapons, as well as surveillance, detection, location, classification, deception and (if necessary) destruction of hostile weapons, activities and forces.

EMC is particularly difficult to achieve in typical military operations because of the requirement that many CE equipments be operated in a confined geographical area. The military problem is further aggravated by the critical life-or-death nature of missions and the total dependence of the mission on successful operation of various CE equipments.

1.4.2 Radio and Television Broadcasting

Based on annual expenditures or revenues, the second largest users of the spectrum are those in the radio and television broadcast industry. Broadcasting accounts for 82 percent of the nongovernment allocations of the spectrum in the frequency range below 1,000 MHz.[2]

EMI problems limit the number of available radio and television broadcast stations that can operate in a given geographical area, and these problems impose severe restrictions on the use of this medium. EMI prediction techniques, however, help to improve channel use by providing information on the affect of various technical considerations such as improved receiver standards, antenna designs and changes in transmission standards.

1.4.3 Aerospace and Marine Services

An important and rapidly growing use of the electromagnetic spectrum is for aeronautical and marine communications and control, radar and radio navigation applications and the launching and tracking of space vehicles. Next to television, these services use the largest portion of the spectrum below 1,000 MHz.[3]

The aeronautical problems are compounded by the large numbers of aircraft that now exist, and the fact that interfering emissions can propagate considerable distances from ground sources to susceptible airborne equipment and vice versa. Besides the congestion of these services in their allocated frequency bands, other potential interference sources present hazards to air traffic. For example, garage-door openers may interfere with aviation navigation.

Congestion in the coastal and inland waterways has created considerable problems in marine communications. Additionally, EMI problems plague maritime navigation along coastal areas. The increase in the number of small craft harbor radars alone is enormous.

1.4.4 Telecommunications

The electromagnetic spectrum is currently used for many forms of communication including long distance radio relay of telephone calls, television and satellite relay. In addition to present services, there will be future requirements for transmitting large quantities of digital data between computers, data processing centers and users. The picture phone has been developed and demonstration services are provided in a number of major cities.

In order to provide only one percent of the current telephone service with picture phone service, it would be necessary to double present telephone bandwidth facilities. Another less costly and possibly more imminent service is the concept of the home communication center for financial and banking transactions, ordering of goods and services, document and publication transmission and many record communications provided by mail today.

Although some of the telecommunication services identified above will probably rely on coaxial cable, waveguide or fiber optics transmission, economic considerations make these modes of transmission less desirable than relay transmission via radio waves. Thus, it is anticipated that the demand for and use of the spectrum for telecommunications will significantly increase, and EMI problems will result because of increased numbers of emitters in densely populated urban areas in which the present spectrum is already congested and overcrowded.

1.4.5 Public Safety Services

The spectrum is used in many ways to help ensure public safety. Some of the more important uses are for law enforcement, fire services, civil defense and rescue operations. It is anticipated that additional spectrum allocations will be required for other services such as a Highway Emergency Location Plan (HELP) to provide emergency radio communication for the motorist, and increased tactical and administrative communications among elements of a law enforcement agency for rapid access to crime information.

Additional spectrum and facilities will be needed for public communication with appropriate agencies in emergencies; regional or national channels interconnecting law enforcement agencies and control data sources, and increased use by the Forest Industries Radio Communication. EMI problems are certain to arise with these increased services because they require providing additional services in those regions of the spectrum such as the land mobile bands in cities that are already overcrowded from spectrum traffic and occupancy.

1.4.6 Other Uses

In addition to the specific users of the spectrum described above, there are many other users that should not be overlooked by the EMC analyst. For example, transportation, public utilities and the petroleum industry make widespread use of the frequency spectrum for information and control of their operations. Power companies use both point-to-point and mobile systems for control, fault location and direction of operation. The petroleum industry uses point-to-point communication systems for linking operations involving refining and pipeline distribution, and two-way radio for communication during exploration drilling, production, refining and distribution. The transportation industry makes widespread use of the spectrum for railroads, trucking, buses, taxis, etc. Other uses include research, citizen's band, amateur radio and dissemination of time and frequency standards.

1.5 Telecommunication System Analysis

The EMC analysis requirement is illustrated in Fig. 1.11. The typical EMI problem results from the fact that transmitters and receivers must be operated in close geographical proximity without interfering with each other. In Fig. 1.11 the receiver is attempting to intercept a signal from a distant transmitter while operating close to several other potentially interfering transmitters.

A basic telecommunication system may consist of single-channel analog-voice amplitude or frequency modulated transmitter and receiver. A more complex system may be required to transmit multiple channels of digital data which may be encoded and encrypted for error detection and correction and message security. A typical digital system may use time-division multiplexing and any one of several modulation schemes to include phase modulation or spread spectrum modulation techniques such as frequency hopping or pseudo-random sequences. A typical digital communication system is illustrated in Fig. 1.12. A given system may not provide all of the functions indicated in Fig. 1.12.

In performing an EMC analysis of telecommunication systems, it is necessary to identify and describe all potentially interfering signal sources, determine and describe the mechanism by which these signals may couple from the source to a potentially susceptible device and describe the susceptibility threshold and performance degradation mechanisms for the susceptible device.

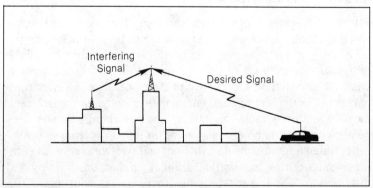

Figure 1.11—Illustration of Typical EMI Problem

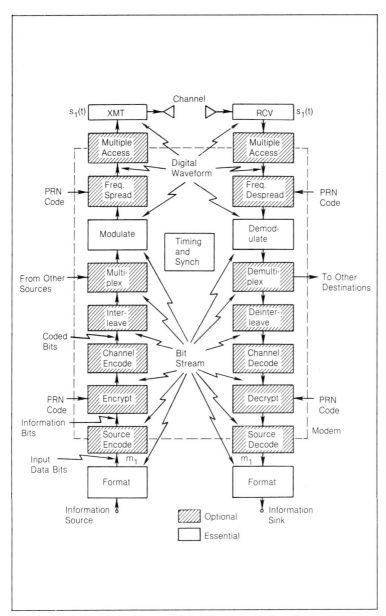

Figure 1.12—Typical Modern Digital Communication System

1.27

The overall EMC analysis elements are illustrated in Fig. 1.13. The source is an interfering transmitter with an output which may be described either as a function of time $v_i(t)$ or as a function of frequency $V_i(f)$. The coupling media may be described in terms of a transfer function in either the time domain $h(t)$ or the frequency domain $H(f)$. If the source is deterministic and the coupling media is linear and time-invariant, the output, $v_o(t)$ or $V_o(f)$, of the coupling media (which is the input to the potentially susceptible device) may be calculated as follows:

$$v_o(t) = \int_{-\infty}^{\infty} h(\tau) \, v_i(t-\tau) \, d\tau$$

or,
$$V_o(f) = H(f) \, V_i(f) \tag{1.1}$$

In analyzing telecommunication systems it is usually possible to use the frequency domain equations and to make assumptions that simplify these equations for specific situations of interest.

A telecommunication system designer must carefully consider the various electromagnetic interactions between his system and the overall environment in which the system must operate. The system designer must be able to analyze the interactions between his system and all emitters and receptors in the environments. In order to perform the required systems analysis, it is necessary to develop systems equations which relate appropriate electromagnetic source (emitter output) characteristics to appropriate responses.

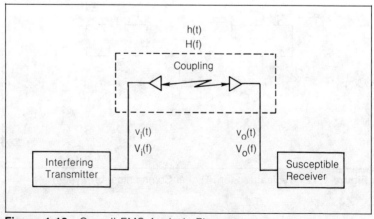

Figure 1.13—Overall EMC Analysis Elements

These responses might be in the form of: (1) waveforms such as time varying voltages at receptor inputs, (2) waveform parameters such as average power or (3) interference indicators such as average power susceptibility margins.

The main purpose for identifying systems equations is that they express a problem by relating input (sources, emitters) to output (receptor response parameter) within the constraints of the problem. This formulation is usually expressible in mathematical form with emitter, receptor and coupling terms explicit. Thus pertinent attributes of emitter, receptor and coupling models are readily apparent from systems equations. For example, an average power susceptible receptor and linear media may be evident in a systems equation given in terms of frequency domain transfer functions. These attributes, in turn, provide a guide to choosing appropriate emitter models such as an average power density description or a waveform description. They also guide the choice of coupling models with regard to computing desired receptor parameters or margins and with regard to the type of media whether it is linear, nonlinear, time-variant, etc.

Two categories of systems equations are presented here: (1) "waveform systems equations," defined as those relating arbitrary time waveforms between emitters and receptors and (2) "parameter systems equations," defined as those relating emitter outputs to receptor waveform parameters or interference indicators.

1.5.1   Waveform System Equations

In considering the interactions between emitters and potentially susceptible devices, it is important to recognize that there are different types of emissions and that each may produce different interference effects and may require different analysis methods. For the purpose of classifying waveform systems equations, emissions are considered to be aperiodic, periodic or random. This is a general method of classifying emissions.

Aperiodic emissions are, with relatively few exceptions, of finite energy and can be represented in terms of their time waveforms or continuous frequency spectra. They are assumed to be deterministic here. Periodic emissions can be represented in terms of their time waveforms or discrete frequency spectra. Fourier analysis methods may be applied to either of these two types of waveforms. Random processes generally must be represented by their N-dimensional joint probability distribution functions. However, for certain situations (e.g., stationary Gaussian processes) they may be represented by their autocorrelation functions or power spectral densities.

The transfer of energy from an emitter to a potentially susceptible device may, in general, involve a nonlinear, time-varying, dispersive and even random process. The randomness generally reflects a lack of precise information about the system. For example, reflection and scattering from objects in the propagation path of a signal may either be impractical to obtain or so varied between systems of a given type that only a statistical representation is meaningful.

The general type of transfer process is very difficult to treat analytically. However, in many cases of practical interest, it is possible to assume that the process is deterministic and time-invariant or to separate the time-variant process from the remainder of the transfer process. Furthermore, in some cases it is possible to assume that the process is deterministic and linear, or to separate the nonlinearity from the remainder of the transfer process. Each of these assumptions results in certain limitations. Table 1.2 shows the basic systems equations which result for each of the cases of interest. General equations are provided only for the linear, deterministic transfer process. They are given for three different types of temporal dependencies and for both continuous and discrete spectrum emissions.

1.5.2   Waveform Parameter Equations

Some waveform parameters to which receptors may be sensitive include average power, total energy and peak voltage (current or power). For example, certain explosive devices are triggered by the burning away of a wire (resistive heating). This is a total energy susceptibility. Also, many digital devices are susceptible to instantaneous waveform level ("peak" sensitivity).

This parameter list is far from complete, of course, and one could think of many other parameters that a device may be sensitive to: for example, pulse width or pulse repetition frequency. There are a large number of conceivable parameters; however, the characteristics of almost all known receptors are likely to warrant consideration of only the above three.

Table 1.2—Waveform System Equations (continued next page)

Transfer / Emission	Linear and Deterministic		
	Time Variant		**Time Invariant**
	General	**Special Case (Time & Frequency Separable)**	
Aperiodic (Continuous Spectrum)	$v_o(t) = \int_{-\infty}^{\infty} v_i(\tau) h_g(t - \tau,\, t)\, d\tau$ $V_o(f) = \int_{-\infty}^{\infty} V_i(f') H_g(f',\, f - f')\, df'$	$V_o(t) = \int_{-\infty}^{\infty} a(t) v_i(\tau) h(t - \tau)\, d\tau$ $V_o(f) = A(f) * [V_i(f) H(f)]$	$v_o(t) = \int_{-\infty}^{\infty} v_i(\tau) h(t - \tau)\, d\tau$ $V_o(f) = V_i(f) H(f)$
Periodic (Discrete Spectrum)	$v_o(t) = \frac{1}{T} \sum_{n=-\infty}^{\infty} h_g\!\left(\frac{n}{T},\, t\right) v_n^i\, e^{j\frac{2\pi n}{T} t}$ $V_o(f) = \frac{1}{T} \sum_{n=-\infty}^{\infty} V_n^i\, H_g\!\left(\frac{n}{T},\, f - \frac{n}{T}\right)$	$v_o(t) = \frac{a(t)}{T} \sum_{n=-\infty}^{\infty} h\!\left(\frac{n}{T}\right) v_n^i\, e^{j\frac{2\pi n}{T} t}$ $V_o(f) = \frac{1}{T} \sum_{n=-\infty}^{\infty} H\!\left(\frac{n}{T}\right) v_n^i\, A\!\left(f - \frac{n}{T}\right)$	$v_o(t) = \frac{1}{T} \sum_{n=-\infty}^{\infty} h\!\left(\frac{n}{T}\right) v_n^i\, e^{j\frac{2\pi n}{T} t}$
Random	General solution not available. Solution may be obtained for special case of a Gaussian random process.		

Table 1.2—Waveform System Equations (continued)

Nonlinear	Random
General solution not available. Time-domain analysis methods are available for special cases that may be considered as piecewise linear, e.g., hard limiting, mixing, etc. Effort should be directed toward developing computer programs for these special cases. Volterra analysis may be used for periodic signals that have a limited number of frequency components. Aperiodic or periodic signals may be represented in either time domain or frequency domain, and Fourier transforms may be used. In general, random signals must be described in terms of their N-Dimensional joint probability distribution functions. A stationary Gaussian random process may be described in terms of the autocorrelation function or power spectral density.	Monte Carlo method offers general solution. Methods for solving cable bundle problems, where relative wire locations and terminals loads are random, are discussed in Morgan, Feb. 1978.

v_i, V_i = the input voltage as a function of time (t) or frequency (f)

h = the impulse response of the coupling media

H = the transfer function of the coupling media

τ = delay

T = the period of a waveform

a, A = the time variation of the coupling media

1.32

The above three parameters are often related to corresponding interference indicators such as "susceptibility margins." These margins are numbers which indicate the level to which specified unwanted emissions cause unacceptable receptor performance. Table 1.3 gives equations for various waveform parameters. Although the parameters are in terms of current waveforms, corresponding voltage waveform equations would be similar. Also, the receptor and detector input impedances are assumed to be 1 Ω each. Only minor changes in the tabulated margins would result if the impedances were arbitrary.

Table 1.3—Susceptibility Margins

	Deterministic	Stochastic
Average Power	$\int_{f_a}^{f_b} \dfrac{G_r(f)}{|I_r^s(f)|^2}\, df$	$\int_{f_a}^{f_b} \dfrac{G_r(f)}{|I_r^s(f)|^2}\, df$
Total Energy	Periodic: Use average power margin Aperiodic: $\int_{f_a}^{f_b} \dfrac{|I_r(f)|^2}{E_r^s(f)^2}\, df$	Stationary: Use average power margin "Switched" Stationary: $\quad \Delta \int_{f_a}^{f_b} \dfrac{G_r(f)}{E_r^s(f)}\, df$
Peak Current	$\int_{f_a}^{f_b} \dfrac{|I_r(f)|}{|I_r^s(f)|}\, df$	Stationary: $\quad \dfrac{\sigma_r^2}{\alpha|I_r^s(f_p)|^2}$

The definitions of all quantities in Table 1.3 are included in the list below. The term "switched stationary" as a susceptibility margin for total energy sensitive receptors indicates that the input waveform is an otherwise stationary process that is "turned" on and off at regular intervals.

$i_r(t)$ = detector output current

$I_r(f)$ = Fourier transform of $i_r(t)$ (finite energy)

$I_r^s(f)$ = level of $I_r(f)$ which induces the interference threshold level at the detector

$G_r(f)$ = spectral power density at receptor input (Note: $G_r(f)$ is defined for negative f.)

$E_r^s(f)$ = the CW energy at frequency f which generates the energy equal to the standard response energy level at the detector input with cooling included

Δ = duration of interference on receptor

σ_r^2 = variance of detector input waveform

α = fraction of time that a stochastic waveform peak at detector input must exceed K to trigger interference

f_a, f_b = lower, upper frequencies defining common frequency band between interferer and receptor

f_p = frequency for which receptor input is maximum

1.5.3 Application of System Equations to EMC Analysis

In order to determine whether an EMI problem exists between a potentially interfering transmitter and a receiver, it is necessary to consider the susceptibility of the receiver to both the design and spurious outputs (individually and collectively) of the potentially interfering transmitters. The factors that must be included in the analysis for each transmitter output (or group of transmitter outputs) include: the transmitter power (P_T), the transmitting antenna gain in the direction of the receiver (G_T), the propagation loss between the transmitter and receiver (L), the receiver antenna gain in the direction of the transmitter (G_R) and the amount of power required to produce interference in the receiver (P_R) in the presence of the desired signal.

Factors that must be considered in EMC analysis include both the design (intentional) and operational performance characteristics of equipment and the nondesign (unintentional) and nonoperational characteristics. The necessity of considering parameters such as transmitter spurious output emissions, receiver spurious responses, antenna side-and-back lobe radiation and unintentional propagation paths introduces complications since it is now necessary to obtain information on equipment nondesign characteristics.

Unlike equipment design characteristics (which are usually well-defined and may be easily found from equipment specifications), equipment spurious characteristics are not usually identified or described in equipment specifications. It is therefore difficult to obtain information on the spurious characteristics of specific equipments.

Performance measurements clearly demonstrate that there are large inherent variations in equipment spurious characteristics. As a result of these inherent variations, two electronic equipments that are identical in all visible physical respects (two different serial number equipments of a particular nomenclature) may exhibit wide-ly different spurious characteristics. For this reason it is better to specify equipment spurious characteristics statistically, i.e., in terms of the likelihood that a particular spurious level will be equaled or exceeded. If the spurious characteristics are described as cumulative probability distributions, the analysis results will also be defined in terms of the probability that a particular interference situation exists.

The procedure that is used for each transmitter output emission can be demonstrated by considering the interference situation that exists between a particular output of one of a number of potential-ly interfering transmitters and a specimen receiver. In the case of a particular transmitter output (which may be either a fundamen-tal or a spurious emission), the power available at the receiver is given by:

$$P_A(f,t,d,p) = P_T(f,t) + C_{TR}(f,t,d,p) \qquad (1.2)$$

where, $P_A(f,t,d,p) =$ power available at the receiver (in dBm) is a function of frequency (f), time (t), distance separation (d) and direction (p) of both transmitter and receiver and their antennas

$P_T(f,t,) =$ transmitter power (in dBm)

$C_{TR}(f,t,d,p) =$ transmission coupling between the transmitter and receiver (in dB)

In intersystem EMC analysis problems, the function $C_{TR}(f,t,d,p)$ includes the effects of both the transmitting and receiving anten-na characteristics, G_T and G_R and the intervening propagation media. For some situations (emphasis certain radars), the antenna performance is not readily separable from the transmitter/receiver characteristics. When this exists, the transmitter antenna characteristics are grouped with P_T (units now dBm/m^2) and backed out of the C_{TR} term. This is explained in more detail in subsequent chapters.

By comparing the power available at the receiver input terminals to the power required at the input to produce interference in the receiver at the frequency in question $P_R(f,t)$, it is possible to deter-mine the interference situation for the particular transmitter out-put being considered. The requirement for EMC is that the power available at the receiver be less than the power required to produce interference in the receiver. Thus, the condition for electromagnetic compatibility is:

$$P_A(f,t,d,p) < P_R(f,t) \qquad (1.3)$$

On the other hand, if the power available at the receiver input terminals is equal to or greater than the power required to produce interference in the receiver, as given below, an electromagnetic interference problem may exist:

$$P_A(f,t,d,p) \geq P_R(f,t) \qquad (1.4)$$

While the foregoing may seem basic, it is the essence of all intersystem EMI situations. The P_R terms appearing in Eqs. (1.3) and (1.4) are rather complicated. First, P_R in reality is greater than the receiver internal noise referred to the input and is related to the intended signal reception level. Secondly, to determine if interference is actually disturbing or damaging, calculations must be made of the result of a particular signal-to-interference (S/I) ratio and the impact that this will have on system performance. Two relatively simple situations will illustrate this.

Illustrative Example 1.2

Assume that an FPS-T, L-Band radar, radiating 2 MW of peak pulse power at its 1,300 MHz fundamental, will radiate -50 dB down ($P_{Ti} = 20$ W $= +43$ dBm) at the third harmonic, 3.9 GHz (P_{Ti} = transmitter interference power). Also assume a TD-R microwave relay link is in line of sight with this radar 9.7 m away and that the transmitter and receiver antenna gains in the direction of each other at 3.9 GHz are $G_{Ti} = 20$ dB and $G_{Ri} = -15$ dB, respectively. Finally, assume the TD-R threshold sensitivity is $P_R = -95$ dBm for a 3 MHz bandwidth. It follows then that:

$$P_{Ti} = +43 \text{ dBm}$$

$$C_{TRi} = G_{Ti} - L_i + G_{Ri} \qquad (1.5)$$

where,
$$L_i = 20 \log(4\pi R^2/\lambda) = 125 \text{ dB (see Chap. 6)} \qquad (1.6)$$

Thus,

$$C_{TRi} = 20 \text{ dB} - 125 \text{ dB} - 15 \text{ dB} = -120 \text{ dB} \qquad (1.7)$$

Equation (1.2) then becomes:

$$P_{Ai} = P_{Ti} + C_{TRi}$$

$$= 43 \text{ dBm} - 120 \text{ dB} = -77 \text{ dBm} \qquad (1.8)$$

Since $P_R = -95$ dBm, Eq. (1.4) applies for a potentially interfering situation:

$$P_{Ai} = -77 \text{ dBm} \geqslant P_R = -95 \text{ dBm} \qquad (1.9)$$

or,

$$P_{Ai} - P_R = 18 \text{ dB above TD-R receiver noise level} \qquad (1.10)$$

Thus, in the absence of an intentional signal, it would appear that EMI would exist in the TD-R receiver from the FPS-T radar when the latter's scanning antenna is looking at (bore sighting) the former.

Illustrative Example 1.3

The second situation considers the effect of a TD-T microwave relay transmitter located 51 km away in line of sight with its intentional receiver. For this situation, $P_{Ts} = 1$ W ($+30$ dBm), $G_{Ts} = G_{Rs} = 40$ dB for horn antennas ("s" in subscripts = intentional signal). $P_R = -95$ dBm as before. Applying these data to the above yields:

$$P_{Ts} = +30 \text{ dBm}$$

$$C_{TRs} = C_{Ts} - L_s + G_{Rs}$$

$$= 40 \text{ dB} - 139 \text{ dB} + 40 \text{ dB} = -59 \text{ dB}$$

Equation (1.2) becomes:

$$P_{As} = P_{Ts} + C_{TRs}$$

$$= 30 \text{ dBm} - 59 \text{ dB} = -29 \text{ dBm}$$

Since $P_R = -95$ dBm, Eq. (1.4) applies for the intentional transmitter situations:

$$P_{As} = -29 \text{ dBm} \geqslant P_R = -95 \text{ dBm}$$

$$P_{As} - P_R = 66 \text{ dB above TD-R receiver noise level}$$

The intentional microwave relay signal is 66 dB above receiver threshold, while the unintentional radar third harmonic is 18 dB above threshold. The net effect is that the intentional signal is 48 dB (66 dB – 18 dB) above the potentially interfering source. Thus, the S/I ratio is about 48 dB as long as the intentional transmitting source is communicating with the microwave relay. It should be recognized that the desired signal may be subject to fading. Allowing for 30 dB fades, the S/I ratio will still be 18 dB. Because of receiver AGC action (desensitization), EMI will not exist.

1.6 Input Information Required

To perform an EMC analysis, it is necessary to provide certain basic information on each source and responding equipment to be included in the analysis. Examples of information that are usually required include equipment nomenclature, geographical location and operating or assigned frequency. Nominal equipment data such as the following are required:

1. transmitter power output, emission types and emission bandwidth;
2. receiver sensitivity, bandwidth, IF and local oscillator frequencies and anti-jamming logic, if applicable and
3. antenna gain, polarization, height, orientation and beamwidth.

It is best, but not always necessary, to have terrain data, specific information on equipment interference characteristics and data on special fixes which may be supplied on specific equipment. Equipment interference characteristics that are useful for EMC analysis include transmitter spurious outputs; receiver selectivity, spurious responses, intermodulation and adjacent-channel interference characteristics and antenna gain characteristics for side and back lobe regions as a function of polarization.

It is often difficult to gather all the needed information for an EMC analysis; therefore, it is necessary to synthesize missing data. In many cases it is possible to use nominal equipment characteristics to generate needed characteristics data for transmitters, receivers and antennas. The use of synthesized data permits the user to perform an EMC analysis of a system containing equipments for which specific interference characteristics are not available. Figure 1.14 shows the interrelationship between various types of required and synthesized data.

One source of detailed equipment characteristic data required to perform an EMC analysis is the spectrum signature measurement program conducted in accordance with MIL-STD-449D (see Vol. 1). EMC characteristics of a number of transmitters, receivers and antennas have been measured and collected under this program which is sponsored by the Department of Defense (DoD). All information obtained under this program has been collected and reviewed by the Electromagnetic Compatibility Analysis Center (ECAC).

ECAC is a major source of data used in EMC analysis. The four basic types of data files established and maintained by ECAC include:

1. The Environmental File shows the use and operation of CE equipment by various civilian, military and governmental agencies in the United States and other selected areas of the world. Among the agencies included are the Department of Defense, Coast Guard, National Aeronautical Space Agency, Weather Bureau, Office of Emergency Preparedness, Federal Communications Commission, American Telephone and Telegraph, Western Union and General Telephone and Electronics Company. Outputs from the file can be sorted alphabetically by city or military base, frequency, equipment nomenclature or a number of other parameters.

2. The Spectrum Allocation and Use File consists of information on the frequency allocation status of present and future United States military CE systems. The file contains detailed data on both the operational and functional features of the system. The file may be sorted by application number, frequency, operational data, geographical area, operational environment, equipment function and many other major fields and outputs provided accordingly.

3. The Nominal Characteristics File contains information on the technical characteristics of U.S. military and civilian CE systems. The bulk of the information comes from military technical manuals and technical orders and from manufacturers' brochures. Special computer programs are used to sort the file on one or more of the available parameters.

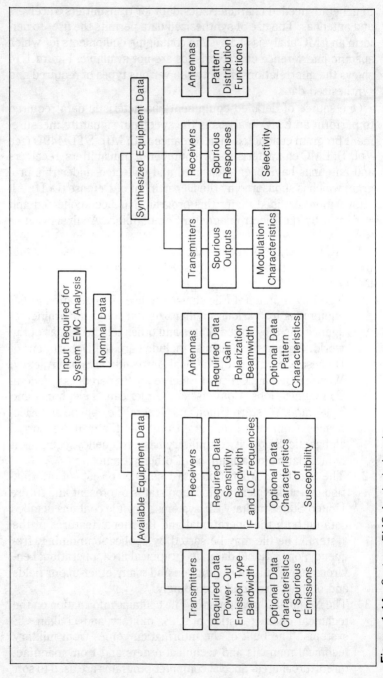

Figure 1.14—System EMC Analysis Inputs

4 . The ECAC Topographic File consists of terrain elevation data extracted from standard Army Topographic Command maps. Elevation data are in feet and the coordinate system conforms to the latitude/longitude grid system. Outputs from this file are used to determine line-of-sight conditions between equipments and as input to propagation path loss calculation models which depend on a knowledge of path profiles.

Information contained in ECAC files is provided to qualified users in the form of computer printouts or publications; contact your contracting officer's technical representative. Capabilities are provided for gathering data contained in the files by selective retrieval on the basis of different categories using designated descriptor words. One problem encountered in trying to get data from ECAC or other DoD agencies is that much of the data is classified SECRET or CONFIDENTIAL and are therefore not generally available.

Another major source of data for EMC analysis is the Federal Communication Commission (FCC) which maintains detailed files and records on all applications for a licensee to use the spectrum. FCC data is available in the form of computer tapes which can be purchased by users. These tapes include information on the location and frequency for all licensees.

Information of government users of the spectrum can be obtained from the National Telecommunications Information Agency (NTIA) which is under the Department of Commerce.

A lot of information for EMC analysis is also available through reports on programs that have been performed at various DoD agencies, civilian government, and private organizations. Many of the more significant works are referenced in the bibliography at the end of each chapter.

1.7 Output Results Obtained

EMC analysis will yield a variety of answers. The types of answers obtained in a particular problem are determined by the extent to which one chooses to carry the analysis. For example, if only a preliminary analysis is performed, the results may (1) identify potentially interfering equipment transmitter-receiver pairs by nomenclature, (2) define the frequency range over which interference problems may exist and (3) specify the interference margin (the amount by which the interfering signal exceeds the level required to produce a standard response at the receiver output) over each frequency range of interest. Other outputs may include the distance separation between potentially interfering equipment pairs and their respective tuned frequencies to just avoid an EMI problem. The answers from an analysis will also provide information regarding specific transmitter outputs and receiver responses which may result in interference problems.

A detailed EMC analysis is used to provide additional answers, such as the elimination of potentially interfering equipment pairs by considering specific propagation modes and antenna directivity characteristics. Other output results may contain a statistical description of the interference, details of time-dependent statistics and a summary of the combined effects of time-dependent and time-independent statistics.

Another aspect of an EMC analysis is relating EMI conditions to operational performance or operational effectiveness. This is a system analysis problem that must consider the effect of interference on a particular equipment, and factors such as the importance of the equipment to a particular operation or mission and redundancy that may be present in the system, operator, etc.

All classes of results described above may be found by applying EMC analysis techniques presented in this volume. There are also many fringe benefits that the user can get from this handbook. These include statistical summaries of transmitter, receiver and antenna EMC characteristics; description of general mathematical models that are used for representing equipment EMC characteristics; summary of propagation models and a discussion of operational performance and operational effectiveness.

1.8 References

1. *Electromagnetic Spectrum Utilization, the Silent Crisis* (Washington, DC: U.S. Dept. of Commerce).
2. Ibid.
3. Ibid.

1.9 Bibliography

1. Beckmann, P., "Amplitude-Probability Distribution of Atmospheric Radio Noise," *NBS Radio Science Journal of Research*, Vol. 68D, No. 6, June 1964.

2. Bello, P.A., "Error Probabilities Due to Atmospheric Noise and Flat Fading in HF Ionospheric Communications Systems," *IEEE Transactions on Communications Technology*, Vol. 13, No. 3, September 1965.

3. Bernard, C.R.W., "VHF Noise Levels over Large Towns," Royal Aircraft Establishment Technical Report 67213, August 1967.

4. Buehler, W.E., and Lunden, C.D., "Signatures of Man-Made High-Frequency Radio Noise," *IEEE Transactions on Electromagnetic Compatibility*, Vol. EMC-8, No. 8, September 1966, pp. 143-52.

5. Buehler, W.E.; King, C.H.; and Lunden, C.D., "VHF City Noise," *1968 IEEE EMC Symposium Record*, pp. 113-18 (New York: IEEE, 1986).

6. CCIR Report 322, *World Distribution and Characteristics of Atmospheric Radio Noise* (Geneva: CCIR, 1964).

7. "Control of Electronic Product Radiation," Federal Register, Vol. 35, No. 100, May 22, 1970, pp. 7851-954.

8. Crichlow, W.Q.; Robique, C.J.; Spaulding, A.D.; and Berry, W.M., "Determination of the Amplitude-Probability Distribution of Atmospheric Radio Noise from Statistical Moments," *Journal of Research NBS*, Vol. 64D, No. 1, January/February 1960, pp. 49-56.

9. Crichlow, W.Q., and Disney, R.T., *Man-Made Radio Noise Measurements at the NBS Gaithersburg Site and NBS, Washington, DC*, Memorandum Report (Boulder Laboratories: National Bureau of Standards, February 1961).

10. Crichlow, W.Q.; Spaulding, D.J.; Robique, A.D.; and Disney, R.T., "Amplitude-Probability Distribution for Atmospheric Radio Noise," NBS Monograph 23, November 1960.

11. Crichlow, W.Q.; Smith, D.F.; Morton, R.N.; and Corliss, W.R., "World-Wide Radio Noise Levels Expected in the Frequency Band 10 Kilocycles to 100 Megacycles," NBS Circular 557A, August 1955.

12. Deterding, J.M., "Electromagnetic Compatibility Assurance—A Step in Planning for Communications of the Future," IIT RI ECAC, *1969 IEEE International Communication Conference Record*, pp. 24-1 to 24-s (New York: IEEE, 1969).

13. Duff, W.G., et. al., "Airborne Electromagnetic Environment Survey," *1974 IEEE EMC Symposium Record* (New York: IEEE, 1974).

14. Duff, W.G., et. al., "Overview of Weapon Assessments in an Electromagnetic Environment," *1983 IEEE EMC Symposium Record* (New York: IEEE, 1983).

15. Ellis, A.G., "Site Noise and Its Correlation with Vehicular Traffic Density," *Proceedings of the IRE*, January 1963, pp. 45-52.

16. Federal Communications Commission," *Man-Made Noise*, Report to Technical Committee of the Advisory Committee for Land Mobile Radio Services from Working Group 3, Vol. 2, Part 2, November 1967.

17. Garlan, H., and Whipple, G.L., *Field Measurements of Electromagnetic Energy Radiated by RF Stabilized Arc Welders*, FCC Technical Div. Report T-6401, February 1964.

18. George, R.W., "Field Strength of Motor Car Ignition between 40 and 450 Megacycles," *Proceedings of the IRE*, Vol. 28, September 1940, pp. 409-13.

19. International Telephone and Telegraph Corp., *Reference Data for Radio Engineers*, 5th ed. (New York: Howard W. Sams & Co., Inc., 1968).

20. Joint Technical Advisory Committee (JTAC) of the IEEE and EIA, *Spectrum Engineering—the Key to Progress* (New York: IEEE, 1968).

21. Lichter, I.; Borris, J.; and Miller, W.M., "Radio-Frequency Hazards with Cardiac Pacemaker," *British Medical Journal*, Vol. 1, pp. 1513-18, June 12, 1965.

22. Pakala, W.E.; Taylor, E.R.; and Harrold, R.T., "Radio Noise Measurements on High Voltage Lines," *1968 IEEE EMC Symposium Record*, pp. 96-107 (New York: IEEE, 1971).

23. Pearce, S.F. and Bull, J.H., "Interference from Industrial, Scientific and Medical Sea Radio-Frequency Equipment," Electrical Research Assn., Leatherhead, Surry, England, Report No. 5033, October 1964.

24. Skomal, E.N., "Analysis of Airborne VHF/UHF Incidental Noise over Metropolitan Areas," *IEEE Transactions on EMC*, Vol. EMC-11, No. 2, May 1969, pp. 75-83.

25. Skomal, E.N., "Distribution and Frequency Dependence of Incidental Man-Made HF/VHF Noise in Metropolitan Areas," *IEEE Transactions on Electromagnetic Compatibility*, Vol. EMC-11, No. 3, May 1969, pp. 66-75.

26. Skomal, E.N., "Analysis of the Frequency Dependence of Man-Made Radio Noise," *1966 IEEE International Convention Record*, pp. 125-9. Part 2, March 1966.

27. Skomal, E.N., "Comparative Radio Noise Levels of Transmission Lines, Automotive Traffic and RF Stabilized Arc Welders," *IEEE Transactions on Electromagnetic Compatibility*, Vol. EMC-7, September 1967, pp. 73-6.

28. Skomal, E.N., "Distribution and Frequency Dependence of Unintentionally Generated Man-Made UH/VHF Noise in Metropolitan Areas, Part 2, Theory," *IEEE Transactions on EMC*, Vol. EMC-7, December 1965, pp. 263-78, 420-28.

29. Spaulding, D.C.; Robique, C.J.; and Crichlow, W.Q., "Conversion of the Amplitude-Probability Distribution Function for Atmospheric Radio Noise from One Bandwidth to Another," *NBS*, Vol. 66D, No. 6, November-December 1962, pp. 713-20.

30. Telecommunication Science Panel of the Commerce Technical Advisory Board, U.S. Dept. of Commerce, "Electromagnetic Spectrum Utilization, the Silent Crisis," a report on telecommunication science and the federal government, 1966.

31. White, D.R.J., et. al., "Spectrum Pollution in Metropolitan Washington, DC," *1970 IEEE Regional EMC Symposium Record*, pp. II-A-1 to II-A-9 (New York: IEEE, 1970).

Chapter 2

Telecommunication System EMC Analysis

This chapter describes electromagnetic relationships that exist between telecommunications systems and presents equations that define these relationships. The chapter also defines basic concepts, procedures and techniques that are used in performing an EMC analysis. An organized analysis procedure is presented for telecommunications system interference which is characterized via energy emitted by and received from antennas and may be applied to either operational systems or systems in the planning and design stages.

In order to give adequate attention to EMC at all stages, from original system definition to operation, it is necessary that an organized and well-defined mathematical process exist. This covers predicting, analyzing and evaluating compatibility considerations before the actual development and production of systems. This requirement establishes a need for techniques for analyzing and evaluating EMI between transmitters, emitters, receivers or other devices that are potentially susceptible to electromagnetic energy.

To be useful at all stages in the life cycle of an equipment, the basic analysis techniques should be applicable to a broad range of different types of problems. These include the capability to determine EMI between equipments for which available data may be either limited (as in the case of preliminary design stages) or extensive (as in the case of existing equipments for which specific measured data are already available).

As explained in later sections, the analysis techniques contain a repertoire of mathematical models and EMI forecasting processes. A math model is a term used in the trade to represent the mathematical relationship between two or more parameters. Just as a physical model of a device or structure is a three-dimensional scale representation of the real item, a math model is a conceptual (mathematical) representation with emphasis on external, i.e., input-output, characteristics.

2.1 Major EMI Interactions

In the planning and design of a CE system, it is important to recognize that there are several different means by which EMI may occur, and for each situation the appropriate types of EMC analysis must be considered. Figure 2.1 illustrates the important types of EMI which may exist between a transmitter-receiver pair.

The important types of EMI shown in Figure 2.1 may be considered to be in one of three basic categories: (a) co-channel, (b) adjacent-signal or (c) out-of-band.

Co-channel EMI refers to interference resulting from signals that exist within the narrowest passband of the receiver. For superheterodyne receivers (which is the type used for many applications) the frequency of co-channel interference must be such that the interference is translated to the intermediate frequency (IF) passband in the same way as the desired signal. This requires that the frequency of co-channel interfering signals equals the tuned radio frequency plus or minus one-half the narrowest IF bandwidth.

Although the receiver is sensitive to this type of interference, it is usually easily controlled by avoiding co-channel assignments within a relatively large zone over which this type of interference may occur.

Adjacent-signal EMI refers to potentially interfering signals that exist within or near the receiver radio frequency (RF) passband, but after conversion, fall outside of the IF passband. The most significant adjacent-signal EMI effects result from intermodulation and transmitter noise. The adjacent-signal EMI region may extend over a considerable range of frequencies on each side of the tuned frequency. For example, for a typical UHF communication transceiver having 50 kHz channel spacing, the adjacent-channel EMI region may include 200 channels (10 MHz) on each side of the desired channel. Although the adjacent-signal EMI

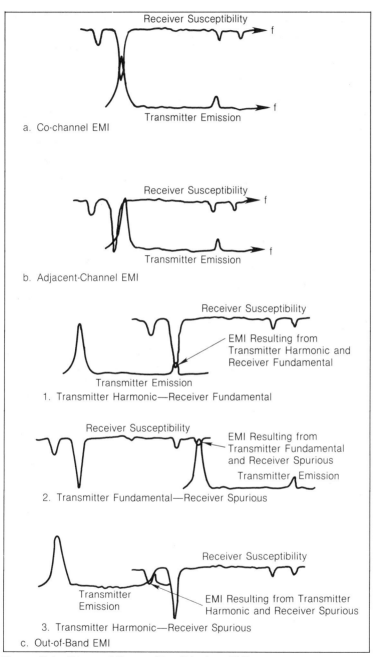

a. Co-channel EMI

b. Adjacent-Channel EMI

1. Transmitter Harmonic—Receiver Fundamental

2. Transmitter Fundamental—Receiver Spurious

3. Transmitter Harmonic—Receiver Spurious

c. Out-of-Band EMI

Figure 2.1—Types of Transmitter-Receiver EMI

2.3

region includes a relatively wide range of frequencies, the receiver is not particularly sensitive to these signals. As a result, adjacent-signal EMI is usually limited to co-site situations involving transceivers which are located within several kilometers of each other.

Out-of-band EMI refers to signals having frequency components which are significantly outside of the widest receiver passband. The most significant out-of-band EMI effects result from transmitter harmonics interfering with receiver fundamentals or transmitter fundamentals interfering with receiver spurious. EMI between transmitter harmonics and receiver spurious is also possible but extremely unlikely. Because of the power levels involved, out-of-band EMI is usually restricted to co-site situations.

2.2 Analysis Input Functions

In order to describe the basic prediction and analysis procedures that are used in determining telecommunication system EMI, an introduction to the fundamental input functions and the basic analysis equation is presented. While they may appear to be simple, these initial introductions and relations serve to establish the basic frame from which the analysis processes are derived. With the basic elements of the problem defined, the next steps are to explore the form of the input functions and to combine them to achieve a meaningful and useful process.

A single, potentially interfering source and a single, susceptible device are used to define the input functions. The equation used to predict EMI involving CE equipments is then derived. The basic input functions are:

1. The electromagnetic emitting source output or emitter function, $P_T(f,t)$ in dBm, where P_T represents the power transmitted as a function of frequency (f) and time (t), and where dBm = decibel above 1 mW and dBm = 10 log mW = 30 + 10 log W

2. The susceptibility threshold function $P_R(f,t)$ in dBm represents the minimum power received for producing interference in the potentially susceptible device.

3. The transmission coupling (transmit-receive) function $C_{TR}(f, t, d, p)$ in dB describes the power transfer relationship between the source function and the susceptible device. The symbol d represents the separation distance and p represents the direction of the antennas. In the case of telecommunica-

tion system problems involving interference coupled from a transmitting antenna to a receiving antenna, the transmission coupling function is represented by:

$$C_{TR}(f,t,d,p) = G_{TR}(f,t,d,p) - L(f,t,d,p) + G_{RT}(f,t,d,p) \quad (2.1)$$

where,

G_{TR} (f,t,d,p) = the transmitting source antenna gain in dB
L (f,t,d,p) = the propagation loss function in dB
G_{RT} (f,t,d,p) = the receiving antenna gain in dB
Subscript TR = from transmitter to receiver, and vice versa

2.2.1   Independent Variables

The input functions defined above are expressed in terms of frequency, time, distance and direction. These are the four fundamental and most important dimensions of EMI problems and are the basic variables in EMC analysis. When electromagnetic radiation is used for communication, navigation, radar, etc., it is necessary to separate the desired signal from its electromagnetic environment. This separation may be made on the basis of time, frequency, distance or direction. Figure 1.9 of Chapter 1 illustrates this. Direction includes both three-dimensional direction and polarization.

2.2.1.1   Frequency Separation

Signal emission on the basis of frequency is one of the basic principals in communication and radar. Carrier frequency separation is the best-known and most widely used EMI-control technique. This is especially important since more emissions are being added to the already crowded spectrum each year.

EMC analysis is compounded in the frequency domain because transmitters, which are designed to radiate at an assigned frequency, actually produce spurious radiations at many other frequencies. This greatly increases the complexity of the electromagnetic environment and its pollution. Similarly, receivers tuned to a given frequency are susceptible to emissions at other frequencies. The frequency variable, therefore, also requires that both the selectivity associated with each receiver response and the emission bandwidth of each intentional and unintentional transmitter emission be considered in the prediction and analysis process.

2.2.1.2   Time Separation

The element of time is also important in any interference problem. In many instances EMI may be avoided if the intentional signal and unintentional emitting sources are not present simultaneously. Situations which result in severe interference may often be resolved when a time-sharing plan is put into effect. Time-dependent quantities must be considered for both random and continuous operations. These include longer time situations such as diurnal effects (day-night propagation changes), seasonal effects and even 11-year solar cycles (emphasis on sudden ionospheric disturbances-SIDs) in estimating propagation transmission losses. Short-time effects such as antenna rotation and scanning as well as moving CE equipments must also be considered. Percentages of time in which useful communication is required and provided are included.

2.2.1.3   Distance Separation

Distance separation is the third basic independent variable that is considered in an EMC analysis. This variable is fundamental to all antenna and propagation considerations. Equipments which do not have sufficient distance separation are potential sources of, or responders to, interference. The maximum distance separation to be considered is as unlimited as the potential range to earth from a space vehicle. The minimum separation lies within the near-field region and presents a challenging problem.

2.2.1.4   Directional Selectivity

The fourth independent variable in EMC analysis involves direction of transmitted and received signals. Specifically, it is a three-dimensional directional selectivity offered by both antennas, and it includes polarization match or alignments.

2.2.2   Dependent Variables

In addition to the preceding basic independent variables of the EMI problem, it is necessary to consider the dependent variables. These variables are normally referred to as amplitude, signal or emission levels, transmission coupling and susceptibility. For the purpose of EMC analysis, the dependent variables are more correctly referred to as "directly contributing to interference." Their definitions are different for each of the three analysis input functions, but the effects of their respective contributions to the total interference problem are identical.

The dependent variable contributing to interference for the source emitting function P_T is the power delivered to the transmission media which includes the transmitting antenna. As the power output from the potentially interfering source increases, its contribution to EMI increases and the potential for interference becomes greater.

For the transmission coupling function C_{TR}, the primary contribution to interference is the electromagnetic coupling between emission sources and potentially susceptible devices. Thus, as the transmission coupling increases, the contribution to interference increases and the potential interference becomes greater. For antenna coupling, C_{TR} is composed of the contribution of EMI associated with transmitting and receiving antenna functions and propagation.

For the contribution to interference associated with transmitting and receiving antenna functions, the dependent variable contributing to interference is the directional antenna gain versus frequency, time, direction and orientation (polarization). As the contribution to EMI attributed to antenna gain function increases, potential interference becomes greater.

For the contribution to interference associated with the propagation, the dependent variable is the propagation loss L. As the propagation loss decreases, its contribution to EMI increases and a potential interference becomes greater. The dependent variable contributing to EMI for the susceptibility function P_R is expressed in terms of the power required to interfere with the receiver or other receptor output devices. As this power decreases, the relative contribution to interference increases.

The preceding relationships are illustrated in Fig. 2.2. A marginal interference condition (one in which the received power P_A is approximately equal to the receiver susceptibility threshold) is represented in Fig. 2.2a. If either (1) the transmitter power or antenna gains were increased or (2) the propagation loss or receiver susceptibility threshold were decreased, an interference condition would exist. This corresponds to one in which the received power is greater than the receiver susceptibility threshold as illustrated

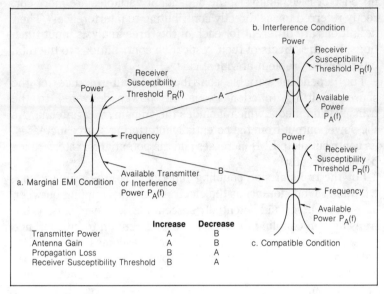

Figure 2.2—EMI Relationships

in Fig. 2.2b. On the other hand, if (1) the transmitter power or effective antenna gains were decreased or (2) the propagation loss or receiver susceptibility threshold were increased, a compatible condition would exist. This situation is one in which the received power is less than the receiver susceptibility threshold as shown in Fig. 2.2c.

2.3 EMC Analysis

To analyze EMC between a single emitting source and a single susceptible device, the source function and transmission function (which may consist of both propagation and antenna functions) are combined. This results in the power available at the receiver or other potentially susceptible device. The next step is to compare the power available with the susceptibility function to determine whether a potential interfering problem will in fact exist.

The expression which defines the power available (P_A) in units of dBm at the susceptible device was presented in Chapter 1:

$$P_A(f,t,d,p) = P_T(f, t) + C_{TR}(f,t,d,p) \qquad (2.2)$$

If the power available at the susceptible device from a potentially interfering source is less than the susceptibility threshold of the

2.8

device, EMC is ensured. Thus, a compatible condition exists when:

$$P_A(f,t,d,p) < P_R(f, t) \tag{2.3}$$

On the other hand, if the power available at the susceptible device is equal to or greater than the susceptibility threshold, a compatibility problem (EMI) may be present. Thus, an interference problem may exist when:

$$P_A(f,t,d,p) \geqslant P_R(f,t) \tag{2.4}$$

When $P_A = P_R$, EMC is marginal and an EMI problem may or may not exist. Specifics regarding this situation are discussed in later sections.

An indication of the magnitude of a potential interference problem may be found by considering the difference between the power available and the susceptibility threshold. This difference is called interference margin (IM) and provides a measure of the total contribution to intereference, i.e.:

$$IM(f,t,d,p) = P_A(f,t,d,p) - P_R(f,t) \tag{2.5}$$

The interference margin is defined such that there is a potential interference problem if the margin is positive and there is little to no chance of interference if the interference margin is negative.

The expression $IM(f,t,d,p)$ in Eq. (2.5) can be considered to represent an equivalent on-tune interference-to-noise ratio (I/N) at the receiver input terminals. If the expressions for $P_A(f,t,d,p)$ and $P_R(f,t)$ are expanded, Eq. (2.5) becomes:

$$IM(f,t,d,p) = I/N = P_T(f_E) + G_{TR}(f_E, t,d,p) - L(f_E,t,d,p)$$

$$+ G_{RT}(f_E,t,d,p) - P_R(f_R) + CF(B_T, B_R, \Delta f) \tag{2.6}$$

where,

$$P_T(f_E) = \text{power transmitted in dBm at emission frequency } f_E$$
$$G_{TR}(f_E,t,d,p) = \text{transmitter antenna gain in dB at emission frequency } f_E \text{ in the direction of the receiver}$$

$L(f_E,t,d,p)$ = propagation loss in dB at emission frequency f_E between transmitter and receiver

$G_{RT}(f_E,t,d,p)$ = receiver antenna gain in dB at emission frequency f_E in direction of transmitter

$P_R(f_R)$ = receiver susceptibility threshold in dBm at response frequency f_R

$CF(B_T,B_R,\Delta f)$ = factor in dB that accounts for transmitter and receiver bandwidths B_T and B_R respectively and the frequency separation Δf between transmitter emission and receiver response

The EMC analysis equations presented above apply to various types of interference problems. In most cases, the major difficulty is to determine the parameters in the equation. Although this may appear to be a relatively simple undertaking, where transmitting and receiving equipments are involved it is not. This occurs because each transmitter produces many undesired spurious emissions and each receiver has many spurious responses in addition to the desired response. Furthermore, it is necessary to consider radiation in unintended directions via unintended propagation paths. Interactions between transmitters and receivers having totally different operational functions, purposes and technical characteristics also must be determined. Hence, for the simple case of an EMC analysis involving a single transmitter and receiver pair, information must be obtained for each transmitter output and receiver response, and the basic EMC analysis equation must be applied for each output-response combination.

Illustrative Example 2.1

To illustrate the above, consider a situation like that of Example 1.2 in Chapter 1, which involves a radar transmitter and a microwave tropospheric scatter communication receiver operating at the same radio frequency. Assume that the transmitter has a fundamental power output of 100 kW (+80 dBm), and the receiver sensitivity is −100 dBm. Also assume that the transmission coupling between the transmitter and receiver due to spatial separation, scattering criteria, and antenna gain is −180 dB. Thus, from Eq. (2.2), the power available at the receiver is:

$$P_A = P_T + C_{TR}$$
$$= 80 \text{ dBm} - 180 \text{ dB} = -100 \text{ dBm}$$

The notation here is simplified because this example involves specified conditions of the independent variables. The contributing elements to P_A and C_{TR} are in reality quite complicated as discussed in subsequent chapters. The interference margin for this case from Eq. (2.5) is:

$$IM = P_A - P_R$$
$$= -100 \text{ dBm} - (-100 \text{ dBm}) = 0 \text{ dB}$$

For this simple example a marginal interference condition exists. If either the transmitter power is increased or the coupling loss is decreased, a potential interference problem would exist.

2.4   Probability Considerations

Do not underestimate the complexity of the EMC analysis problem because of the apparent simplicity of Eq. (2.6). Recall that individual contributions to EMI are functions of four basic independent variables: frequency, time, distance and direction. Each depends on many factors such as transmitter-receiver equipment type, age, maintenance condition and seasonal, environmental and atmospheric parameters. In most cases the effects of these parameters can be described only tentatively. Each of the basic input functions in some respect is probabilistic, and therefore the interference prediction and analysis process includes elements of probability analysis.

The use of probabilistic parameters for describing the input functions means that the interference margin as defined by Eq. (2.5), in reality, has a distribution of possible values. These are defined as a function of probability of occurrence. The basic answer to "does EMI exist?" is not a definite yes or no; it depends on whether the interference margin is above zero. Thus, it is expressed in terms of the probability that the interference margin exceeds zero. This in turn may be expressed in terms of the probability of interference. Note that the probability of interference is itself time dependent.

This is more clearly illustrated when interference may exist from a scanning radar antenna during boresighting conditions (when the radar antenna looks at the victim receiver) and interference may not exist when the antenna beam is looking elsewhere.

The basic concept of defining EMI in a probabilistic manner is illustrated in Fig. 2.3 where three situations are defined. The first situation is one in which interference is not likely to occur (probability of interference is about 10 percent). The second situation

Telecommunication System EMC Analysis

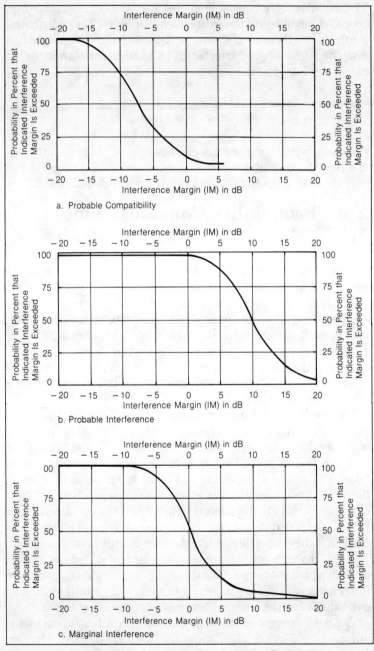

Figure 2.3—Interference Situations Expressed as Probabilities

corresponds to almost certain interference (probability of about 98 percent). For the third situation illustrated, the probability of interference is about 50 percent. Thus, it is not possible to assign "yes" or "no" answers to the EMI outcome.

It is important to weigh the relative merits of a simple yes-or-no type of interference prediction answer against a knowledge of the full range of potential possibilities and a measure of the relative likelihood of each possibility. Recognizing that each of the input functions for EMC analysis has many elements that are difficult to specify exactly, even when subjected to a rigorous form of analysis, it is apparent that predicting on a strictly yes-or-no basis is not practical.

2.4.1   No EMI Permitted

The design and installation of CE systems which result in absolutely interference-free situations are ideal. However, under the criterion of absolutely no interference (zero probability of EMI), most systems used today would have to be shut down. This criteria would not result in a cost-effective or useful design of new systems. One cannot realistically hope to fulfill even a small fraction of present electromagnetic requirements that can be applied based on what might happen in the worst possible case.

2.4.2   An Average EMI Situation

The prediction of an average or most probable interference situation is a sensible first step. Application of the results, however, is still limited because only the average condition is known. This corresponds to choosing one point on a statistical distribution as a division between usefulness and uselessness. In the complex decision processes of the system planning or installation stages, the system planner must have information on all of the odds and consequences of each so he can make sensible and practical tradeoffs.

2.4.3   Acceptable EMI Situations

It is much more likely that systems whose probability of interference-free operation is relatively high (90 to 99 percent) will be chosen rather than those whose probability of interference-free operation is only 50 percent (the average). This is tempered by cost and many other considerations. It is necessary to examine the input function and analysis practices from more than a deterministic point of view. The inherent variability of the problem and user needs and consequences must be considered by including probable concepts in the analysis process.

2.5   Other Analysis Considerations

Another factor that complicates the analysis problem is that each of the input functions described in Eq. (2.6) is defined over a wide range of frequencies, often in excess of three octaves or one decade. Consequently, in analyzing EMC between transmitters and receivers it is necessary to apply the basic analysis equation for each transmitter-output/receiver-response pair. For example, if the analysis is to be applied to a single transmitter having 10 significant emissions and a receiver with 10 significant spurious responses, the analysis equation must be applied for each 100 emission-response pairs. Additionally, the results must be combined for the more significant surviving pairs.

If a CE site that consists of many transmitters and receivers is being analyzed for identifying EMI situations, it is necessary to apply Eq. (2.6) many times for each transmitter-receiver pair. Consequently, a large number of individual combinations will be considered. In such situations, it is best to structure the analysis process so that calculations are performed efficiently. It is then particularly appropriate to use digital computers to perform multi-emitter/receptor analysis calculations.

A final significant factor that creates problems in performing an EMC analysis is finding detailed input information of the type required. For example, to perform an EMC analysis for a CE site, it is necessary to have quantitative information on transmitter spurious emission levels, receiver spurious responses and antenna radiation characteristics. The latter includes gain (or loss) for both polarizations in all three dimensional directions over a wide range of frequencies. In many cases, this type of information is not available.

For cases in which specific detailed data are not available, several different sources may be used. This handbook presents analysis techniques that are implemented with different types of input data. These sources include results of detailed measurements, statistical summaries of equipment characteristics and equipment performance limits as defined in military EMI/EMC standards and specifications.

2.6 Multi-level Analysis Process

In EMI problems involving many transmitters and receivers, the application of the analysis equation to every transmitter-output receiver-response pair results in an unwieldy number of calculations. Since doing this would be inefficient, the philosophy that is often adopted in EMC analysis is to perform the calculations in different stages. For example, it is possible to take a quick look at the total problem using rather simple representations of the input functions. This eliminates many output-response pairs which would probably not represent EMI situations. This multilevel analysis can be extended to several levels of analysis detail. At each subsequent level, additional factors are considered and more noninterfering cases are eliminated from further consideration. This situation, of course, does not apply where only one or a few pairs are involved. Readers having interests involving a relatively simple electromagnetic environment only may skip this section of the handbook.

When the analysis is performed in the above manner it is only necessary to carry out a complete analysis on those surviving cases that exhibit a significant potential for creating interference. The number of analysis levels that gainfully should be used and the specific assumptions and calculations that should be performed at each level depend on the particular EMC analysis problem being considered. As a general objective, each particular level of analysis should remove about 90 percent of the noninterference situations.

For the purpose of this handbook, four analysis levels are considered. They are based on considerations of amplitude, frequency, parameter detail and performance. These analysis levels, the factors that are considered in each and the results that are obtained are illustrated in Fig. 2.4.

The most fundamental level of EMC analysis is based on a consideration of emission-response amplitude. Frequency, time, distance and direction effects are considered only in a relatively gross sense. The amplitude analysis uses simple, reasonable and conservative approximations for each of the input functions. This separates the many unimportant interference possibilities from the relatively few cases which represent significant interference threats. For those cases that survive the amplitude analysis, there remains at least a small probability that interference will occur.

The amplitude analysis is more than just a weeding-out process because the basic functions computed during this stage remain meaningful throughout the remainder of the finer-level analyses.

It forms a nucleus to which a number of adjustment models are applied.

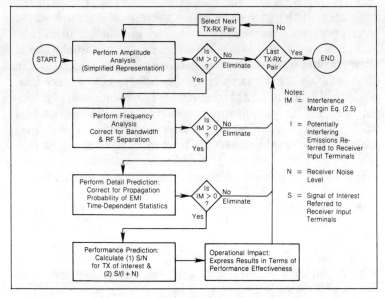

Figure 2.4—The EMC Analysis Process for Multiple Transmitter/Receiver Pairs Showing Four Levels of Analysis

The frequency analysis shown in Fig. 2.4 is the second sorting level to be considered. During this stage, those cases which remain as potential interference culprits are analyzed further using the results of the amplitude analysis as a base. Frequency analysis treats the frequency variables provided as a result of frequency separation (lack of alignment) between a susceptible response and a potentially interfering source.

The third stage of analysis includes detailed consideration of the distance and directional variables. Here potential interference amplitudes resulting from previous stages of analysis are translated into probabilities of interference and time-dependent terms.

The final stage of analysis described in this handbook for multi-transmitter/receiver pairs includes a consideration of factors such as transmitter and receiver modulation characteristics and operational response and performance analysis. At this stage, analysis results are translated into terms that are more meaningful to the user from an operational standpoint. Interference conditions are interpreted in quantities such as intelligibility of voice systems, digital error-rates, scope presentation conditions, false alarms, missed targets, reduction in range of radar systems and other measures that are related to overall system effectiveness and performance. They are based on signal-to-noise or signal-to-interference-plus-noise ratios.

In the final analysis and interpretation of system effectiveness, it is necessary to give careful consideration to mission or operational requirements and priorities. For example, although an identical communication set has the same voice intelligibility to either a private or to a general, the latter has greater demands because of the increased impact resulting from loss of text, error in judgment, etc.

2.6.1 Amplitude Analysis

The amplitude analysis is a first step in EMC analysis involving a relatively large number (say, more than 10) transmitter-receiver main and spurious emission and response pairs. It seeks to separate those combinations of signal amplitudes and frequencies which under worst circumstances will not result in interference, from those situations which exhibit at least a small probability of producing interference. The primary purpose of the amplitude analysis is (1) to examine meaningful combinations of emitter outputs and susceptible responses of receptors and (2) to eliminate from further consideration as many obviously noninterfering cases as possible. The basic philosophy used to accomplish this goal is to calculate potential margins assuming that transmission losses are minimized. It also assumes emission outputs and receptor responses are aligned in frequency in such a way that the susceptible device provides minimum rejection to the potential interfering signal.

The specific operations performed during amplitude analysis can best be explained by referring to Eq. (2.6), which was:

$$IM(f,t,d,p) = P_T(f_E) + G_{TR}(f_E,t,d,p) - L(f_E,t,d,p) \\ + G_{RT}(f_E,t,d,p) - P_R(f_R) + CF\ (B_T,B_R,\Delta f)$$

First, the amplitude analysis considers (1) transmitter fundamental and spurious emission power levels $P_T(f)$, and (2) receiver fundamental and spurious response susceptibility threshold levels $P_R(f)$. Second, amplitude analysis considers antenna gains and propagation loss, but uses simple conservative approximations to represent the effects of time, distance separation and direction on these parameters. Third, the correction factor CF $(B_T, B_R, \Delta f)$ is not considered during the amplitude analysis. In other words, CF $(B_T, B_R, \Delta f)$ is assumed to be zero.

If the resulting interference margin exceeds a preselected analysis level, the emission-response combination is retained for the next finer level of prediction. On the other hand, if the interference margin is less than the preselected analysis level, the emission-response combination is eliminated from further prediction considerations. When the interference margin level is selected correctly, the cases that are eliminated will have a small probability of interference. The problems of selecting an interference margin level will be discussed later.

For the purpose of describing amplitude analysis, the problem of evaluating potential EMI between transmitters and receivers is considered. See Chapters 3 and 4 for discussion of transmitter and receiver models used in amplitude analysis. Considering the above basic assumptions which are applied to amplitude analysis, the problem of predicting EMI between transmitters and receivers is grouped into four significant and different cases of transmitter output and receiver response pairs. These four cases are:

1. Fundamental Interference Margin (FIM) is the interference level that will exist if the transmitter fundamental frequency output and receiver fundamental response are aligned in frequency in such a way that there is no rejection.

2. Transmitter Interference Margin (TIM) is the interference level that will exist if the transmitter fundamental emission is aligned with a receiver spurious response.

3. Receiver Interference Margin (RIM) is the interference level that will exist if the receiver fundamental response is aligned in frequency with a transmitter spurious emission output.

4. Spurious Interference Margin (SIM) is the interference level that will exist if both a transmitter spurious output and a receiver spurious response are aligned in frequency. The spurious interference level is a function of frequency and this must be taken into consideration in the analysis.

The procedure is to first calculate the fundamental interference margin level. If the interference margin is less than the preselected level it is not necessary to compute the other three cases since their margins will be still lower. On the other hand, if the interference margin for the fundamental interference level exceeds the preselected level, it is then necessary to compute both the transmitter fundamental and the receiver fundamental interference levels. If either of these produce an interference margin that exceeds the preselected level, it is also necessary to calculate the spurious interference level.

One simple level, or margin of intercepted to susceptible power level, would be 0 dB (I/N ratio = 1 or 0 dB). However, this may eliminate some real potential EMI situations because of the probability distributions discussed in Section 2.4. Since mean value interference margins are often calculated, typical analysis levels selected may be −10 to −20 dB to allow for interfering signals that exceed the mean level by 10 to 20 dB, i.e., those whose standard deviation may exceed 5 to 10 dB.

Illustrative Example 2.2

Calculate the potential EMI between a tropospheric scatter communication transmitter and a radar receiver. Assume that the transmitter operates at 1 GHz (f_{OT}), has a fundamental power output $P_T(f_{OT})$ of 1 kW (+60 dBm) and all transmitter spurious outputs are at least 60 dB below the fundamental output, i.e., spurious outputs are less than 0 dBm. Also assume that the radar receiver operates at 1.2 GHz(f_{OR}), has a fundamental sensitivity $P_R(f_{OR})$ of − 100 dBm and all spurious responses are at least 80 dB above the fundamental response, i.e., spurious sensitivity $P_R(f_{SR})$ is greater than − 20 dBm. The problem then is to calculate the interference margin that will exist for each of the four cases if the transmission coupling is − 100 dB.

Figure 2.5 illustrates the functions used in interference analysis and demonstrates the results obtained for this sample problem over a frequency range of 0.1 to 10 GHz. The power available function P_A shown in the figure was obtained by applying Eq. (2.2) using the simplified notation containing only the frequency variable of this particular problem:

$$P_A(f) = P_T(f) + C_{TR}(f) \tag{2.7}$$

For the transmitter fundamental frequency (f_{OT}):

$$P_A (f_{OT}) = 60 \text{ dBm} + (-100 \text{ dB}) = -40 \text{ dBm}$$

For transmitter spurious outputs:

$$P_A(f_{ST}) = 0 \text{ dBm} + (-100 \text{ dB}) = -100 \text{ dBm}$$

The receiver susceptibility threshold P_R is shown immediately below the available power functions, and the interference margin shown at the bottom of the figure is obtained by applying Eq. (2.5) to each of the four cases separately:

$$IM(f) = P_A(f) - P_R(f) \qquad (2.8)$$

Case FIM - Fundamental Interference Margin:

$$FIM = IM\ (f_{OT},\ f_{OR}) = -40\ dBm - (-100\ dBm) = +60\ dB$$

Case TIM - Transmitter Interference Margin:

$$TIM = IM(f_{OT},\ f_{SR}) = -40\ dBm - (-20\ dBm) = -20\ dB$$

Case RIM - Fundamental Interference Margin:

$$RIM = IM(f_{ST},\ f_{OR}) = -100\ dBm - (-100\ dBm) = 0\ dB$$

Case SIM - Fundamental Interference Margin:

$$SIM = IM\ (f_{ST},\ f_{SR}) = -100\ dBm - (-20\ dBm) = -80\ dB$$

If an EMI margin of 0 dB is used as the level, the results of amplitude analysis indicate that the TIM and SIM cases will not result in interference. Thus, these may be eliminated from further consideration. However, the FIM and RIM cases do present a potential problem (especially FIM) and hence must be considered further in the second-stage frequency analysis.

In order for amplitude analysis to be effective in eliminating noninterfering situations from further consideration and to allow for a large percentage of potentially interfering situations to be retained, a choice must be made with respect to the levels which represent the basic input functions. Since each input function is represented by a distribution which describes the probability that a given level will not be exceeded, a choice is made regarding the probability that will be selected for either retaining or limiting a case from further consideration. Because of the probabilistic nature of the EMI problem, it is necessary to establish a criteria for amplitude analysis so that a low probability of eliminating cases with a significant potential of interference during this stage of EMI analysis will result.

Although the specific criteria are optional, there are definite trade-offs involved. In establishing criteria for a particular analysis, it is important to recognize the tradeoffs that exist between the

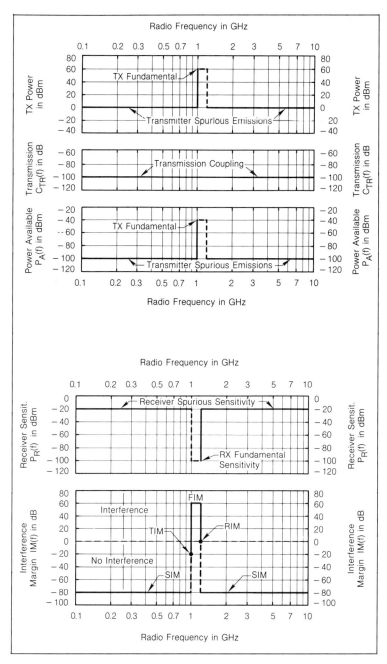

Figure 2.5—Illustrating Amplitude Analysis (See Example 2.2)

efficiency of the amplitude analysis and the possibility of eliminating equipments which may produce EMI. If the interference criterion (interference margin level) used in amplitude analysis is too conservative, the analysis will not be effective in eliminating cases, but no potential cases of interference will be overlooked. If the interference criterion is too liberal, the analysis will eliminate not only a large number of noninterfering cases but also some potentially interfering situations.

Chapter 8 presents specific guidelines for selecting the interference criterion to be used in amplitude analysis. Specific amplitude analysis models used to represent the transmitter, receiver, antenna and propagation loss functions are presented in Chapters 3, 4, 5 and 6 respectively.

2.6.2 Frequency Analysis Process

The second step of the multi-emitter-receptor interference analysis process is referred to as the frequency analysis stage. This step modifies the interference margin obtained in the amplitude analysis stage by accounting for such factors as transmitter bandwidths and modulation characteristics, bandwidth and selectivity of each receiver response and frequency separation between specific transmitter emissions and receiver responses. See Chapters 3 and 4 for discussions of transmitter and receiver models used in frequency analysis.

Within the selected frequency range determined from the preceding amplitude analysis, frequency analysis corrects for bandwidth differences and frequency separations between transmitter output and receiver response frequencies. Each transmitter output frequency (fundamental, harmonics and spurious) is compared with each of the potential receiver response frequencies (spurious heterodyne, intermodulation, co-channel and adjacent-channel receiver response frequencies) to determine specific transmitter emission bands which are capable of producing EMI. Separation between each mating pair of frequencies is considered by applying a composite bandwidth, selectivity and modulation envelope function at the surviving frequencies. The resulting comparison yields a correction to the interference margin obtained from the amplitude analysis.

In the amplitude analysis, no spectrum spread in power is assumed. The total power is considered to exist at each emission or response frequency. No frequency separation (Δf) between a transmitter output and a receiver response was considered in calculating the interference margin.

In the frequency analysis, on the other hand, the transmitter modulation envelope and receiver selectivity curve are considered. Taking into account relative bandwidths, a correction or adjustment factor which is applied to the amplitude-analysis interference margin is defined. Additionally, frequency analysis considers center frequency separation between output response pairs and defines a correction factor to the amplitude analysis to account for this separation. Basically, the method involves superimposing the receiver selectivity on the transmitter modulation envelope.

Specifically, the frequency analysis modifies the amplitude analysis result by the correction factor $CF(B_T, B_R, \Delta f)$. If the resulting interference margin still exceeds the preselected level, the emission-response pair is retained for further consideration during the detailed analysis. If the resulting interference margin is less than the preselected level, the emission-response pair is eliminated from further consideration.

2.6.2.1 On-Tune Case $\Delta f < \dfrac{(B_T + B_R)}{2}$

The basic concept of the frequency analysis is illustrated by considering various possibilities that may exist between particular output response pairs as shown in Fig. 2.6. First, if the output and response occur at the same center frequency ($\Delta f = 0$), there are two basic co-channel possibilities that may be considered:

1. Receiver bandwidth is either equal to or larger than the transmitter bandwidth ($B_R > B_T$). For this case the power associated with the transmitter output is received and no correction is necessary.

2. Receiver bandwidth is less than the transmitter bandwidth ($B_R < B_T$). For this case only a portion of the power associated with the emission output is received, and it is necessary to apply a bandwidth correction CF to account for the bandwidth differences. This correction for $\Delta f = 0$ depends on the bandwidth ratios and is of the form:

$$CF\ (\Delta f = 0) = K \log (B_R/B_T) \text{ dB for } B_R < B_T \qquad (2.9)$$

where,

B_R = receiver 3 dB bandwidth in Hz
B_T = transmitter 3 dB bandwidth in Hz
K = a constant for a particular emission-response combination
= 0 for $B_R > B_T$ and co-channel frequency alignment
= 10 for noise-like signals for which rms levels apply and $B_R < B_T$
= 20 for pulse signals for which peak levels apply and $B_R < B_T$

For pulse signals, peak levels are applicable as long as B_R is greater than the pulse-repetition rate.

Illustrative Example 2.3:
Co-channel Interference ($B_R > B_T$)

Consider a co-channel interference involving a UHF voice transmitter with a 3 dB bandwidth of 10 kHz (B_T = 10 kHz) and a surveillance receiver having a bandwidth of 1 MHz (B_R = 1,000 kHz). Assume that amplitude analysis has indicated that the fundamental interference margin IM is +80 dB and both equipments are operating at the same center frequency ($\Delta f = 0$). For this situation, all the transmitting power will be received as shown in Eq. (2.7) since $B_R > B_T$. Thus, it is not necessary to apply a frequency analysis correction factor to the results of amplitude analysis.

Illustrative Example 2.4:
Co-channel Interference ($B_R < B_T$)

If the previous example were reversed, i.e., the transmitter bandwidth was 1 MHz (B_T = 1,000 kHz) and the receiver bandwidth was 10 kHz (B_R = 10 kHz), then only a portion of the available transmitter power would be received. If the transmitter is pulse modulated at 1,000 pps, the received voltage is directly proportional to the ratios. From Eq. (2.9):

$$CF(\Delta f = 0) = 20 \log (B_R/B_T) \text{ dB}$$

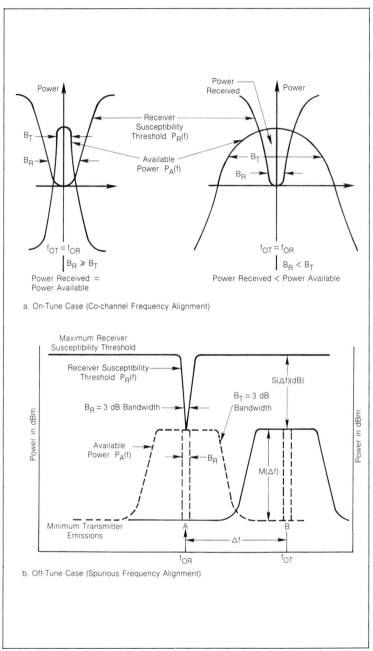

a. On-Tune Case (Co-channel Frequency Alignment)

b. Off-Tune Case (Spurious Frequency Alignment)

Figure 2.6—Illustration of Frequency Analysis

Therefore:

$$CF \ (\Delta f = 0) = 20 \log \left[\frac{10 \text{ kHz}}{1,000 \text{ kHz}} \right] = -40 \text{ dB}$$

When this bandwidth correction factor is applied to the amplitude analysis results of Example 2.3 (interference margin IM = 80 dB), the resulting frequency culling interference margin is reduced to +40 dB (+80 dB − 40 dB). Thus, where frequency alignment exists and the receiver bandwidth is less than the transmitter bandwidth, the frequency analysis results in a reduction in the interference potential obtained by the amplitude analysis.

2.6.2.2 Off-Tune Case $\Delta f > \dfrac{(B_T + B_R)}{2}$

As the transmitter and receiver center frequencies are separated, the transmitter power can enter the receiver in either of two other possible ways (see Fig. 2.6):

1. The transmitter emission modulation sidebands can enter the receiver at the main-response frequency. For this case, the correction factor is:

$$CF_R(\Delta f) = [K \log (B_R/B_T) + M(\Delta f)] \text{ dB} \qquad (2.10)$$

where,

$M(\Delta f)$ = modulation sideband level in dB above transmitter power at frequency separation Δf

K = defined in Eq. (2.9)

2. The power at the transmitter main output frequency can enter the receiver off-tune response. For this case, the correction factor is:

$$CF_T(\Delta f) = -S(\Delta f) \text{dB} \qquad (2.11)$$

where, $S(\Delta f)$ = receiver selectivity in dB above receiver fundamental susceptibility at frequency separation Δf

The final bandwidth correction factor which must be applied to the amplitude-analysis interference margin because of nonalignment of the transmitter output and receiver response is either $CF_R(\Delta f)$ or $CF_T(\Delta f)$, whichever is the largest of the two.

Illustrative Example 2.5:
Off-Channel Interference ($B_R > B_T$)

Consider the transmitter-receiver combinations used for the co-channel Example 2.3. Assume that the center frequency separation Δf is 2 MHz for an AM voice transmitter bandwidth B_T of 10 kHz and a 1 MHz surveillance receiver bandwidth B_R. Also, assume that the transmitter modulation envelope is 90 dB below the fundamental level ($M(\Delta f) = -90$ dB), and the receiver selectivity provides 60 dB of rejection ($S(\Delta f) = 60$ dB) at a 2 MHz frequency separation. These values are developed in subsequent chapters. The correction factor is selected to be the one which has the largest algebraic value. For this case, the correction factor at R and T frequencies are given by Eqs. (2.10) and (2.11) respectively:

$$CF_R(\Delta f) = 10 \log \left[\frac{1,000 \text{ kHz}}{10 \text{ kHz}} \right] - 90 \text{ dB} = -70 \text{ dB}$$

$$CF_R(\Delta f) = -S(\Delta f) = -60 \text{ dB}$$

The final frequency-analysis correction factor is determined by selecting the larger of the two correction factors; in this case it would be -60 dB. In order to obtain the interference margin resulting from the additive effects of the frequency analysis, it is necessary to apply the frequency-analysis correction factor (-60 dB) to the amplitude-analysis interference margin ($+80$ dB, see Example 2.3). The resulting frequency-analysis interference margin is reduced to $+20$ dB.

Illustrative Example 2.6:
Off-Channel Interference ($B_R < B_T$)

Consider another example similar to Example 2.5 except that the transmitter bandwidth and its modulation envelope, and the receiver bandwidth and selectivity are reversed, i.e.:

Transmitter bandwidth, $B_T = 1$ MHz
Transmitter modulation envelope reduction, $M(\Delta f) = -60$ dB

Receiver bandwidth B_R = 10 kHz

Receiver selectivity rejection, $S(\Delta f)$ = 90 dB

Assume the transmitter is pulsed at 1,000 pps. The correction factors at R and T frequencies are obtained by again applying Eqs. (2.10) and (2.11) respectively:

$$CF_R(\Delta f) = K \log B_R/B_T + M(\Delta f) \text{ dB}$$

$$= 20 \log \left[\frac{10 \text{ kHz}}{1,000 \text{ kHz}} \right] - 60 \text{ dB}$$

$$= (-40 - 60) \text{ dB} = -100 \text{ dB}$$

$$CF_T(\Delta f) = S(\Delta f) \text{ dB} = -90 \text{ dB}$$

The frequency analysis correction factor is the larger of the two. In this example it is -90 dB. When this correction factor is applied to the stated value of amplitude-analysis interference margin ($+80$ dB, see Example 2.3), the resulting frequency analysis interference margin is reduced to -10 dB. Thus, by considering both the bandwidth differences and frequency separations, a considerable reduction in the interference potential is obtained over that previously indicated by amplitude analysis.

2.6.3 Detailed Analysis

In the preceding sections, the factors which contribute to interference within a CE system complex were introduced, and methods of obtaining the interference margin were presented. It was pointed out that it is possible to eliminate a large number of noninterfering situations from further analysis by employing amplitude analysis and still retain nearly all potential interfering situations. Those cases that remained after amplitude analysis were considered further during frequency analysis and additional non-EMI situations were eliminated.

The results of frequency analysis yield surviving cases that have a significant potential for producing interference. Each of these cases then must be subjected to still further analysis. The purposes of the detailed analysis are (1) to include those factors depending on time, distance and direction which will influence the interference situation between a specific transmitter and receiver and (2) to determine the probability distribution for the resulting interference margin. Some of the more important factors that are considered in the detailed analysis include: specific propagation modes, near-field antenna gain corrections, multiple interfering signal effects, time-dependent statistics (such as those resulting from rotating antennas) and the probability distribution of interference margin.

One of the important steps in the detailed analysis is determining the probability distribution associated with the interference margin. The probability distribution results from considerations previously discussed in Section 2.4. Probability distributions are associated with the transmitter power, antenna gains, propagation loss and receiver susceptibility threshold; and it is assumed that all of the distributions are log normal. The resulting probability distribution for the interference margin is log normal with standard deviation σ_{IM} dB given by:

$$\sigma_{IM} = \sqrt{\sigma_T^2 + \sigma_{TA}^2 + \sigma_L^2 + \sigma_{RA}^2 + \sigma_R^2} \ \text{dB} \qquad (2.13)$$

where,

σ_T = standard deviation of transmitter emission power in dB

σ_{TA} = standard deviation of transmitter antenna gain in dB

σ_L = standard deviation of propagation loss in dB

σ_{RA} = standard deviation of receiver antenna gain in dB

σ_R = standard deviation of receiver suscep-tibility threshold in dB

The specific steps to be performed in the detailed analysis depend on the particular problem being considered and the results that are desired. Discussions of factors that should be considered in the detailed analysis are presented in Chapters 3, 4, 5 and 6 of this handbook. Chapter 8 contains a further discussion of specific considerations to be applied to the detailed analysis and presents several illustrative examples of different applications of detailed analysis procedures.

2.6.4 Performance Analysis

Any signal which hinders or degrades the operation of an electrical or electronic device in accomplishing its intended or design function can be termed interference. However, to analyze the effects of interference it is necessary to express the results in terms of the impact on operational performance.

The primary problem in expressing results in a form that is useful in evaluating performance is to relate the interference levels to measures of performance. Because of the importance and complexity of this particular aspect of the interference analysis process, a complete chapter is devoted to this subject. The reader is referred to Chapter 7 for a discussion of performance analysis.

2.7 EMC Analysis Short Form

There are many EMC analysis problems for which only a few transmitter-receiver pairs need to be considered and the analysis is either performed manually or with the aid of a small computer program which may be run on a personal computer or a time-sharing terminal. This section presents a step-by-step process for performing a manual EMC analysis through the use of a special form. The user simply fills out the analysis form in the same way as an income tax form. References are provided to specific parts of this volume which may be used to find further descriptions of EMC analysis models or techniques. A brief description of some of the major EMC analysis considerations that apply to a manual analysis process is presented below. Samples of the EMC Analysis Short Form are presented on the following pages.

There are a number of possible combinations of transmitter-receiver (TX-RX) emission-responses for each pair that must be considered. These are classified as:

1. Class Fundamental Interference Margin (FIM) – TX fundamental emission and RX fundamental response
2. Class Transmitter Interference Margin (TIM) – TX fundamental emission and RX spurious response
3. Class Receiver Interference Margin (RIM) – TX spurious emission and RX fundamental response
4. Class Spurious Interference Margin (SIM) – TX spurious emission and RX spurious response

The considerations that apply and the calculations used are different for each of these categories. Thus, the first step in an EMC analysis process is to examine the frequency limits associated with each TX-RX pair order to determine which emission-response categories apply. The specific data required for this step are the frequency limits over which each type of interference must be considered for the particular TX-RX pair.

After it is determined that one or more of the above cases apply, the next step is to calculate the interference level for that particular case. Thus, the second step is to calculate a preliminary level based on considerations of emission and response amplitudes and free space propagation loss as given by Fig. 2.7. An adjustment is made in the third step using Figs. 2.8 or 2.9 to account for differences between the transmitter and receiver bandwidths. In the fourth step, a correction is made to account for frequency

EMC Analysis Short Form

Frequency:
☐ kHz; ☐ MHz

Transmitter and Receiver Frequency Limits

1. TX Fundamental Frequency (f_{OT})
2. TX Minimum Spurious Frequency ($f_{ST})_{min}$ or $0.1f_{OT}$
3. TX Maximum Spurious Frequency ($f_{ST})_{max}$ or $10f_{OT}$
4. RX Fundamental Frequency (f_{OR})
5. RX Minimum Spurious Frequency ($f_{SR})_{min}$ or $0.1f_{OR}$
6. RX Maximum Spurious Frequency ($f_{SR})_{max}$ or $10f_{OR}$
7. TX-RX Maximum Allowable Frequency Separation for Fundamental EMI, Δf_{max} or $0.2f_{OR}$

Applicability of Four EMI Prediction Cases:

SIM = TX Harmonic & RX Spurious
Is (2) _____ < (6) _____ ?   ☐ Yes, ☐ No
Is (3) _____ > (5) _____ ?   ☐ Yes, ☐ No
If either is No, there is no EMI Problem—Stop.

RIM = TX Harmonic & RX Fundamental
Is (2) _____ < (4) _____ ?   ☐ Yes, ☐ No
Is (3) _____ > (4) _____ ?   ☐ Yes, ☐ No
If either is No, skip RIM and enter N/A on line 38.

TIM = TX Fundamental & RX Spurious
Is (1) _____ < (6) _____ ?   ☐ Yes, ☐ No
Is (1) _____ > (5) _____ ?   ☐ Yes, ☐ No
If either is No, skip TIM and enter N/A on line 38.
If both RIM and TIM were N/A, skip FIM and enter N/A on line 38.

FIM = TX Fundamental & RX Fundamental

Is $|(1)$ _____ $- (4)$ _____ $| <$

(7) _____ ?   □ Yes, □ No

If No, skip FIM and enter N/A on line 38.

Surviving cases   □ SIM,   □ RIM,   □ TIM,   □ FIM

  □ No cases survived—No EMI problem.

Amplitude Analysis

	FIM	TIM	RIM	SIM
8. TX Power, $P_T(f_{OT})$, (peak power if pulsed)				
9. TX Spurious Power Output: $P_T(f_{ST})$ or $P_T(f_{OT}) - 60$ dB				
10. TX Antenna Gain in RX Direction: $G_{TR}(f)$ or 0 dB				
11. RX Antenna Gain in TX Direction: $G_{RT}(f)$ or 0 dB				
12. Propagation Loss, L Using Frequency No.	(1)	(1)	(4)	(2)
Loss in dB from Fig. No. 2.7	-	-	-	-
13. Unintentional Power Available $P_A(f)$ Add 8 to 12				
14. RX Fundamental Susceptibility $P_R(f_{OR})$				
15. RX Spurious Suscept.: $P_R(f_{SR})$ or $P_R(f_{OR}) + 80$ dB				
16. Preliminary EMI Prediction: Line 13-14 or 13-15				

  If EMI margin < -10 dB, EMI Highly Improbable

   —Stop

  If EMI margin > -10 dB, Start Frequency Culling

Frequency Analysis

Bandwidth Correction

Frequency:
□ kHz; □ MHz

17. TX PRF (if pulse)			pps
18. TX Bandwidth ($B_T = 2/\pi\tau$ if pulse; $\tau =$ width			
19. RX Bandwidth B_R			
20. Adjustment (from lines 17 to 19, use Fig. 2.8 and 2.9)			dB
21. Bandwidth Corrected, EMI Margin = lines 16 + 20			dB

  If EMI Margin $\leqslant -10$ dB, EMI Highly Improbable—Stop

Frequency Correction

Frequency:
□ kHz; □ MHz

22. RX Local Oscillator Frequency f_{LO}		
23. RX Intermediate Frequency f_{IF}		

	FIM	TIM	RIM	SIM
24. TX-RX Frequency Separation: $\Delta f = |(1) - (4)|$				
25. $\Delta f > (B_T + B_R)/2$ (from line 24, use Fig. 2.10)				

26. Calculate $f_{OT}/f_{LO} \pm f_{IF}$ to nearest integer
27. Multiply lines 22 × 26   MHz
28. $\Delta f = |1 - 23 - 27| = $ _____: $| + 23 - 27| = $ _____
29. Select smaller Δf from line 28   MHz
30. $\Delta f > (B_T + B_R)/2$ (from line 29, use Fig. 2.10)   dB

31. Calculate f_{OR}/f_{OT} to nearest integer
32. Multiply lines 1 × 31   MHz
33. $\Delta f = |(4) - (32)|$ MHz
34. $\Delta f > (B_T + B_R)/2$ (from line 33 use Fig. 2.10)   dB

35. Calculate Minimum Δf (see Form A)   MHz
36. If $\Delta f > (B_T + B_R)/2$ (from line 35 use Fig. 2.10)   dB

EMI Frequency Corrected Summary

25	30	34	36

37. Add line 21 to line
38. Total here   dB

    If EMI Margin < -10 dB, EMI Highly Improbable

Detailed Analysis
Harmonic or Spurious Response Correction*

    FIM TIM RIM SIM

39. Correction from Form B   dB
40. Corrected EMI add line 38 to line 39*   dB

Modulation Correction

41. Correction from Form C   dB
42. Corrected EMI Add line 40 to line 41   dB

Polarization Correction

43. Correction from Form D   dB
44. Corrected EMI Add line 42 to line 44   dB

Propagation Loss Correction

45. Correction from Form E   dB
46. Corrected EMI Add line 44 to line 46   dB

    If EMI < -10 dB EMI Highly Improbable
    -10 dB $\leqslant$ EMI $\leqslant 10$ dB EMI Marginal
    EMI > 10 dB EMI Probable

*Apply corrections only if nominal -60 dB TX (line 9) and/or $+80$ dB RX (line 15) corrections were used.

Form A—SIM Frequency Separation Correction in dB

TX Fund (f_{OT}): _____; RX LO (f_{LO}): _____; RX IF (f_{IF}): _____

N	$(Nf_{OT} + f_{IF})/f_{LO}$	Δp^*	$(Nf_{OT} - f_{IF})/f_{LO}$	Δp^*
2				
3				
4				
5				
6				
7				
8				
9				
10				

Select Minimum Value for Δp
Minimum Spurious Frequency Separation $= (\Delta p)_{min} \, f_{LO}$

*Δp is the magnitude of difference between value obtained for $p \pm \Delta p = N(f_{OT} \pm f_{IF})/f_{LO}$ and the nearest integer.

Form B—Harmonic and/or Spurious Response Correction in dB

FIM—No Correction
TIM—Spurious Response Correction Use p from Line 26
RIM—Harmonic Correction Use N from Line 31
SIM—Add Spurious and Harmonic Correction Use p and N from Form A above

Category		N or p*								
		2	3	4	5	6	7	8	9	10
HF &	Harmonic	+ 19	+ 7	− 2	− 9	− 14	− 19	− 23	− 27	− 30
Below	Response	− 13	− 17	− 20	− 22	− 24	− 26	− 27	− 29	− 30
VHF	Harmonic	+ 6	− 8	− 18	− 26	− 32	− 37	− 42	− 46	− 50
	Response	− 15	− 22	− 26	− 29	− 32	− 35	− 37	− 38	− 40
UHF &	Harmonic	+ 5	− 4	− 10	− 15	− 19	− 22	− 25	− 28	− 30
Above	Response	+ 8	+ 1	− 4	− 8	− 11	− 14	− 16	− 18	− 20

*For the receiver image response use a + 20 dB correction.

Form C—Modulation Correction in dB*

Modulation Type	B_T Line 18	B_R Line 19	Modulation Correction in dB
(Use Δf's from lines 24, 29, 33 or 35)			
Pulse			0
AM			$20 \log (B_T + B_R)/2\Delta f$
FM			$40 \log (B_T + B_R)/2\Delta f$

*The combined Frequency Separation Correction from lines 25, 30, 34 or 36 plus Modulation Correction must not exceed 100 dB

Form D—Antenna Polarization Correctly in dB*

TX Pol: □H; □V; □C.
RX Pol: □H; □V; □C.

RX \ TX		Horizontal		Vertical		Cir
		G < 10 dB	G ⩾ 10 dB	G < 10 dB	G ⩾ 10 dB	
	G < 10 dB	0	0	− 16	− 16	− 3
	G ⩾ 10 dB	0	0	− 16	− 20	− 3
	G < 10 dB	− 16	− 16	0	0	− 3
	G ⩾ 10 dB	− 16	− 20	0	0	− 3
	Circular	− 3	− 3	− 3	− 3	0

*Applies only to intentional radiation region and design frequency.

2.35

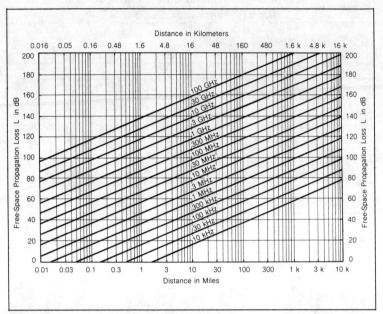

Figure 2.7—Free-Space Propagation Loss

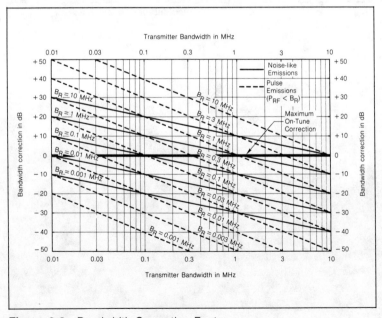

Figure 2.8—Bandwidth Correction Factor

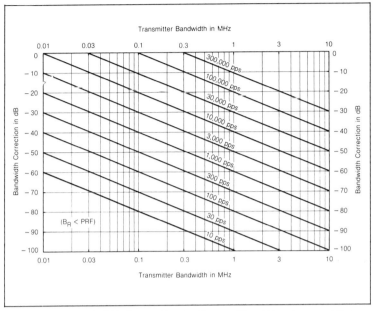

Figure 2.9—Bandwidth Correction for Narrow Band Receiver and Pulses

separation between the particular transmitter output and receiver response. In this step, if specific transmitter and receiver frequencies are not known, the calculations may be repeated for different frequencies. Alternately, the relationship plotted in Fig. 2.10 may be used to determine the frequency separation required for compatibility.

2.7.1 Factors Pertinent to the Use of the EMC Analysis Form

One of the problems in performing an EMC analysis of the type described is getting all the information required for the analysis. In order to assist the user, values that may be used in the absence of certain specific data are provided. Also, references are provided to specific sections of this handbook which the reader may use to find more detailed discussions of various EMC analysis considerations.

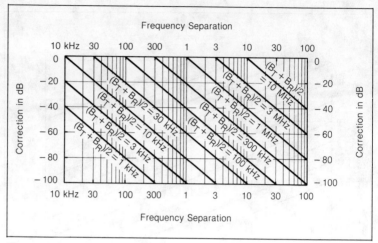

Figure 2.10—Frequency Separation Correction

The specific values and techniques provided in the short-form EMC analysis process are intended to be as realistic as possible. Users may want to regard situations that result in an interference margin between −10 and +10 dB as marginal. They may determine whether the specific values and relationships used in the analysis process are realistic for the specific problem. In this case, users should refer to the referenced sections to find more descriptions and models for the relationships. If significant differences exist, it may be necessary to conduct a detailed EMC analysis. It may appear premature to some readers to introduce an overall EMC analysis process at this early point in the handbook. However, experience has shown that the principal problem is one involving the ability to assimilate a comprehensive topic. Thus, the earlier the broad picture is introduced, the easier it is to follow and assimilate subsequent material.

The major assumptions used or implied by the short-form EMC analysis process and the suggested values provided are:

1. Frequency limits for transmitter spurious emissions and receiver spurious responses are from 0.1 to 10 times the fundamental frequency. This assumes that there are no significant emissions or responses outside these limits.

2. Maximum TX-RX frequency separation for fundamental interference is 0.2 the times receiver fundamental. This assumes fundamental interference is not significant for larger frequency separations.
3. Free-space propagation loss is assumed.
4. Levels for transmitter spurious emissions are 60 dB below fundamental emission.
5. Levels for receiver spurious susceptibility are 80 dB above fundamental susceptibility.
6. An additional 20 dB rejection each is assumed for transmitter and receiver minor emissions and responses.
7. Values for antenna gains in unintentional radiation directions and at unintentional frequencies are 0 dB.
8. Differences in transmitter and receiver bandwidth are assumed to modify the power available in the manner specified in Table 2.1.
9. Frequency separation Δf between transmitter emission and receiver response are assumed to reduce the effective power available by an amount given by $40 \log (0.5 [B_T + B_R])/\Delta f$.
10. A go, no-go interference margin level of -10 dB is used. Thus, potentially interfering situations are eliminated only if the mean signal level is less than -10 dB relative to the receiver susceptibility threshold.

A relatively detailed application of the short-form EMC analysis process is presented in Section 2.7.2. It is suggested that the reader

Table 2.1—Bandwidth Corrections in dB

Modulation Type	Bandwidth Conditions	On-Tune $\Delta f \leqslant (B_T + B_R)/2$	Off-Tune $\Delta f > (B_T + B_R)/2$	Remarks
Noise-like Continuous	$B_R \geqslant B_T$	No Correction	$10 \log \dfrac{B_R}{B_T}$	Rms Power Proportional to Bandwidth
	$B_R < B_T$	$10 \log \dfrac{B_R}{B_T}$		
Pulse	$B_R \geqslant B_T$	No Correction	$20 \log \dfrac{B_R}{B_T}$	Peak Voltage Proportional to Bandwidth
	$PRF < B_R < B_T$	$20 \log \dfrac{B_R}{B_T}$		
	$B_R < PRF$	$20 \log \dfrac{PRF}{B_T}$	$20 \log \dfrac{PRF}{B_T}$	Power in $B_R \approx PRF$

review Example 2.7 before attempting to use the process if the uses of specific parts of the form are not clear.

2.7.2 Composite Illustrative Example

This section summarizes much of the material presented in this chapter and illustrates the application of the short-form analysis process presented in Section 2.7.

Illustrative Example 2.7

Consider the potential EMI which may exist between a P-band radar transmitting at 220 MHz and a UHF AM voice receiver tuned to 360 MHz, used for communicating with aircraft. Assume that both the P-band radar and the UHF receiver are located on the same ship and their antennas are only 30.5 m (100') apart but are vertically separated enough so that the radar antenna main beam does not illuminate the UHF antenna. Assume that the nominal TX-RX characteristics are:

Parameter	P-Band Radar	UHF Receiver
Operating Frequency (f_o)	220 MHz	360 MHz
Peak Power Output	100 kW	NA
Pulse Width	10 μs	NA
Pulse Repetition Rate	100 pps	NA
Antenna Gain	23 dB	0 dB
Receiver Bandwidth	NA	10 kHz
Receiver Sensitivity	NA	-100 dBm
Receiver IF	NA	40 MHz
Receiver LO	NA	($f_{OR} + f_{IF}$)

The EMC analysis short form is executed for this problem in the following pages. Referring to the short form, the spurious (SIM), receiver (RIM) and transmitter (TIM) interfering cases are applicable to this problem. The fundamental (FIM) case is not applicable because the fundamental frequency separation is greater than 0.2 f_{OR} = 0.2 (360 MHz) = 72 MHz.

As a result of performing the amplitude analysis, a positive EMI margin is obtained for the TIM, RIM and SIM cases. It is therefore necessary to continue with the frequency analysis. When the frequency analysis is applied, the corrected TIM and RIM are both below the -10 dB level. Hence, EMI is highly improbable for these cases and it is not necessary to examine them further in the detailed analysis. On the other hand, the frequency analysis corrected SIM case results in an EMI margin that is above the -10 dB level and hence the SIM case must be examined further during the detailed analysis.

When the detailed analysis is applied to the SIM case, it is seen that a $+26$ dB correction is obtained for the harmonic or spurious response correction. This positive correction results because the SIM case in this particular example involves the transmitter second harmonic ($N = 2$) interfering with the receiver image response. Transmitter second harmonics result in a $+6$ dB harmonic correction for VHF equipments. This positive correction occurs because second harmonics tend to exceed the nominal level ($PT(f_{OR}) - 60$ dB) used on line 9. Receiver image responses result in a $+20$ dB correction because receivers tend to be more susceptible to the image than the nominal level ($PR(f_{OR}) + 80$ dB) used on line 15. Application of the detailed analysis results in a $+21$ dB EMI margin for the SIM case.

To summarize results of this illustrative example, EMI is probable for the particular conditions considered. The potential EMI results from the transmitter second harmonic falling on the receiver image response frequency of 440 MHz. This potential EMI problem may be avoided by changing the receiver operating frequency so that there is sufficient frequency separation between the transmitter second harmonic and the image response to provide the -31 dB rejection required to reduce the EMI margin below the -10 dB analysis level.

Referring to Fig. 2.10, if the output-response frequency separation is greater than 200 kHz, more than 31 dB of rejection will be provided, and the potential EMI problem will be eliminated. For example, if the receiver is tuned to a frequency of 360.5 MHz, no EMI problem should result from the transmitter second harmonic and the receiver image response.

Telecommunication System EMC Analysis

Illustrative Example 2.7—EMC Analysis Short Form

Transmitter and Receiver Frequency Limits

Frequency:
☐ kHz; ☒ MHz

1. TX Fundamental Frequency (f_{OT}) — **220**
2. TX Minimum Spurious Frequency (f_{ST})$_{min}$ or $0.1f_{OT}$ — **22**
3. TX Maximum Spurious Frequency (f_{ST})$_{max}$ or $10f_{OT}$ — **2200**
4. RX Fundamental Frequency (f_{OR}) — **360**
5. RX Minimum Spurious Frequency (f_{SR})$_{min}$ or $0.1f_{OR}$ — **36**
6. RX Maximum Spurious Frequency (f_{SR})$_{max}$ or $10f_{OR}$ — **3600**
7. TX-RX Maximum Allowable Frequency Separation for Fundamental EMI, Δf_{max} or $0.2f_{OR}$ — **72**

Applicability of Four EMI Prediction Cases:

SIM = TX Harmonic & RX Spurious
Is (2) **22** < (6) **3600** ?   ☒ Yes, ☐ No
Is (3) **2200** > (5) **36** ?   ☒ Yes, ☐ No
If either is No, there is no EMI Problem—Stop.

RIM = TX Harmonic & RX Fundamental
Is (2) **22** < (4) **360** ?   ☒ Yes, ☐ No
Is (3) **2200** > (4) **360** ?   ☒ Yes, ☐ No
If either is No, skip RIM and enter N/A on line 38.

TIM = TX Fundamental & RX Spurious
Is (1) **220** < (6) **3600** ?   ☒ Yes, ☐ No
Is (1) **220** > (5) **36** ?   ☒ Yes, ☐ No
If either is No, skip TIM and enter N/A on line 38.
If both RIM and TIM were N/A, skip FIM and enter N/A on line 38.

FIM = TX Fundamental & RX Fundamental
Is |(1) **220** – (4) **360** | <
(7) **40** ?   ☐ Yes, ☒ No
If No, skip FIM and enter N/A on line 38.

Surviving cases   ☒ SIM,   ☒ RIM,   ☒ TIM,   ☐ FIM
☐ No cases survived—No EMI problem.

Amplitude Analysis

	FIM	TIM	RIM	SIM
8. TX Power, $P_T(f_{OT})$, (peak power if pulsed)	NA	80	////	////
9. TX Spurious Power Output: $P_T(f_{ST})$ or $P_T(f_{OT}) - 60$ dB	////	////	20	20
10. TX Antenna Gain in RX Direction: $G_{TR}(f)$ or 0 dB	NA	0	0	0
11. RX Antenna Gain in TX Direction: $G_{RT}(f)$ or 0 dB	NA	0	0	0
12. Propagation Loss, L Using Frequency No.	(1)	(1)	(4)	(2)
Loss in dB from Fig. No. 2.7	NA	-49	-49	-30
13. Unintentional Power Available $P_A(f)$ Add 8 to 12	NA	31	-29	-10
14. RX Fundamental Susceptibility $P_R(f_{OR})$	NA	////	-100	////
15. RX Spurious Suscept.: $P_R(f_{SR})$ or $P_R(f_{OR}) + 80$ dB	////	-20	////	-20
16. Preliminary EMI Prediction: Line 13-14 or 13-15	NA	51	71	10

      If EMI margin < -10 dB, EMI Highly Improbable
      —Stop
      If EMI margin > -10 dB, Start Frequency Culling

Frequency Analysis

Bandwidth Correction

Frequency: ☒ kHz; ☐ MHz

17. TX PRF (if pulse)	100	pps
18. TX Bandwidth ($B_T = 2/\pi\tau$ if pulse; τ = width	64	
19. RX Bandwidth B_R	10	

	FIM	TIM	RIM	SIM	
20. Adjustment (from lines 17 to 19, use Fig. 2.8 and 2.9)	NA	-15	-15	-15	dB
21. Bandwidth Corrected, EMI Margin = lines 16 + 20	NA	36	56	-5	dB

      If EMI Margin $\leqslant -10$ dB, EMI Highly Improbable—Stop

Frequency Correction

Frequency: ☐ kHz; ☒ MHz

22. RX Local Oscillator Frequency f_{LO}	400
23. RX Intermediate Frequency f_{IF}	40

	FIM	TIM	RIM	SIM	
24. TX-RX Frequency Separation: $\Delta f = |(1) - (4)|$	NA	////	////	////	
25. $\Delta f > (B_T + B_R)/2$ (from line 24, use Fig. 2.10)	NA	////	////	////	

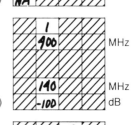

26. Calculate $f_{OT}/f_{LO} \pm f_{IF}$ to nearest integer	////	1	////	
27. Multiply lines 22 × 26	////	400	////	MHz
28. $\Delta f = |1 - 23 - 27| =$ **220** $:	+ 23 - 27| =$ **140**	////	////	////	
29. Select smaller Δf from line 28	////	140	////	MHz
30. $\Delta f > (B_T + B_R)/2$ (from line 29, use Fig. 2.10)	////	-100	////	dB

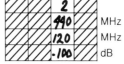

31. Calculate f_{OR}/f_{OT} to nearest integer	////	2	////	
32. Multiply lines 1 × 31	////	440	////	MHz
33. $\Delta f = |(4) - (32)|$	////	120	////	MHz
34. $\Delta f > (B_T + B_R)/2$ (from line 33 use Fig. 2.10)	////	-100	////	dB

35. Calculate Minimum Δf (see Form A)  **0** MHz

36. If Δf > (B$_T$ + B$_R$)/2 (from line 35 use Fig. 2.10) **0** dB

EMI Frequency Corrected Summary

37. Add line 21 to line

25	30	34	36

38. Total here

NA	**-49**	**-29**	**-5**	dB

If EMI Margin < − 10 dB, EMI Highly Improbable

Detailed Analysis

Harmonic or Spurious Response Correction*

	FIM	TIM	RIM	SIM	
39. Correction from Form B		**NA**	**NA**	**26**	dB
40. Corrected EMI add line 38 to line 39*	**NA**	**NA**	**NA**	**21**	dB

Modulation Correction

	FIM	TIM	RIM	SIM	
41. Correction from Form C	**NA**	**NA**	**NA**	**0**	dB
42. Corrected EMI Add line 40 to line 41	**NA**	**NA**	**NA**	**21**	dB

Polarization Correction

	FIM	TIM	RIM	SIM	
43. Correction from Form D	**NA**				dB
44. Corrected EMI Add line 42 to line 44	**NA**	**NA**	**NA**	**21**	dB

Propagation Loss Correction

	FIM	TIM	RIM	SIM	
45. Correction from Form E	**NA**	**NA**	**NA**	**0**	dB
46. Corrected EMI Add line 44 to line 46	**NA**	**NA**	**NA**	**21**	dB

If EMI < − 10 dB EMI Highly Improbable
− 10 dB ⩽ EMI ⩽ 10 dB EMI Marginal
EMI > 10 dB EMI Probable

*Apply corrections only if nominal − 60 dB TX (line 9) and/or + 80 dB RX (line 15) corrections were used.

Form A—SIM Frequency Separation Correction in dB

TX Fund (f_{OT}): __*220*__; RX LO (f_{LO}): __*400*__; RX IF (f_{IF}): __*40*__

N	$(Nf_{OT} + f_{IF})/f_{LO}$	Δp*	$(Nf_{OT} - f_{IF})/f_{LO}$	Δp*
2	*1.2*	*.2*	*1.0*	*0*
3	*1.75*	*-.25*	*1.55*	*-.45*
4	*2.30*	*.30*	*2.10*	*.10*
5	*2.85*	*-.15*	*2.65*	*-.35*
6	*3.40*	*.40*	*3.20*	*.20*
7	*3.95*	*-.05*	*3.75*	*-.25*
8	*4.50*	*.50*	*4.30*	*.30*
9	*5.05*	*.05*	*4.85*	*-.15*
10	*5.60*	*-.40*	*5.40*	*.40*

Select Minimum Value for Δp
Minimum Spurious Frequency Separation = $(\Delta p)_{min} f_{LO}$

*Δp is the magnitude of difference between value obtained for $p \pm \Delta p = N(f_{OT} \pm f_{IF})/f_{LO}$ and the nearest integer.

Form B—Harmonic and/or Spurious Response Correction in dB

FIM—No Correction
TIM—Spurious Response Correction Use p from Line 26
RIM—Harmonic Correction Use N from Line 31
SIM—Add Spurious and Harmonic Correction Use p and N from Form A above

Category		N or p*								
		2	3	4	5	6	7	8	9	10
HF &	Harmonic	+ 19	+ 7	− 2	− 9	− 14	− 19	− 23	− 27	− 30
Below	Response	− 13	− 17	− 20	− 22	− 24	− 26	− 27	− 29	− 30
VHF	Harmonic	+ 6	− 8	− 18	− 26	− 32	− 37	− 42	− 46	− 50
	Response	− 15	− 22	− 26	− 29	− 32	− 35	− 37	− 38	− 40
UHF &	Harmonic	+ 5	− 4	− 10	− 15	− 19	− 22	− 25	− 28	− 30
Above	Response	+ 8	+ 1	− 4	− 8	− 11	− 14	− 16	− 18	− 20

*For the receiver image response use a + 20 dB correction.

Form C—Modulation Correction in dB*

(Use Δf's from lines 24, 29, 33 or 35)			
Modulation Type	B_T Line 18	B_R Line 19	Modulation Correction in dB
Pulse			0
AM			$20 \log (B_T + B_R)/2\Delta f$
FM			$40 \log (B_T + B_R)/2\Delta f$

*The combined Frequency Separation Correction from lines 25, 30, 34 or 36 plus Modulation Correction must not exceed 100 dB

Form D—Antenna Polarization Correctly in dB*

TX Pol: □H; □V; □C.					
RX Pol: □H; □V; □C.					
TX RX	Horizontal		Vertical		Cir
	G < 10 dB	G ≥ 10 dB	G < 10 dB	G ≥ 10 dB	
G < 10 dB	0	0	− 16	− 16	− 3
G ≥ 10 dB	0	0	− 16	− 20	− 3
G < 10 dB	− 16	− 16	0	0	− 3
G ≥ 10 dB	− 16	− 20	0	0	− 3
Circular	− 3	− 3	− 3	− 3	0

*Applies only to intentional radiation region and design frequency.

2.8 EMC Analysis Form for Analog Voice Systems

The EMC analysis short form described in the previous section was a general form that may be used to analyze interactions between various types of communication, navigation and radar transmitters and receivers. This section discusses an even simpler form that is designed for analyzing AM and FM analog voice communication systems such as those used for land mobile applications.

One of the problems in performing an EMC analysis of the type described is gathering all the information required for the prediction. In order to assist the user, values that may be used in the absence of certain specific data are provided. Also, the reader is referred to specific sections of this handbook for more detailed discussion of various EMC analysis considerations.

The specific values and techniques provided in the short-form EMC analysis process are intended to be as realistic as possible. Users may want to regard situations that result in an interference margin between − 10 and + 10 dB as marginal. They may wish to determine whether the specific values and relationships used in the prediction process are realistic for the specific problem. In this case, users should refer to the applicable sections for more detailed descriptions and models for the relationships. If significant differences exist, it may be necessary to conduct a detailed EMC analysis.

EMC Analysis Form for Analog Voice Systems

Adjacent Signal Interference*	
Transmitter Noise	
1. Transmitter Power, P_T (dBm/Channel)	
2. Noise Constant	56
3. 20 log Δf_{TR} (kHz)	
4. Noise per Channel dBm/channel) (1) − (2) − (3)	
5. Transmitter Antenna Gain, G_{TR} (dB)	
6. Effective Radiated Noise Power (dBm/Channel); (4) + (5)	
7. Propagation Constant	32
8. 20 log d_{TR} (km)	
9. 20 log f_R (MHz)	
10. Propagation Loss, L (dB): (7) + (8) + (9)	
11. Receiver Antenna Gain, G_{RT} (dB)	
12. Noise Power Available, P_A (dBm); (6) − (10) + (11)	
13. Receiver Sensitivity Level (dBm)	
14. Allowable Degradation of Receiver Sensitivity (dB)	
15. Receiver Susceptibility Level, P_R (dBm); (13) + (14)	
16. Interference Margin (dB); (12) − (15)	

Third Order Intermodulation

Frequency Check

- Select Receiver fo Analysis
17. Receiver/Frequency, f_R (MHz)
- Select Cosite Transmitter, T_1, with Frequency Nearest to f_R
18. Transmitter Frequency, f_{T_1} (MHz)
19. Frequency Separation ΔF_{TR} (MHz); (18) − (17)
20. Frequency, f_{T_2}, for Intermodulation; (18) + (19)
21. Channel Width, (MHz)
22 Band for Intermodulation; (20) ± (21)

- Check Other Cosite Transmitters for Frequency within Band Specified by (22). If one is found, continue with analysis. If none, eliminate selected transmitter from consideration and repeat process with another transmitter.

Interference Margin < 0.10 dB, EMI Highly Improbable
10 dB < Interference Margin < 10 dB, EMI Marginal
Interference Margin > 10 dB, EMI Probable.

*Applies to cosite transmitters and receivers with frequency separations (Δf)

©Copyright 1987, Interference Control Technologies, Inc.

2.47

EMC Analysis Form for Analog Voice Systems

Adjacent Signal Interference*	T_1	T_2
Receiver Intermodulation		
23. Transmitter Power, P_T (dBm/Channel)		
24. Transmitter Antenna Gain, G_{TR} (dB)		
25 Effective Radiated power (dBm) (23) + (24)		
26. Propagation Constant	32	32
27. 20 log d_{TR} (km)		
28. 20 log f_T (MHz)		
29. Propagation Loss (dB); (26) + (27) + (28)		
30. Receiver Antenna Gain, (dB)		
31. Power Available at Receiver, (dBm); (25) − (29) + (30)		
32. Multiply T_1 Power Available, Line (31), by Two		
33. T_2 Power Available, Line (31)		
34. Intermodulation Constant	−93	
35. Frequency Separation, $\Delta\infty/o$ [19) ÷ (17)] × 100		
36. 60 log $\Delta\infty/o$ or 0		
37. Equivalent Intermodulation Power (dBm); (32) + (33) + (34) − (36)		
38. Receiver Susceptibility Level, P_R (dBm)		
39. Interference Margin, (dB); (37) − (38)		
Transmitter Intermodulation		
40. Power of T_2 (dBm)		
41. T_2 Antenna Gain (dB)		
42. T_2 Effective Radiated Power (dBm), (40) + (41)		
43. Propagation Constant		32
44. 20 log $d_{T_1 T_2}$ (km)		
45. 20 log f_{T_2} (MHz)		
46. Propagation Loss L (dB); (43) + (44) + (45)		
47. T_1 Antenna Gain (dB)		
48. T_2 Signal at T_1 (dBm); (42) − (46) + (47)		
49. Intermodulation Constant		10
50. 30 log ($\Delta\infty/o$, (line 35), or 0; Whichever Is Larger		
51. Intermodulation Power at T_1 (dBm); (48) − (49) + (50)		
52. T_1 Antenna Gain (dB)		
53. Intermodulation ERP (dBm); (51) + (52)		
54. Propagation Constant (dB)		32
55. 20 log $d_{T_1 R}$ (km)		
56. 20 log f_R (MHz)		
57. Intermodulation Propagation Loss (dB); (54) + (55) + (56)		
58. Receiver Antenna Gain (dB)		
59. Intermodulation Power at Receiver (dBm); (53) − (57) + (58)		
60. Receiver Susceptibility Level (dBm)		
61. Interference Margin (dB)		

Interference Margin < .10 dB, EMI Highly improbable
−10 dB < Interference Margin < 10 dB, EMI Marginal
Interference Margin > 10 dB, EMI Probable.

EMC Analysis Form for Analog Voice Systems

Out of Band Interference*	
Transmitter Harmonic to Receiver Fundamental; $f_R > f_{Tq}$	
1. Receiver Frequency, f_R (MHz)	†
2. Transmitter Frequency, f_T (MHz)	†
3. (1) ÷ (2) and Round Off to Nearest Integer, N	
4. Transmitter Harmonic Frequency, Nf_T (MHz; (3) × (2)	
5. Frequency Separation, | (4) − (1) |, (MHz)	
6. Receiver Bandwidth	†
• If (5) > (6) No Harmonic Interference If (5) < (6) Continue	
7. Transmitter Power, P_T (dBm)	
8. Harmonic Correction, (dB); from Table 8.2	
9. Harmonic Power (dBm); (7) + (8)	
10. Propagation Constant	32
11. 20 log d_{TR} (km)	
12. 20 log f_R (MHz)	
13. Propagation Loss, L, (dB) (10) + (11) + (12)	
14. Receiver Antenna Gain, G_R (dB)	
15. Power Available at Receiver (dBm); (9) − (13) + (14)	
16. Receiver Susceptibility Level, P_R (dBm)	
17. Interference Margin, (dB); (15) − (16)	
Transmitter Fundamental to Receiver Spurious: $f_T > f_R$	
18. (2) ÷ (1) and Round Off to Nearest Integer, P	
19. Local Oscillator Frequency, f_{LO} (MHz)	
20. Intermediate Frequency, f_{IF} (MHz)	
21. $\|Pf_{LO} \pm f_{IF} - f_T\|$;(18) × (19) ± (20) − (2)|	
If (21 +) or (21 −) > (6) No Spurious Interface If (21 +) or (21 −) < (6) Continue	
22. Transmitter Power, P_T(dBm)	
23. Transmitter Antenna Gain, G_T (dB)	
24. Propagation Constant	32
25. 20 log d_{TR} (km)	
26. 20 log f_T (MHz)	
27. Propagation Loss, L (dB); (24) + (25) + (26)	
28. Power Available at Receiver, (dBm); (22) + (23) − (27)	
29. Receiver Fundamental Susceptibility, P_R (dBm)	
30. Spurious Correction, from Table 8.3	
31. Spurious Susceptibility, (dBm); (29) + (30)	
32. Interference Margin, (dB); (28) − (31)	

Interference Margin < − 10 dB, EMI Highly Improbable
− 10 dB < Interference Margin < 10 dB, EMI Marginal
Interference Margin > 10 dB, EMI Probable.

*Applies to cosite transmitters and receivers with frequency
separations (Δf) greater than 10% of operating frequency.
†These entries are also required for transmitter fundamental to receiver
spurious.

Illustrative Example 2.8: Transmitter Noise

Consider the case of a land mobile receiver operating at 150 MHz. Determine whether EMI will result if a land mobile transmitter is installed 122 m from the receiver at a frequency of 150.1 MHz. The pertinent transmitter and receiver characteristics are:

Transmitter power (P_T) = 50 dBm
Transmitter antenna gain (G_T) = 3 dB
Receiver antenna gain (G_R) = 3 dB
Receiver sensitivity = -107 dBm
Allowable degradation = 0 dB

This is clearly a co-site adjacent-signal situation, and the primary cause of potential interference would be transmitter noise. The complete short form is provided for this example. The results indicate that a $+8$ dB interference margin will be obtained, and a marginal interference situation exists.

Illustrative Example 2.9: Intermodulation

Consider the case of a land mobile receiver operating at 450 MHz within 12.2 m of a land mobile transmitter at 451 MHz. Determine whether an intermodulation problem will result if a second transmitter operating at 452 MHz is located 30.5 m from the receiver on a site which is 24.4 m from the first transmitter. The pertinent transmitter and receiver characteristics are:

Transmitter power $(T_1$ and $T_2)$ = 50 dBm
Transmitter antenna gain $(G_{T1}$ and $G_{T2})$ = 3 dB
Receiver antenna gain (G_R) = 3 dB
Receiver sensitivity = -107 dBm
Allowable degradation = 0 dB
Channel width = 50 kHz

This situation could potentially result in either transmitter or receiver third-order intermodulation. To determine whether third-order intermodulation is possible, it is necessary to first perform the frequency check indicated on the short form. This has been

EMC Analysis Form for Analog Voice Systems

Illustrative Example 2.8—Transmitter Noise

Adjacent Signal Interference*	
Transmitter Noise	
1. Transmitter Power, P_T (dBm/Channel)	50
2. Noise Constant	56
3. 20 log Δf_{TR} (kHz)	40
4. Noise per Channel dBm/Channel) (1) − (2) − (3)	− 46
5. Transmitter Antenna Gain, G_{TR} (dB)	3
6. Effective Radiated Noise Power (dBm/Channel); (4) + (5)	− 43
7. Propagation Constant	32
8. 20 log d_{TR} (km)	− 18
9. 20 log f_R (MHz)	44
10. Propagation Loss, L (dB): (7) + (8) + (9)	58
11. Receiver Antenna Gain, G_{RT} (dB)	3
12. Noise Power Available, P_A (dBm); (6) − (10) + (11)	− 98
13. Receiver Sensitivity Level (dBm)	− 107
14. Allowable Degradation of Receiver Sensitivity (dB)	0
15. Receiver Susceptibility Level, P_R (dBm); (13) + (14)	− 107
16. Interference Margin (dB); (12) − (15)	9

Third Order Intermodulation

Frequency Check

- Select Receiver fo Analysis ///////////
17. Receiver/Frequency, f_R (MHz)
- Select Cosite Transmitter, T_1, with Frequency Nearest to f_R ///////////
18. Transmitter Frequency, f_{T_1} (MHz)
19. Frequency Separation ΔF_{TR} (MHz); (18) − (17)
20. Frequency, f_{T_2}, for Intermodulation; (18) + (19)
21. Channel Width, (MHz)
22. Band for Intermodulation; (20) ± (21) | (−) | (+) |
- Check Other Cosite Transmitters for Frequency within Band Specified by (22). If one is found, continue with analysis. If none, eliminate selected transmitter from consideration and repeat process with another transmitter.

Interference Margin < 0.10 dB, EMI Highly Improbable
10 dB < Interference Margin < 10 dB, EMI Marginal
Interference Margin > 10 dB, EMI Probable.

*Applies to cosite transmitters and receivers with frequency separations (Δf)

2.51

performed on the accompanying form, and the results indicate that an intermodulation problem may occur.

Next it is necessary to calculate the interference margin resulting from both receiver and transmitter intermodulation situations to determine the corresponding interference potential. These straightforward calculations have been performed on the accompanying form. The calculations indicate that receiver intermodulation results in a +30 dB interference margin and that transmitter intermodulation results in a +57 dB interference margin. For this situation, transmitter intermodulation will predominate and EMI is probable.

Illustrative Example 2.10: Out-of-Band EMI

Consider that an industrial user wants to operate a land mobile base receiver at 158.1 MHz. The receiving antenna will be located on top of a building, and a survey of the immediate vicinity reveals that there is a public safety transmitter operating at 39.525 MHz and a land transportation transmitter operating at 452.9 MHz. The separations between the industrial receiver, and the public safety and transportation transmitters are 30.5 m and 6.1 m, respectively. Determine whether an EMI problem exists if the system characteristics are as follows:

Industrial Receiver
   Frequency = 158.1 MHz
   Intermediated frequency = 10.7 MHz
   Local oscillator = 147.4 MHz
   Fundamental sensitivity = −107 dBm
   Antenna gain = 3 dB

Public Safety Transmitter
   Frequency = 39.535 MHz
   Power output = 100 W
   Antenna gain = 0 dB

Land Transportation Transmitter
   Frequency = 452.9 MHz
   Power output = 50 W
   Antenna gain = 6 dB

EMC Analysis Form for Analog Voice Systems

Illustrative Example 2.9—Intermodulation (continued next page)

Adjacent Signal Interference*	
Transmitter Noise	
1. Transmitter Power, P_T (dBm/Channel)	
2. Noise Constant	56
3. 20 log Δf_{TR} (kHz)	
4. Noise per Channel dBm/Channel) (1) $-$ (2) $-$ (3)	
5. Transmitter Antenna Gain, G_{TR} (dB)	
6. Effective Radiated Noise Power (dBm/Channel); (4) $+$ (5)	
7. Propagation Constant	32
8. 20 log d_{TR} (km)	
9. 20 log f_R (MHz)	
10. Propagation Loss, L (dB): (7) $+$ (8) $+$ (9)	
11. Receiver Antenna Gain, G_{RT} (dB)	
12. Noise Power Available, P_A (dBm); (6) $-$ (10) $+$ (11)	
13. Receiver Sensitivity Level (dBm)	
14. Allowable Degradation of Receiver Sensitivity (dB)	
15. Receiver Susceptibility Level, P_R (dBm); (13) $+$ (14)	
16. Interference Margin (dB); (12) $-$ (15)	

Third Order Intermodulation

Frequency Check

• Select Receiver fo Analysis	///////
17. Receiver/Frequency, f_R (MHz)	450
• Select Cosite Transmitter, T_1, with Frequency Nearest to f_R	///////
18. Transmitter Frequency, f_{T_1} (MHz)	451
19. Frequency Separation ΔF_{TR} (MHz); (18) $-$ (17)	$+1$
20. Frequency, f_{T_2}, for Intermodulation; (18) $+$ (19)	452
21. Channel Width, (MHz)	.050

22. Band for Intermodulation; (20) $\pm$ (21) $(-)$ 451.95 $(+)$ 452.05

• Check Other Cosite Transmitters for Frequency within Band Specified by (22). If one is found, continue with analysis. If none, eliminate selected transmitter from consideration and repeat process with another transmitter.

Interference Margin < 0.10 dB, EMI Highly Improbable
10 dB < Interference Margin < 10 dB, EMI Marginal
Interference Margin > 10 dB, EMI Probable.

*Applies to cosite transmitters and receivers with frequency separations (Δf)

EMC Analysis Form for Analog Voice Systems

Illustrative Example 2.9—(continued)

Adjacent Signal Interference*	T_1	T_2
Receiver Intermodulation		
23. Transmitter Power, P_T (dBm)	50	50
24. Transmitter Antenna Gain, G_{TR} (dB)	3	3
25 Effective Radiated Power (dBm) (23) + (24)	53	53
26. Propagation Constant	32	32
27. 20 log d_{TR} (km)	−38	−38
28. 20 log f_T (MHz)	53	53
29. Propagation Loss (dB); (26) + (27) + (28)	47	55
30. Receiver Antenna Gain, (dB)	3	3
31. Power Available at Receiver, (dBm); (25) − (29) + (30)	9	1
32. Multiply T_1 Power Available, Line (31), by Two	18	
33. T_2 Power Available, Line (31)		1
34. Intermodulation Constant	−93	
35. Frequency Separation, $\Delta\infty$/o [19) ÷ (17)] × 100	0.22	
36. 60 log $\Delta\infty$/o or 0	0	
37. Equivalent Intermodulation Power (dBm); (32) + (33) + (34) − (36)	−74	
38. Receiver Susceptibility Level, P_R (dBm)	−107	
39. Interference Margin, (dB); (37) − (38)	+33	
Transmitter Intermodulation		
40. Power of T_2 (dBm)		50
41. T_2 Antenna Gain (dB)		3
42. T_2 Effective Radiated Power (dBm), (40) + (41)		53
43. Propagation Constant		32
44. 20 log $d_{T_1 T_2}$ (km)		−32
45. 20 log f_{T_2} (MHz)		53
46. Propagation Loss L (dB); (43) + (44) + (45)		53
47. T_1 Antenna Gain (dB)		3
48. T_2 Signal at T_1 (dBm); (42) − (46) + (47)		3
49. Intermodulation Constant		10
50. 30 log ($\Delta\infty$/o, (line 35), or 0; Whichever Is Larger		0
51. Intermodulation Power at T_1 (dBm); (48) − (49) + (50)		−7
52. T_1 Antenna Gain (dB)		3
53. Intermodulation ERP (dBm); (51) + (52)		−4
54. Propagation Constant (dB)		32
55. 20 log $d_{T_1 R}$ (km)		−38
56. 20 log f_R (MHz)		53
57. Intermodulation Propagation Loss (dB); (54) + (55) + (56)		47
58. Receiver Antenna Gain (dB)		3
59. Intermodulation Power at Receiver (dBm); (53) − (57) + (58)		−48
60. Receiver Susceptibility Level (dBm)		−107
61. Interference Margin (dB)		59
Interference Margin < .10 dB, EMI Highly Improbable − 10 dB < Interference Margin < 10 dB, EMI Marginal Interference Margin > 10 dB, EMI Probable.		

2.54

These two potential interference situations clearly are examples of out-of-band EMI. The most probable causes of interference for these situations would be a harmonic of the public safety transmitter interfering with the industrial receiver fundamental, and a spurious response of the industrial receiver being interfered with by the fundamental of the land transportation transmitter. The calculations have been performed on the accompanying forms. The results indicate that both transmitters pose a potential EMI problem to the receiver.

2.9 Computer EMC Analysis

The previous section presented forms which may be used to perform a manual of EMC analysis. All of the operations indicated on the forms may be easily programmed on a personal computer to assist the system designer in performing an EMC analysis. If one is to be involved in the planning and design of a large system (such as a statewide public safety system), it is recommended that a computer be used for the many calculations that will be required for an EMC analysis. Also, it is suggested that a computer data base be established and maintained on all other users in the area.

Illustrative Example 2.10—EMI from Public Safety Transmitter

Out of Band Interference*	
Transmitter Harmonic to Receiver Fundamental; $f_R > f_{Tq}$	
1. Receiver Frequency, f_R (MHz)	158.1†
2. Transmitter Frequency, f_T (MHz)	39.525†
3. (1) ÷ (2) and Round Off to Nearest Integer, N	4
4. Transmitter Harmonic Frequency, Nf_T (MHz); (3) × (2)	158.1
5. Frequency Separation, | (4) − (1) |, (MHz)	0
6. Receiver Bandwidth	0.015†
• If (5) > (6) No Harmonic Interference If (5) < (6) Continue	////////
7. Transmitter Power, P_T (dBm)	50
8. Harmonic Correction, (dB); from Table 8.2	−72
9. Harmonic Power (dBm); (7) + (8)	−22
10. Propagation Constant	32
11. 20 log d_{TR} (km)	−30
12. 20 log f_R (MHz)	44
13. Propagation Loss, L, (dB) (10) + (11) + (12)	46
14. Receiver Antenna Gain, G_R (dB)	3
15. Power Available at Receiver (dBm); (9) − (13) + (14)	−65
16. Receiver Susceptibility Level, P_R (dBm)	−107
17. Interference Margin, (dB); (15) − (16)	+42
Transmitter Fundamental to Receiver Spurious: $f_T > f_R$	
18. (2) ÷ (1) and Round Off to Nearest Integer, P	
19. Local Oscillator Frequency, f_{LO} (MHz)	
20. Intermediate Frequency, f_{IF} (MHz)	
21. $\|Pf_{LO} \pm f_{IF} - f_T\|$;(18) × (19) ± (20) − (2)|	
If (21+) or (21−) > (6) No Spurious Interface If (21+) or (21−) < (6) Continue	////////
22. Transmitter Power, P_T(dBm)	
23. Transmitter Antenna Gain, G_T (dB)	
24. Propagation Constant	32
25. 20 log d_{TR} (km)	
26. 20 log f_T (MHz)	
27. Propagation Loss, L (dB); (24) + (25) + (26)	
28. Power Available at Receiver, (dBm); (22) + (23) − (27)	
29. Receiver Fundamental Susceptibility, P_R (dBm)	
30. Spurious Correction, from Table 8.3	
31. Spurious Susceptibility, (dBm); (29) + (30)	
32. Interference Margin, (dB); (28) − (31)	

Interference Margin < − 10 dB, EMI Highly Improbable
− 10 dB < Interference Margin < 10 dB, EMI Marginal
Interference Margin > 10 dB, EMI Probable.

*Applies to cosite transmitters and receivers with frequency separations (Δf) greater than 10% of operating frequency.
†These entries are also required for transmitter fundamental to receiver spurious.

Illustrative Example 2.10—EMI from Land Transportation Transmitter

Out of Band Interference*	
Transmitter Harmonic to Receiver Fundamental; $f_R > f_{Tq}$	
1. Receiver Frequency, f_R (MHz)	158.1†
2. Transmitter Frequency, f_T (MHz)	452.9†
3. (1) ÷ (2) and Round Off to Nearest Integer, N	
4. Transmitter Harmonic Frequency, Nf_T (MHz; (3) × (2)	
5. Frequency Separation, | (4) − (1) |, (MHz)	
6. Receiver Bandwidth	0.015†
• If (5) > (6) No Harmonic Interference If (5) < (6) Continue	/////
7. Transmitter Power, P_T (dBm)	
8. Harmonic Correction, (dB); from Table 8.2	
9. Harmonic Power (dBm); (7) + (8)	
10. Propagation Constant	32
11. 20 log d_{TR} (km)	
12. 20 log f_R (MHz)	
13. Propagation Loss, L, (dB) (10) + (11) + (12)	
14. Receiver Antenna Gain, G_R (dB)	
15. Power Available at Receiver (dBm); (9) − (13) + (14)	
16. Receiver Susceptibility Level, P_R (dBm)	
17. Interference Margin, (dB); (15) − (16)	
Transmitter Fundamental to Receiver Spurious: $f_T > f_R$	
18. (2) ÷ (1) and Round Off to Nearest Integer, P	3
19. Local Oscillator Frequency, f_{LO} (MHz)	147.4
20. Intermediate Frequency, f_{IF} (MHz)	10.7
21. $\|Pf_{LO} \pm f_{IF} - f_T\|$;(18) × (19) ± (20) − (2)| $\boxed{(+)\ 0}$	(−) 21.4
If (21+) or (21−) > (6) No Spurious Interface If (21+) or (21−) < (6) Continue	/////
22. Transmitter Power, P_T(dBm)	47
23. Transmitter Antenna Gain, G_T (dB)	6
24. Propagation Constant	32
25. 20 log d_{TR} (km)	− 44
26. 20 log f_T (MHz)	53
27. Propagation Loss, L (dB); (24) + (25) + (26)	41
28. Power Available at Receiver, (dBm); (22) + (23) − (27)	− 12
29. Receiver Fundamental Susceptibility, P_R (dBm)	− 107
30. Spurious Correction, from Table 8.3	92
31. Spurious Susceptibility, (dBm); (29) + (30)	− 15
32. Interference Margin, (dB); (28) − (31)	+ 27

Interference Margin < − 10 dB, EMI Highly Improbable
− 10 dB < Interference Margin < 10 dB, EMI Marginal
Interference Margin > 10 dB, EMI Probable.

*Applies to cosite transmitters and receivers with frequency
separations (Δf) greater than 10% of operating frequency.
†These entries are also required for transmitter fundamental to receiver
spurious.

2.10 Bibliography

1. Atlantic Research Corp., "Electromagnetic Compatibility Prediction Studies," RADC TR-66-560, 1966.
2. Duff, W.G., "EMC Design of Telecommunications Systems," *EMC Expo 1986 Symposium Record* (Gainesville, Virginia: Interference Control Technologies, Inc., 1986).
3. Duff, W.G., et. al., "Intrasystem EMI Prediction and Analysis," *1973 IEEE EMC Symposium Record* (New York: IEEE, 1973).
4. Duff, W.G., et. al., "Electromagnetic Compatibility Prediction Studies," RADC-RE-66-650, November 1966.
5. Jansky and Bailey, a Div. of Atlantic Research Corp., "Interference Analysis Study," Vol. 1, Contract No. AF 30(602)-1934, RADC-TDR-59-224, January 1960.
6. Jansky and Bailey, a Div. of Atlantic Research Corp., "Interference Analysis Study," Vols. 1 and 2, Contract No. AF 30(602)-1934, RADC-TDR-61-154, January 1961.
7. Jansky and Bailey, a Div. of Atlantic Research Corp., "Interference Prediction Study," Contract No. AF 30(602)-1934, RADC-TR-59-224, January 1960.
8. Jansky and Bailey, a Div. of Atlantic Research Corp., "Interference Notebook, Vol. 2," Contract AF 30(602)-68-C-0050, RADC-TR-66-1.
9. Jansky and Bailey, a Div. of Atlantic Research Corp., "Interference Analysis Study," Final Report, Contract No. AF 30(602)-2665, RADC-TDR-63-379, June 1963.
10. Jansky and Bailey, a Div. of Atlantic Research Corp., Contract No. AF 30(602)-1934, RADC-TDR-61-312, January 1962.
11. Office of Manned Space Flight, "Electromagnetic Compatibility Principles and Practices," Apollo Program, NASA, October 1985.
12. Salati, O.M.; Ruston, H.; and Kritikos, H., "Interference Studies," Institute of Cooperative Research, Univ. of Pennsylvania, Final Report, RADC-TDR-62-206, AF 30(602)-1785, February 1, 1962.
13. Spagon, J., and Morrison, E.L., Jr., "System Analysis, Prediction, Hardware Implications and Program Control," *1971 IEEE international EMC Symposium Record*, pp. 66-75 (New York: IEEE, 1971).

14. Wetherington, R.D.; Donaldson, E.E.; and Moss, R.W., "Interference Predictions-Philosophies, Objectives and Future Directions," *1969 IEEE International EMC Symposium Record*, pp. 80-4 (New York: IEEE, 1969).

15. White, D.R.J., "Design of Electromagnetic Interference Reduction Using Computer Simulation Techniques," *Proceedings of the Fifth Conference on Radio Interference Reduction and Electronic Compatibility*, October 1959.

16. White, D.R.J., "CE Equipment Characteristics Needed for RFI Prediction," *Second National IRE Radio Frequency Interference Symposium Record*, 1960.

Chapter 3

Transmitter Considerations
for EMC Design

This chapter describes transmitter characteristics that are used in EMC design and analysis. Also included are methods and techniques for representing these transmitter characteristics in the form of mathematical models for analysis. Methods of selecting the pertinent models for a specific transmitter are provided.

The primary function of a transmitter is to generate radio-frequency power containing direct or latent intelligence within a specified frequency band. In addition to the desired power, transmitters produce many unintentional emissions at spurious frequencies. A spurious emission is any radiated output that is not required for transmitting the desired information. The desired or undesired radio-frequency power generated by transmitters may produce EMI in receivers or other equipments. Therefore, in evaluating EMC, it is important that all transmitters are considered as potential sources of interference.

For EMC analysis it is necessary to describe both the desired and undesired emission power spectrum of each transmitter. In general, the transmitter emission spectrum is a composite of several different transmitter interference functions. The next section briefly describes various transmitter functions, identifies the type of information required and discusses problems involved in specifying each of these functions.

3.1 Transmitter EMC Characteristics

Transmitter emissions are classified into one of four categories: (1) fundamental emissions, (2) harmonically related emissions, (3) nonharmonic emissions and (4) broadband noise. Examples of emissions in each of these categories are illustrated in Fig. 3.1. Although it is convenient for the purpose of EMC analysis to consider discrete transmitter emissions, the power associated with any given emission is actually spread over a finite frequency range. Furthermore, broadband electrical noise is superimposed on a discrete emission spectrum. Thus, the complete transmitter spectral emissions example would more nearly appear as shown in Fig. 3.2, where the overall spectrum-amplitude relations represent one example of a mathematical model. The term "broadband noise" refers to that portion of the transmitter output spectrum that results from thermal noise in the final power amplifiers. This noise generally extends over several octaves but does not include the modulation sidebands in the immediate vicinity of a discrete emission.

For EMC analysis, the important parameters that are described for each type of emission are: (1) the output power used in amplitude analysis, (2) a reference frequency and envelope that define the power content in the sidebands around the reference frequency for use in frequency analysis and (3) a description of the modulation for use in both the detailed and performance analyses.

EMC analysis may be performed at several different levels of varying complexity, each giving different results. The term amplitude analysis refers to the simplest type of EMC analysis which is based on a general consideration of transmitter power, antenna gains, propagation loss and receiver susceptibility. Parameters such as frequency, time, separation and direction are only considered in a limited sense. Frequency analysis refers to an EMC analysis in which the frequency parameter is considered in detail but the other parameters are only considered in a rather limited sense. For the purpose of this handbook, the term "detailed analysis" refers to the level of prediction complexity in which all parameters, (e.g., frequency, time, separation and direction) are considered in detail. The final analysis level (performance analysis) considers the effect of EMI problems on operational performance and mission effectiveness. These topics were discussed in Chapter 2. The following paragraphs discuss some of the major considerations that influence the parameters for different transmitter emissions.

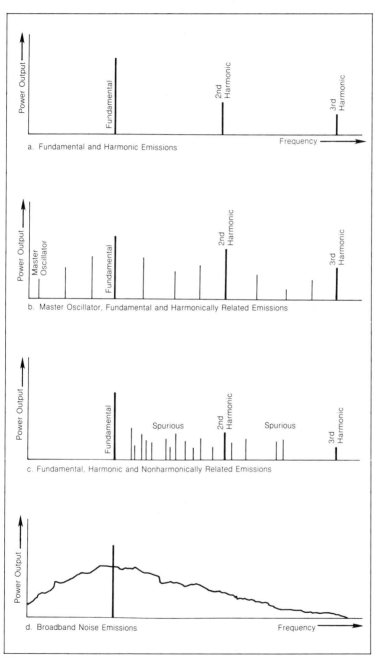

Figure 3.1—Typical Transmitter Emission Spectra

3.3

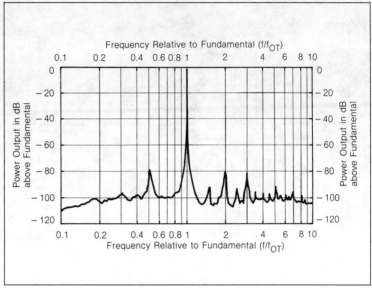

Figure 3.2—Transmitter Output Spectrum Resulting from Composite of Broadband Noise and Discrete Emissions

3.1.1 Fundamental Emission

For amplitude analysis it is necessary to specify power output at the intended fundamental frequency. This information is generally available to the EMI analyst. Typical sources used to determine the fundamental power are the transmitter technical manual, spectrum-signature measurements on the equipment and design specifications. Although the nominal fundamental power is usually specified, there are variations in the actual output from different equipment serial numbers of a particular transmitter nomenclature. Therefore, a statistical representation of the transmitter fundamental output level is recommended for use in EMC analysis.

In the second stage of EMC analysis it is necessary to specify the frequency associated with the fundamental emission. This frequency is the nominal operating or carrier frequency for each transmitter to be considered in the analysis. For problems in which different operating frequencies are to be considered for each transmitter (like a frequency band or assignment problem), the analyst considers each fundamental frequency separately.

The other transmitter parameter that is required for frequency analysis and must be specified for the fundamental emission is the relative power in the sidebands around the carrier frequency. The sidebands on either side of the carrier result from the time-domain modulation process and from nonlinearities that exist in the transmitter. A baseband modulation envelope is used to describe relative power levels of the sideband with respect to the carrier.

For detailed and performance analyses, consider information concerning the transmitter and antenna modulation characteristics in the time domain, the type of modulation used and the type of information transmitted.

3.1.2 Harmonically Related Emissions

Harmonically related transmitter emissions include those undesired spurious emissions that are integer multiples of either the fundamental frequency or frequencies used to generate the fundamental, e.g., a master oscillator or crystal-controlled clock. Specification of harmonic-output power is complicated because of significant variations from serial number to serial number for a particular transmitter nomenclature. As a result, harmonic output power level must be represented statistically.

Spectrum signature measurements provide one of the best sources of data on harmonic-emission output levels for use in EMC analysis (see MIL-STD-449D in Vol 1). However, if the spectrum signature data are not available for a particular transmitting equipment, there are other ways of getting the information. Transmitter specifications and standards such as MIL-STD-461C are possible sources of information regarding spurious emission levels. These specifications and standards provide an indication of harmonic emission output levels. Statistical summaries of available measured harmonic output levels are presented in Section 3.3.1 and may also be used to represent harmonic output levels.

For harmonic emissions, as for the fundamental emission, power is spread over a frequency range. Thus, for these emissions it is also important to define relative content of the power over the frequency band associated with the emission. The techniques for representing the modulation envelopes at the fundamental are also applied to harmonic emissions.

3.1.3 Nonharmonic Spurious Emissions

There are certain cases, such as in the operation of a magnetron or other high-peak pulse power sources, where spurious emissions occur at frequencies that are not harmonically related to the fundamental or the frequency used in producing the fundamental. For these emissions, the relative frequency is subject to random variations and it is therefore necessary to define the probability that an output will occur in any given frequency increment. The output power level and the sideband envelope for the nonharmonic emissions are described in a way similar to that for harmonically related emissions.

3.1.4 Transmitter Broadband Noise

With the possible exception of high-power transmitters (power outputs greater than 1 kW), the transmitter noise level is relatively insignificant compared to the other interfering signals that are present in a given electromagnetic environment. For those cases where it is necessary to consider transmitter broadband noise, the level is specified in terms of available power per hertz of bandwidth as a function of frequency (dBm/Hz). Were this not random noise but impulsive, the term would be peak voltage intensity in V/Hz (or dBV/Hz) or peak power intensity in W/Hz^2 (or dBm/Hz^2).

3.1.5 Other Transmitter Functions

In addition to the specific transmitter outputs delineated above, there is another that is considered in EMC analysis: transmitter intermodulation. For analysis purposes, those signals that are produced when the output of one transmitter mixes with the output of another in the nonlinear circuits of a transmitter are considered to be in a different category from those identified above.

3.2 Fundamental Emission Characteristics

Because of the relatively high power levels associated with

transmitter fundamentals, these emissions are potentially the most serious sources of interference and hence must be given careful consideration in EMC analysis. On the other hand, pertinent characteristics associated with fundamental emissions are generally defined by equipment specifications. Because information is readily available, these emissions do not represent serious data-collection problems.

One important characteristic associated with the fundamental power is the variability from equipment to equipment of a given transmitter type. Although this variability is small compared to the other variations that exist in EMC analysis, cases do exist where equipment-to-equipment variations in the fundamental power output are significant.

3.2.1 Fundamental Emission Amplitude Characteristics

For amplitude analysis the power levels associated with various transmitter emissions are represented consistently with both the overall analysis requirements and the other models used in the analysis process. This section discusses the problems involved in mathematically modeling transmitter fundamental emission levels and describes specific models that may be used when data are not available. Also presented are the general models that are used and techniques for evaluating these models for specific transmitters from measured data and summary models.

Figure 3.3 illustrates the maximum effective radiated powers that may apply to various frequency allocations in the United States and Canada. Figure 3.4 illustrates variations in transmitter fundamental emission power from four different transmitter nomenclatures that have been observed experimentally.[1]

For EMC analysis purposes it is assumed that variations in fundamental power, expressed in dB, are normally distributed random variables. Thus, the distributions are specified by the mean value $P_T (f_{OT})$ and the standard deviations $\sigma_T (f_{OT})$. If specific data are not available (which is usually the case) transmitter fundamental power should be represented by a normal distribution with a mean value that is equal to the nominal power output and a standard deviation of 2 dB.[2]

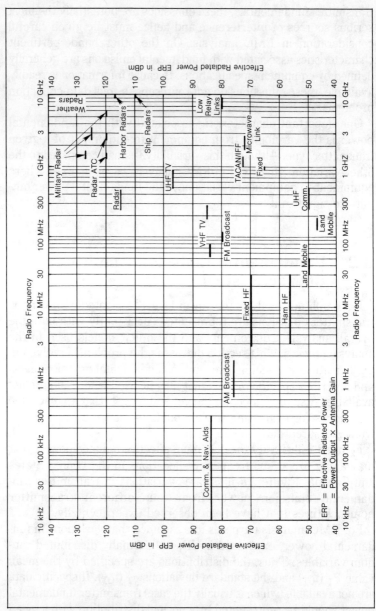

Figure 3.3—U.S. and Canadian Frequency Allocations and Maximum Effective Radiated Powers

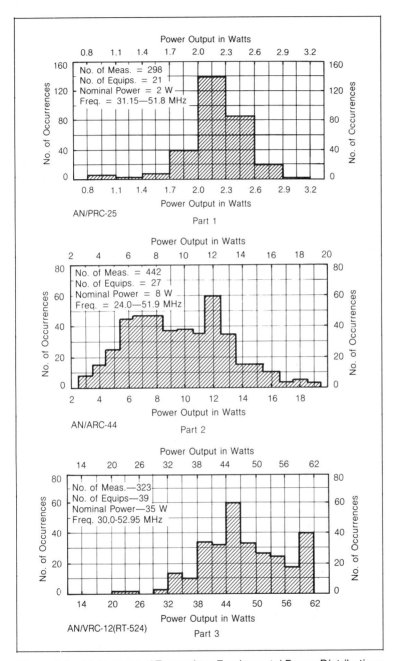

Figure 3.4—Histograms of Transmitter Fundamental Power Distributions (continued next page)

3.9

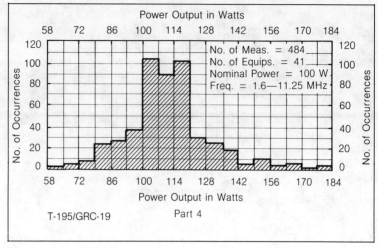

Figure 3.4—(continued)

Illustrative Example 3.1

It is assumed that the nominal power output of a VHF land-mobile transmitter is 8 watts (39 dBm). The resulting probability distribution function of this power is shown in Fig. 3.5. The following observations may be made:

1. The probability of exceeding the nominal power output by more than 3 dB (power output greater than 16 W or 42 dBm) is approximately seven percent.
2. The probability of the power output exceeding a level 3 dB below the nominal (power output greater than 4 W or 36 dBm) is approximately 93 percent.
3. For other power output levels of interest, the probabilities are also obtained from the figure.

Looking at Fig. 3.4, it may be shown that the overall range of levels from Fig. 3.5 correspond to experimental data depicted for the 8 W transmitter.

The graph shown in Fig. 3.5 may be used to obtain the fundamental power output probability distribution function for any transmitter for which specific measured data are not available. The scale that expresses transmitter power in terms of dB relative to the nominal power would be used to specify the probability distribution function for transmitter fundamental emissions.

3.10

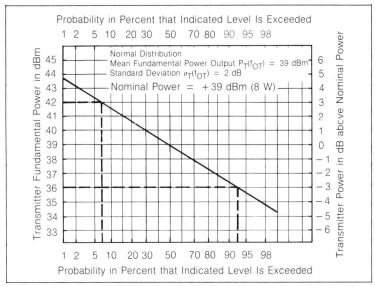

Figure 3.5—Probability Distribution Model for Transmitter Fundamental Power

Relationships have been given for modeling transmitter fundamental power outputs when measured data are not available. On the other hand, when such data are available for several different serial number equipments operating at different tuned frequencies (total samples = M), specific values may be derived. For the mean power $P_T(f_{OT})$ and the standard deviation $\sigma_T(f_{OT})$ the relationships used are:

$$P_T(f_{OT}) \text{ in dBm} = \frac{\displaystyle\sum_{i=1}^{M} P_{T_i}(f_{OT})\text{dBm}}{M} \tag{3.1}$$

$$\sigma_T(f_{OT}) \text{ in dB} = \left[\frac{\displaystyle\sum_{i=1}^{M} [P_T(f_{OT}) - P_{T_i}(f_{OT})]^2}{M-1} \right]^{1/2} \tag{3.2}$$

where, $P_{T_i}(f_{OT})$ = individual measured values of fundamental power output

$\displaystyle\sum_{i=1}^{M}$ = sum over i available samples from i = 1 to M

3.11

Illustrative Example 3.2

Show how Eqs. (3.1) and (3.2) are used to compute $P_T(f_{OT})$ and $\sigma_T(f_{OT})$ for a specific transmitter type (nomenclature) from measured data. Consider a UHF communication transmitter that operates in the 225 to 400 MHz frequency band and has a nominal fundamental power output of 100 W (50 dBm). Assume that power output measurements of three different serial numbers of this transmitter are performed at each of three different frequencies (total of nine measurements). The following data are obtained:

Fundamental Frequency	Power Output for Transmitter Serial No.		
	#1	#2	#3
f_1 = 234 MHz	50 dBm	52 dBm	53 dBm
f_2 = 313 MHz	52 dBm	50 dBm	48 dBm
f_3 = 391 MHz	47 dBm	49 dBm	49 dBm

The mean fundamental power output $P_T(f_{OT})$ is obtained from Eq. (3.1) by adding together the M = 9 individual values and dividing by nine:

$$P_T(f_{OT}) = \frac{50 + 52 + 53 + 52 + 50 + 48 + 47 + 49 + 49}{9} = 50 \text{ dBm}$$

The standard deviation is derived from Eq. (3.2) by subtracting each of the individual values from the mean, squaring, summing, dividing by M − 1 and taking the square root:

$$\sigma_T(f_{OT}) = \left[\frac{\begin{array}{l}(50 - 50)^2 + (50 - 52)^2 + (50 - 53)^2 + \\ (50 - 52)^2 + (50 - 50)^2 + (50 - 48)^2 + \\ (50 - 47)^2 + (50 - 49)^2 + (50 - 49)^2\end{array}}{9 - 1} \right]^{1/2} \text{dB}$$

$$= \left[\frac{32}{8} \right]^{1/2} \text{dB} = 2 \text{ dB}$$

3.2.2 Fundamental Emission Frequency Characteristics

This section presents methods and techniques for modeling transmitter characteristics for use in the second-stage frequency analysis of the EMI analysis process. It identifies sources of information that may be used to determine characteristics of specific transmitters. It also describes general models that may be used to represent transmitter characteristics when specific information is not available.

For frequency analysis, a reference frequency is associated with each transmitter emission, and the distribution of power around this frequency is described. The reference frequency is specified in a simple way for fundamental outputs. In general, the power distribution is described by defining a bandwidth (which is determined by the transmitter modulation characteristics) and an envelope (which describes the way in which the power varies with frequency).

The fundamental emission frequency band, modulation type and emission envelopes for some of the more important CE emitters are described below.

Broadcast Transmitters

Broadcast Bands Cover:
 HF Amplitude Modulation (535-1,605 kHz)
 VHF Frequency Modulation (88-108 MHz)
 VHF Television: Lower Bands (54-88 MHz)
            Upper Bands (174-216 MHz)
 UHF Television (470-890 MHz)
 International AM Broadcasting

Two examples of broadcast spectrum signatures will illustrate spectrum-amplitude profiles. Figure 3.6 shows a typical fundamental emission signature of an FM broadcast transmitter. Note the nominal 200 kHz emission bandwidth around the fundamental frequency and the relatively low (-90 dB) out-of-band levels as controlled by FCC Regulations. Figure 3.7 illustrates the fundamental emission signature of a typical VHF TV emission. The nominal 6 MHz transmission bandwidth levels are readily observed. For both these examples the measurement receiver bandwidth is necessarily much less than the transmitter bandwidth and the amplitude is presented in units of dB relative to the maximum level.

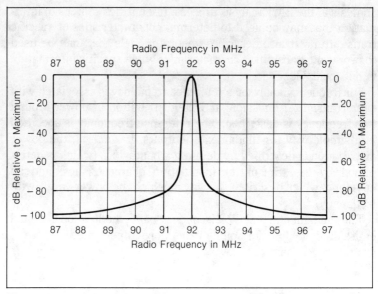

Figure 3.6—Typical Spectrum Signature of an FM Broadcast Transmitter (courtesy of JTAC Spectrum Engineering)

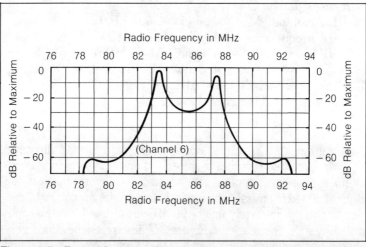

Figure 3.7—Typical Spectrum Signature of a VHF TV Broadcast Transmitter (courtesy of JTAC Spectrum Engineering)

Communication Transmitters

Communication transmitters are the greatest in number and most varied of all CE types. They occupy portions of the spectrum interlaced between other activities from 20 kHz to about 20 GHz.

3.14

The transmitter emission spectrum (resulting from the combined effects of the modulation process and transmitter noise) is one of the most important factors in determining the minimum frequency separation required between communications transmitters and receivers operating in close proximity. Figure 3.8 shows the fundamental emission spectrum signature of a typical VHF voice communication, land mobile transmitter. The 15 kHz transmitter bandwidth is evident. The emission spectrum shows that the levels are below 100 dB down at 150 kHz on either side of the carrier. For frequency separations greater than 15 kHz, the typical emission spectrum given in Fig. 3.8 results from transmitter noise.

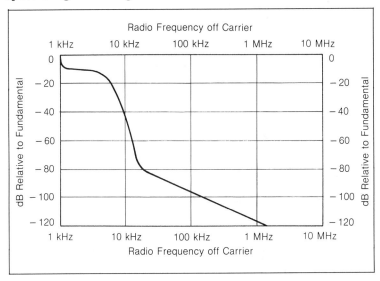

Figure 3.8—Typical Spectrum Signature of a VHF Land-Mobile Transmitter (courtesy of JTAC Spectrum Engineering)

Relay Communication

Relay communications generally consist of four types:
Common Carrier, Microwave Relay (2.1-11.7 GHz interspersed)
Satellite Relay (2.4-16 GHz interspersed)
Ionospheric Scatter (400-500 MHz)
Tropospheric Scatter (1.8-5.6 GHz interspersed)

Figure 3.9 illustrates a spectrum signature for the fundamental of a typical TM, one-watt microwave relay used in the Bell System. Note the rapid emission spectrum falloff. This is typical of most relay communications having a low-spectrum pollution and operating under severe adjacent-channel requirements.

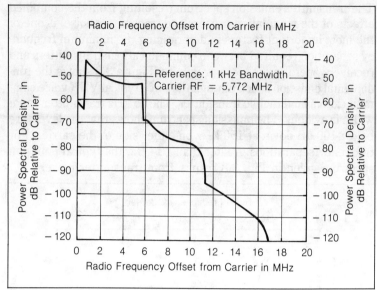

Figure 3.9—Typical Spectrum Signature of a C-Band Microwave Relay Transmitter (courtesy of Bell Telephone Laboratories)

Navigation Transmitters

Navigation transmitters in this classification exclude radars. Typical emitter types included are:
VOR (VHF Omni Range): 108-118 MHz
TACAN (Tactical Air Navigation): 1,000 or 1,180 MHz
Marker Beacons: 74.6-75.4 MHz
ILS (Instrument Landing System):
  ILS Localizer: 108-118 MHz
  Glide Path: 328.6-355.4 MHz
  Altimeter: 4.2-4.4 GHz
  Direction Finding: 405-415 kHz
  Loran C: 90-110 kHz
  A: 1.8-2.0 MHz
  Maritime: 285-325 kHz, 2.9-3.1 GHz, 5.7-5.65 GHz
  Land: 1,638-1,708 kHz

Figures 3.10 and 3.11 show the fundamental signatures of Loran C and VHF doppler VOR transmitters. The 10 kHz variable-phase subcarrier components are readily observed in the spectrum of the VOR transmitter.

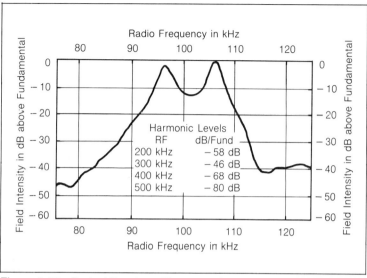

Figure 3.10—Typical Spectrum Signature of a 100 kHz Loran-C Transmitter (courtesy of U.S. Coast Guard)

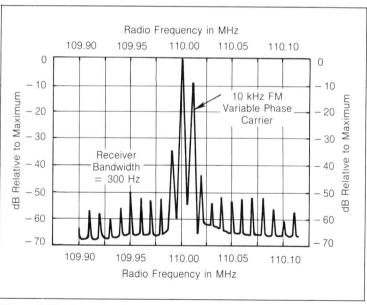

Figure 3.11—Spectrum Signature of FAA, VHF Doppler VOR (courtesy of FAA Frequency Mgmt. Div.)

Radar Transmitters

Radars are perhaps the greatest offenders because of their large peak pulse powers (up to about 5 MW) and attendant spectrum spread due to short pulses occupying broad basebands. They are also offensive because of their relatively high harmonic radiations.

Radars are used in intermittent portions of the spectrum from about 225 MHz to 35 GHz. They are used in many capacities (the Department of Defense is the largest user of the more powerful radars) including air traffic control, air and surface search, harbor surveillance, mapping, tracking and fire control, police speed-monitoring and weather. There may be as many as 100,000 such radars used in the United States alone although most of them are innocuous, low-power speed traps used by the police.

Figures 3.12 and 3.13 illustrate typical spectrum signatures from P-band, long-range search and FAA S-band, air traffic control radars. Note the wide emission sidebands for both radars. Although the harmonic outputs are only illustrated for the P-band radar, they would also be present for the S-band radar and, in fact, for all of the other transmitters discussed in the above subsections. Transmitter spurious output levels are discussed in a later section.

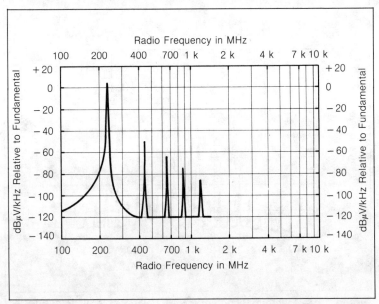

Figure 3.12—Typical Spectrum Signatures of a P-Band (VHF) Long-Range Search Radar

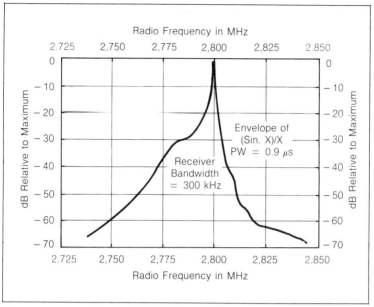

Figure 3.13—Typical Spectrum Signature of an FAA, ASR, S-Band Radar (courtesy of FAA Frequency Mgmt. Div.)

3.2.2.1 Representation of Fundamental Emission

As mentioned previously, the transmitter fundamental output is not actually confined to a single frequency; it is distributed over a range of frequencies around the fundamental. The characteristics of the power distribution in the vicinity of the fundamental are determined primarily by the baseband modulation characteristics of the transmitter. The resulting spectral components are termed modulation sidebands. For frequency analysis, the power distribution in the modulation sidebands is represented by a modulation envelope function. In general, the modulation envelopes are described by specifying bandwidths or frequency ranges and functional relationships which describe the variation of power with frequency, $M(\Delta f)$. The modulation envelope model is:

$$M(\Delta f) = M(\Delta f_i) + M_i \log \left(\frac{\Delta f}{\Delta f_i} \right)$$

(3.3)

$$\text{for } \Delta f_i \leqslant \Delta f_i + 1$$

3.19

where, Δf = separation from reference frequency
          Δf_i = initial frequency of applicable region
          M_i = slope of modulation envelope for applicable region

One example of the resulting functional relationship is shown in Figure 3.14. The parameters that are required to specify the modulation envelope are the bandwidths of applicable regions of constant slope and the rate at which the envelope falls off over the frequency region of interest.

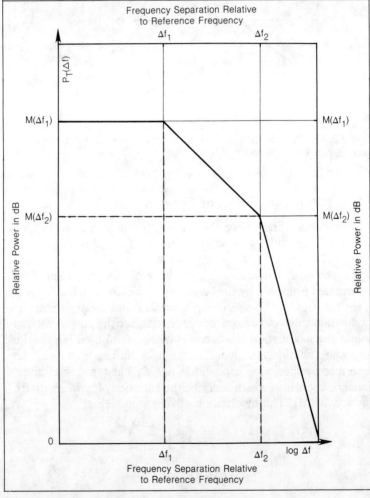

Figure 3.14—Modulation Envelope Representation

3.2.2.2 Bandwidth

One of the most important parameters associated with the modulation envelope is the transmitter nominal bandwidth (usually the 3 dB bandwidth). In general, most of the transmitter power is located within this region, and the power decreases rapidly with frequency separation outside this region. Usually the transmitter nominal bandwidth may be determined from transmitter specifications. In the event that such information is not available, the bandwidth can then be determined by considering the transmitter modulation characteristics.

Amplitude Modulation (AM)

In an amplitude-modulated (AM) wave, the amplitude of a carrier varies according to the baseband intelligence being transmitted. This is shown in Fig. 3.15. When the amplitude of the radio-frequency carrier is varied in this manner, sideband frequencies are generated which carry the intelligence. The nominal width of the frequency spectrum occupied by such an AM wave is twice that of the highest frequency contained in the baseband information. Thus, the bandwidth required of the AM wave is determined by the rate at which the amplitude is varied.

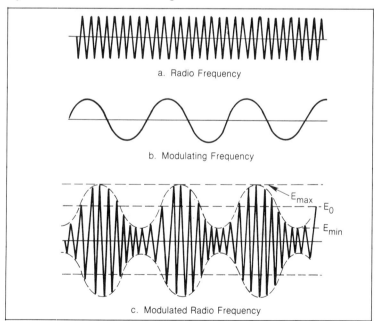

a. Radio Frequency

b. Modulating Frequency

c. Modulated Radio Frequency

Figure 3.15—Amplitude Modulation

Frequency Modulation (FM)

In frequency modulation (FM) the instantaneous frequency of a radio frequency carrier is varied according to the baseband information to be modulated on the wave while the amplitude of the carrier is held constant. This is shown in Fig. 3.16. The rate at which the instantaneous frequency is varied about the carrier is determined by the modulating frequency, whereas the frequency deviation (the excursions or amount that the frequency varies from the central carrier) is proportional to the amplitude of the modulating signal.

For FM, the bandwidth in which most of the energy is contained is a function of the frequency deviation and the highest modulating baseband frequency. The **modulation index (m_f)** is defined as:

$$m_f = \frac{\text{frequency deviation}}{\text{modulation frequency}} = f_d/f_m \qquad (3.4)$$

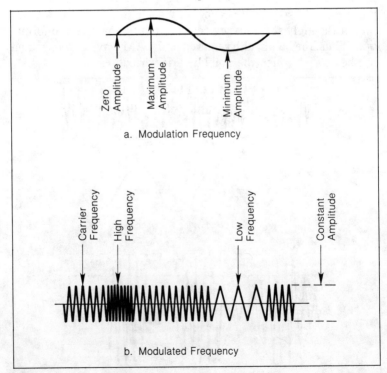

a. Modulation Frequency

b. Modulated Frequency

Figure 3.16—Frequency Modulation

Figure 3.17 illustrates the relationship between modulation index and bandwidth for a given modulating frequency. When the modulation index is less than one-half (the frequency deviation is less than half the modulating frequency), the power distribution is confined to the bandwidth as with AM. On the other hand, if the modulation index is greater than unity (the frequency deviation is greater than the modulating frequency, the FM wave contains significant sideband components on both sides of the carrier. This exists over a frequency interval approximating the sum of the frequency deviation and the modulating frequency. For EMI analysis, the transmitter bandwidth B_T for an FM signal is considered to be twice the sum of the frequency deviation plus the modulating frequency; for example:

$$B_T = 2 \, (f_d + f_m), \text{ for } m_f > 1 \qquad (3.5)$$

where, f_d = frequency deviation
           f_m = modulating frequency

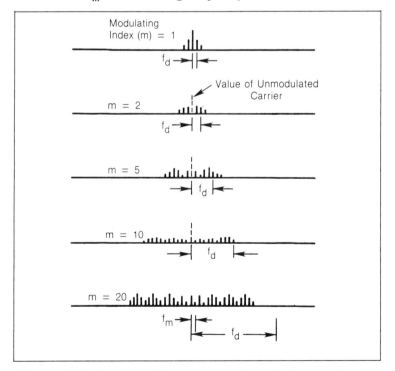

Figure 3.17—Spectra of Frequency-Modulated Waves (Constant Modulating Frequency)

Because the frequency deviation can be expressed as the product of the modulation index and modulating frequency, the bandwidth can be expressed as:

$$B_T = 2 (1 + m_f) f_m \qquad (3.6)$$

When the modulation index (m_f) is one or more orders of magnitude greater than unity, the bandwidth is approximately twice the frequency deviation or twice the product of the modulation index and the modulating frequency. Thus:

$$B_T \cong 2f_d, \text{ for } m_f \gg 1 \qquad (3.7)$$

$$\cong 2m_f f_m$$

Illustrative Example 3.3

Consider an FM transmitter modulated with a baseband signal having a 5 kHz bandwidth (f_m = 5 kHz). Assume that the frequency deviation is 45 kHz. Calculate the bandwidth.

From Eq. (3.4), the modulation index is 9. The bandwidth for this transmitter is given by Eq. (3.6):

$$BT = 2 (1 + m_f) f_m$$

$$= 2 (1 + 9) 5 \text{ kHz}$$

$$= 100 \text{ kHz}$$

Phase Modulation (ϕM)

A phase-modulated (ϕM) wave is one in which the reference phase of the carrier is varied in proportion to the instantaneous amplitude of the modulating baseband signal. ϕM is similar to FM and is merely a way of obtaining an FM wave in which the frequency deviation is proportional to the frequency instead of the amplitude of the modulating wave.

Pulse Modulation (PM)

For pulse-type emissions, such as those used with radar and navigation systems, the transmitter bandwidth B_T used in EMI prediction is given by:

$$B_T = 2/\pi\tau \qquad (3.8)$$

where, τ = pulse width

The bandwidth is calculated from nominal data on the pulse width.

Illustrative Example 3.4

Consider that a radar transmitter has a pulse width of 1 μs. The bandwidth is determined directly from Eq. (3.8):

$$B_T = \frac{2}{(\pi \times 10^{-6})} = 0.63 \times 10^6 \text{ Hz} = 0.63 \text{ MHz} \qquad (3.9)$$

3.2.2.3 Modulation Envelope Model

For performing an EMC analysis, it is necessary to evaluate the constants in the general mathematical model of Eq. (3.3) for the fundamental output modulation envelope. Often, the only available modulation information in the transmitter instruction manual will be the 3 dB points (frequencies) or the 10 dB points. Either measurements or theoretical prediction methods must be used to determine the modulation envelope. When measurements are available for a particular transmitter, the data can be used to determine the constants in the mathematical model for the fundamental output modulation envelope.

Mathematical techniques exist (Fourier analysis) for converting a function in the time domain to an equivalent representation in the frequency domain. In many cases, however, sufficient information is not available to perform the conversion. Thus, general representations of modulation envelopes are required for those cases where detailed information required for the Fourier analysis is not available.

In the event that specific data on transmitter modulation envelopes are not available, the generalized representations shown in Figs. 3.18 through 3.21 may be used to describe the transmitter modulation characteristics for use in EMC analysis. The slope M in dB/decade is always referenced with respect to the baseband notch frequency and not that of the same frequency with carrier inserted. Table 3.1 presents the appropriate values for Δf_i, $M(\Delta f_i)$ and M_i that should be used in the modulation envelope model Eq. (3.3) for the types of modulation indicated.

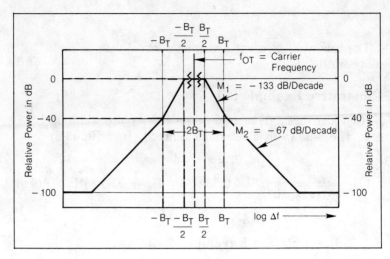

Figure 3.18—Frequency Spectrum Envelope for AM Communication and CW Radar

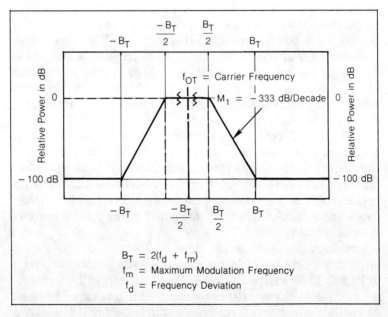

Figure 3.19—FM Modulation Envelope

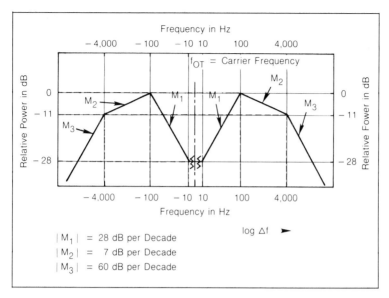

Figure 3.20—Model for AM Voice Modulation

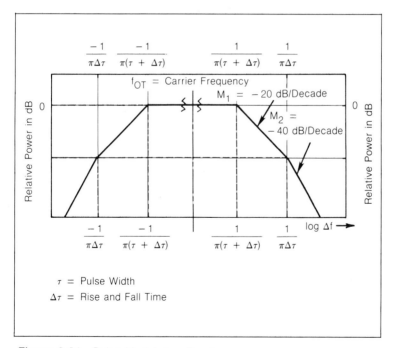

Figure 3.21—Pulse Modulation Envelope

3.27

Table 3.1—Constants for Modulation Envelope Model

Type of Modulation	i	$\|\Delta f_i\|$	$M(\Delta f_i)$ (dB above Fundamental)	M_i (dB/Decade)
AM Communication and CW Radar	0	$0.1\ B_T$	0	0
	1	$0.5\ B_T$	0	-133
	2	B_T	-40	-67
AM Voice	0	1 Hz	-28	0
	1	10 Hz	-28	$+28$
	2	100 Hz	0	-7
	3	1,000 Hz	-11	-60
FM	0	$0.1\ B_T$	0	0
	1	$0.5\ B_T$	0	-333
	2	B_T	-100	0
Pulse*	0	$\dfrac{1}{10\tau}$	0	0
	1	$\dfrac{1}{\pi(\tau + \Delta\tau)}$	0	-20
	2	$\dfrac{1}{\pi\Delta\tau}$	$-20 \log\left(1 + \dfrac{\tau}{\Delta\tau}\right)$	-40

*Modulation Envelope for Trapezoidal Pulse with Half-Voltage Width τ and Rise and Fall Times $\Delta\tau$

Illustrative Example 3.5

Consider an AM communication transmitter with an emission bandwidth of 10 kHz. Use Table 3.1 and Eq. (3.3) to model the modulation envelope for the transmitter.

For an AM transmitter, the modulation envelope shown in Figure 3.18 is completely defined once the emission bandwidth is specified. Thus for a 10 kHz bandwidth, the modulation envelope model, Eq. (3.3) is:

$$M(\Delta f) = 0, \text{ for } |\Delta f| \leqslant 5 \text{ kHz}$$

$$= -133 \log \frac{|\Delta f_{kHz}|}{5 \text{ kHz}}, \text{ for } 5 \text{ kHz} \leqslant |\Delta f| \leqslant 10 \text{ kHz}$$

$$= -40 - 67 \log \frac{|\Delta f_{kHz}|}{10 \text{ kHz}}, \text{ for } 10 \text{ kHz} \leqslant |\Delta f|$$

For this example, the transmitter modulation envelope is -40 dB above the fundamental level at a frequency 10 kHz removed from the fundamental ($|\Delta f| = 10$ kHz), and is -80 dB above the fundamental at a frequency 40 kHz removed from the fundamental.

3.2.2.4 Fourier Analysis Models

If measured data are not available, Fourier analysis methods may be used to determine the modulation envelope. These methods are particularly useful and are widely used for pulse-type signals. Although Fourier analysis methods may also be applied to AM and FM, they are not as readily applied to the complex modulation waveforms associated with these signals.

Periodic PM Signals

Consider a periodic pulse type signal which may either be represented in terms of amplitude versus time or amplitude versus frequency. It is the representation of a pulse signal in the frequency domain which is necessary for interference analysis.

For periodic signals, the relationship between the time and frequency representations is given by Fourier series.[3]

$$f(t) = \sum_{n = -\infty}^{+\infty} d_n e^{-j\omega_n t} \qquad (3.10)$$

where,

$$d_n = \frac{1}{T} \int_{-T/2}^{T/2} f(t) e^{-j\omega_n t} \, dt \qquad (3.11)$$

and,

$$\omega_n = 2\pi f_n = \frac{2n\pi}{T} \qquad (3.12)$$

$f(t) = $ the signal as a function of time

$n = $ a summing index which successively assumes all positive and negative integer values including zero

$T = $ period of repetition

As an example of a Fourier series, consider a periodic train of rectangular-shape current pulses, I(t). Figure. 3.22 depicts the pulse train, in which f_r = pulse repetition frequency; $T = 1/f_r$ and τ = pulse width. Equation (3.10) becomes:

$$I(t) = \sum_{n = -\infty}^{+\infty} I_n e^{-j\omega n t} \tag{3.13}$$

where,

$$I_n = \frac{1}{T} \int_{-T/2}^{T/2} I(t) e^{-j\omega n t} \, dt \tag{3.14}$$

From Fig. 3.22, $I(t) = I_m$ in the region $-\tau/2$ to $+\tau/2$ and is zero over the remainder of the period. Substituting this into Eqs. (3.13) and (3.14) and integrating them yields:

$$I_n = \tau f_r I_m \frac{\sin(n\pi f_r r)}{n\pi f_r \tau} \tag{3.15}$$

and the relative magnitude is:

$$\frac{I_n}{I_o} = \frac{\sin(n\pi f_r \tau)}{n\pi f_r \tau} \tag{3.16}$$

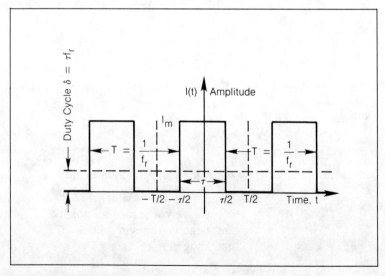

Figure 3.22—Ideal Pulse Train

The spectrum amplitude distribution of a rectangular pulse is described by the (sin x)/x function which is illustrated in Fig. 3.23 along with the resulting envelope described by the function 1/x. From Eq. (3.16), the "x" term equals $n\pi f_r \tau$. The notion of discrete spectral lines existing at nf_r frequencies within the (sin x)/x envelope (centered about the carrier frequency) only applies in certain situations.

An actual pulse is never a perfectly rectangular pulse as suggested in Fig. 3.22 because zero rise and decay times are not physically realizable. Thus, an actual spectrum amplitude would fall off more rapidly with frequency than suggested by the theoretical rectangular pulse spectrum.

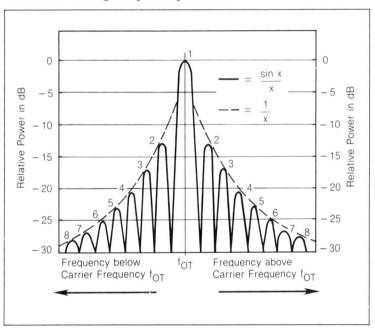

Figure 3.23—(Sin x)/x Distribution

Nonperiodic PM Signals

In most cases of pulse widths, pulse repetition rates and receiver bandwidths the spacing between pulses is such that the individual pulses are considered as nonperiodic signals. In this case the Fourier integral given by Eq. (3.17) is used to determine the spectrum-amplitude distribution.

$$g(\omega) = \frac{1}{2\pi} \int_{-\infty}^{\infty} f(t)e^{-j\omega t}\, dt \tag{3.17}$$

where, $g(\omega)$ = signal amplitude as a function of radial frequency

ω = frequency in radians per second, $2\pi f$ Hz

$f(t)$ = signal amplitude as a function of time

t = time

e = natural logarithm to the base e = 2.718

j = operator $\sqrt{-1}$

Application of the Fourier integral to a nonperiodic signal results in a continuous function of frequency instead of a succession of discrete frequency components. Laplace transforms may also be used. Figure 3.24 depicts four basic pulse types with their corresponding time and frequency functions. Figures 3.25 through 3.28 represent the envelope of the modulation spectrum for various values of pulse widths for each of the four basic pulse types. Figure 3.29 shows a spectral comparison of the four pulses for a 1 μs pulse width.

In many cases involving EMC analysis, the pulse may be represented by a trapezoidal shape with width τ and rise and fall times $\Delta\tau$. In this case, the resulting envelope of the modulation spectrum is illustrated in Fig. 3.30 for several different pulse widths and rise times. To use Fig. 3.30 consider the appropriate lines corresponding to pulse width, τ, and rise-and-fall times, $\Delta\tau$, and select the one that gives the lowest relative power at the frequency separation of interest.

AM and FM Signals

AM and FM waveforms are, in general, quite complex. If the modulating waveform is periodic and can be specified, the Fourier series representation given by Eqs. (3.10) and (3.11) can be used to derive the frequency spectrum of the signal. The frequency spectrum resulting from the modulation process using a single sine wave and a square wave for both AM and FM modulations are presented in Figs. 3.31 through 3.33. Figure 3.31 shows the frequency spectrum resulting from the FM modulation process when the modulation index is five. Figure 3.32 shows similar graphs for a modulation index of 20. For AM modulation, Fig. 3.33 illustrates the resulting spectrum for 25, 50 and 100 percent modulations.

Pulse Shape	Time Function e(t)	Frequency Spectrum E(f)
Rectangular: 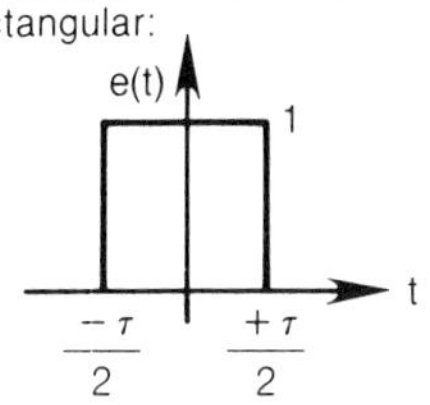 	$1, \ -\dfrac{\tau}{2} \leqslant t \leqslant +\dfrac{\tau}{2}$ $0,$ Elsewhere	$\dfrac{\tau \sin \pi f \tau}{\pi f \tau}$
Half-Cosine: 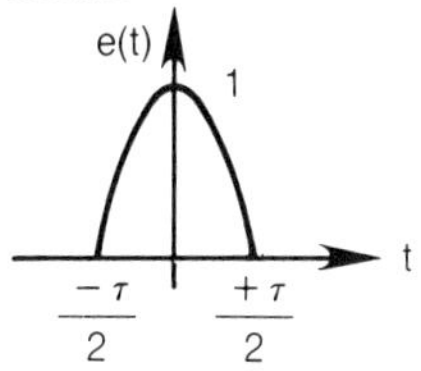 	$\cos \omega_0 t, \ -\dfrac{\tau}{2} \leqslant t \leqslant +\dfrac{\tau}{2}$ $0,$ Elsewhere $\omega_0 = \dfrac{\pi}{\tau}$	$\dfrac{2\tau \cos \pi f \tau}{\pi(1 - 4\tau^2 f^2)}$
Cosine Squared: 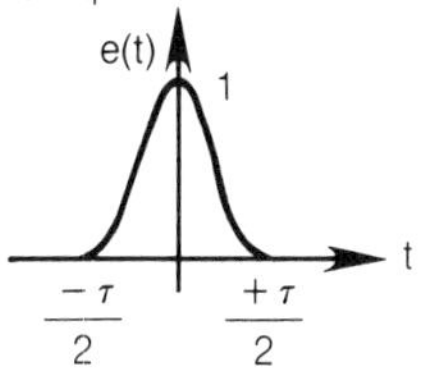 	$\cos^2 \omega_0 t, \ -\dfrac{\tau}{2} \leqslant t \leqslant +\dfrac{\tau}{2}$ $0,$ Elsewhere $\omega_0 = \dfrac{\pi}{\tau}$	$\dfrac{\tau \sin \pi f \tau}{2\pi f \ \tau(1 - \tau^2 f^2)}$
Gaussian: 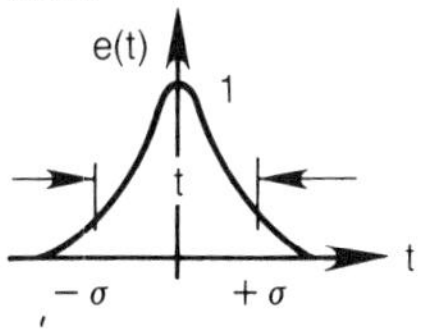 	$e - \dfrac{1}{2}(\omega_0 t)^2$ $-\infty \leqslant t \leqslant +\infty$ $\omega_0 = \dfrac{1}{\tau}$	$\tau\sqrt{2\pi e} \ -2\pi^2 f^2 \tau^2$

Figure 3.24—Four Basic Pulse Types with Their Corresponding Time and Frequency Functions

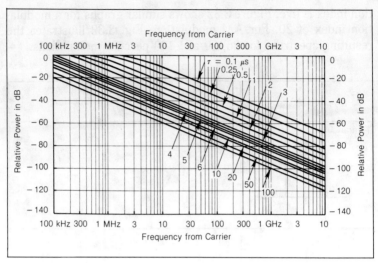

Figure 3.25—Envelope of Power Spectrum of a Rectangular Pulse, Pulse Energy Held Constant

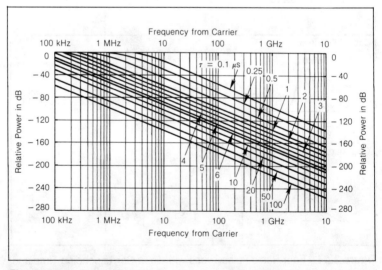

Figure 3.26—Envelope of Power Spectrum of a Half-Cosine Pulse, Pulse Energy Held Constant

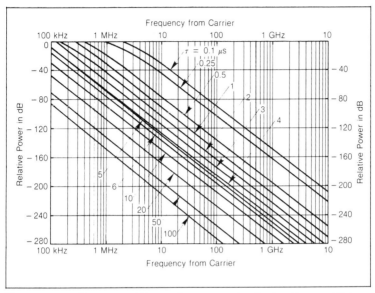

Figure 3.27—Envelope of Power Spectrum of a Cosine Squared Pulse, Pulse Energy Held Constant

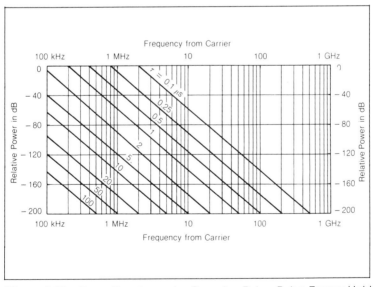

Figure 3.28—Power Spectrum of a Gaussian Pulse, Pulse Energy Held Constant

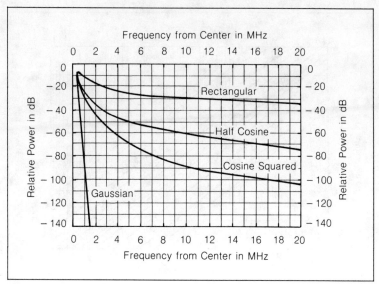

Figure 3.29—Envelopes of Power Spectra, Pulse Energy Constant, for 1 µs Pulse Width

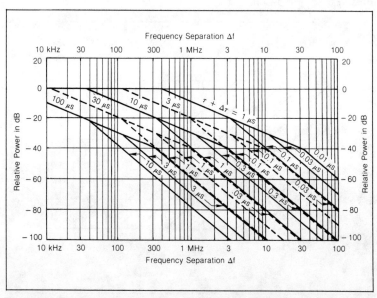

Figure 3.30—Envelope of Power Spectrum of Trapezoidal Pulse, Pulse Energy Field Constant

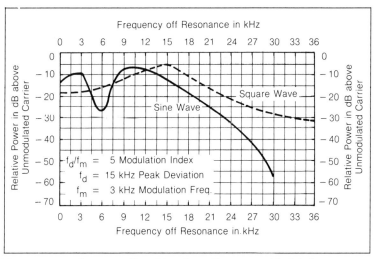

Figure 3.31—Spectrum Resulting from Frequency Modulation

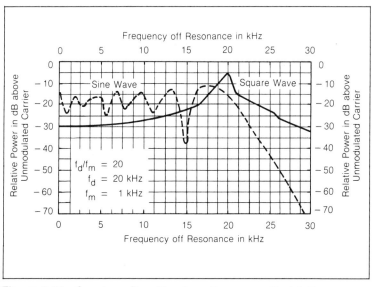

Figure 3.32—Spectrum Resulting from Frequency Modulation

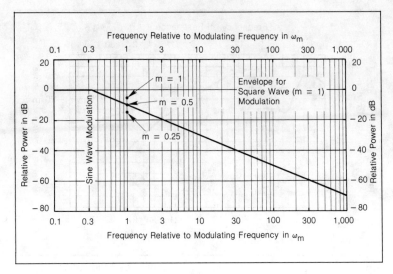

Figure 3.33—Spectrum Resulting from Amplitude Modulation

3.3 Harmonic Emission Characteristics

From an EMI standpoint, harmonic emissions are typically the most serious of the transmitter spurious emissions. Harmonic emissions are generally higher in amplitude than other spurious emissions and therefore they have more potential for causing EMI. In general, information on harmonic emission amplitudes is not readily available, and this poses problems for the EMC analyst. This section describes the important EMC characteristics associated with harmonic emissions and presents models that may be used for EMC analysis.

3.3.1 Harmonic Emission Amplitude Characteristics

For amplitude analysis, the relative power associated with transmitter harmonic emissions must be specified. In modeling these emission outputs, spectrum amplitudes of supposedly identical transmitters (transmitters of the same nomenclature differing only in serial number) have revealed random differences up to 50 dB in harmonic amplitudes.[4, 5] Since these variations occur in transmitter spectra, it is neither necessary nor practical to define a deterministic spectrum for a particular type of transmitter. Instead, the spectrum of a transmitter should be expressed in terms of the likelihood that the harmonic emission output at that harmonic will exist within certain limits.

One of the major problems that occurs in modeling transmitter harmonic emissions is finding specific data on the characteristics of individual transmitter types. One of the primary sources of data on transmitter spurious characteristics is from the spectrum signature measurement program performed under MIL-STD-449D.[6] If this type of data is available, it should be used in the manner described in this section to derive specific transmitter models.

On the other hand, when spectrum signature data are not available, it is necessary to use transmitter harmonic emission models that have been derived from statistical summaries of measured data or from equipment specifications. Models based on these techniques are presented in Sections 3.3.1.2 and 3.3.1.3 and may be used in the absence of specific data.

Although the category of spurious emissions includes all undesired transmitter outputs, harmonics of the fundamental usually have the most significant amplitudes. Thus, transmitter spurious emission models used in the amplitude analysis stage of prediction for frequencies above the fundamental are based on harmonic emission levels.

Figure 3.34 shows scatter diagrams for harmonic emission outputs for a typical transmitter. Harmonic emission data for two serial numbers and 25 different fundamental frequencies are presented. These data are typical of a large number of transmitters which have been examined and reported by different sources. The figure clearly shows that there are large variations between harmonic output levels for a specific transmitter nomenclature. Because of these variations a comprehensive EMC analysis process should treat harmonic outputs in a probabilistic manner.

Illustrative Example 3.6

Figure 3.34 shows that the ninth harmonic of a transmitter varies from -60 to -100 dB relative to the fundamental power output. The corresponding average value is approximately -80 dB. Assume that the transmitter fundamental power output is 100 W

(+50 dBm) and that a microwave relay receiver having a sensitivity P_R of −100 dBm (S = N) is operating at the ninth harmonic. Further, consider a transmission coupling (transmitter to receiver) C_{TR} of −70 dB.

The following EMI prediction results may then be obtained:

Case I: worst case, transmitter ninth harmonic emission output is −60 dB above fundamental. Since $P_T(f_{OT})$ = +50 dBm, $P_T(f_{9T})$ = +50 dBm − 60 dBm = −10 dBm. The potential interfering power available, P_A, at the receiver input terminals is obtained from Eq. (1.2) by adding the transmission coupling C_{TR} to the ninth harmonic power $P_T(f_{9T})$:

$$P_A = P_T(f_{9T}) + C_{TR}$$
$$= -10 \text{ dBm} - 70 \text{ dB} = -80 \text{ dBm}$$

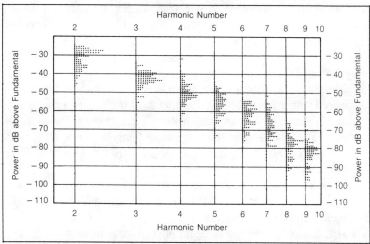

Figure 3.34—Transmitter Harmonic Outputs

Since the receiver sensitivity is −100 dBm, the power available exceeds the potential power required to produce interference by 20 dB. Thus, from the worst case analysis, it appears that an EMI problem exists.

Case II: average case, transmitter ninth harmonic emission output is −80 dB above fundamental. Since $P_T(f_{OT})$ = +50 dBm, $P_T(f_{9T})$ = +50 dBm − 80 dB = −30 dBm. The potential interfering power available at the receiver is now:

$$P_A = P_T(f_{9T})$$
$$= -30 \text{ dBm} - 70 \text{ dB} = -100 \text{ dBm}$$

The power available is equal to the receiver sensitivity of -100 dBm. Thus, from the average case prediction, it appears that a marginal EMI situation exists.

Case III: best case, transmitter ninth harmonic emission output is -100 dB above fundamental. Since $P_T(f_{0T}) = +50$ dBm, $P_T(f_{9T}) = +50$ dBm $- 100$ dB $= -50$ dBm. For this case, the potential interfering power available at the receiver is:

$$P_A = P_T(f_{9T}) + C_{TR}$$
$$= -50 \text{ dBm} - 70 \text{ dB} = -120 \text{ dBm}$$

For the best case, the power available at the receiver is 20 dB less than the -100 dBm receiver sensitivity. Thus, it appears that no EMI problem exists.

From the three cases presented above, it is clearly seen that in predicting EMI between the ninth harmonic of this communication transmitter and the fundamental tuning of the microwave relay receiver, it is not sufficient to consider only the worst case, average case or best case. Instead, the entire range and relative probabilities of each of the possible values should be considered. The following section presents mathematical models that allow transmitter harmonic emissions to be represented in probabilistic terms.

3.3.1.1 General Harmonic Amplitude Models

To properly represent transmitter harmonic emission outputs of the type illustrated in Fig. 3.34, it is necessary to define both the average output level and the statistical distribution which describes the variance at each harmonic. Mathematical models that are used in EMI prediction and analysis to represent the statistics of transmitter harmonic amplitudes are based on the following two principles:[7]

1. The harmonic average emission levels from transmitters decrease with increasing harmonic number. The average level may be represented as one or more straight line segments when plotted as a function of the logarithm of harmonic number.

2. A number of random variables introduce a random deviation from the transmitter harmonic emission average output which

is normally distributed at each harmonic. The standard deviation is independent of harmonic number.

Based on the above, the harmonic average amplitude is represented by the following expression:

$$P_T(f_{NT}) = P_T(f_{OT}) + A \log N + B, \text{ for } N \geqslant 2 \qquad (3.18)$$

where, $P_T(f_{NT})$ = average power in dBm at the Nth harmonic

$P_T(f_{OT})$ = fundamental power in dBm

N = harmonic number

A, B = constants for specific transmitters where A corresponds to the slope in dB per decade and B corresponds to the amplitude intercept at the fundamental in dB above fundamental

The statistical disribution at each harmonic is specified in terms of the standard deviation $\sigma_t(f_{NT})$. The constants A, B and σ are required to specify the transmitter output amplitude statistics for harmonically related frequencies and may be determined from measured data as described in Section 3.3.1.4.

Because the amplitude-analysis process considers the frequency variable only in a general sense, the discrete harmonic emission characteristics of transmitters are not considered. Instead, for amplitude analysis, it is assumed that the transmitter is capable of producing emissions at any frequency, and transmitter spurious emissions are represented as a continuous function of frequency. Thus, for amplitude analysis Eq. (3.18) becomes:

$$P_T(f) = P_T(f_{OT}) + A \log f/f_{OT} + B \qquad (3.19)$$

Illustrative Example 3.7

To illustrate the use of Eq. (3.18) for modeling transmitter harmonic output emission levels, consider a UHF AM voice transmitter with a fundamental power output $P_T(f_{OT})$ of 100 W (+50 dBm). Assume that slope A = −60 dB/decade, intercept B = −20 dB and $\sigma_T(f_{NT})$ = 10 dB.

The average power emitted at any harmonic is then determined from Eq. (3.18):

$$P_T(f_{NT}) = P_T(f_{OT}) + A \log N + B \qquad (3.20)$$
$$= +50 \text{ dBm} - 60 \log N \text{ dB} - 20 \text{ dB}$$
$$= (30 - 60 \log N) \text{ dBm}$$

For the second harmonic (N = 2), the average power is:

$$P_T(f_2 T) = (30 - 60 \log 2) = (30 - 18) = +12 \text{ dBm} \qquad (3.21)$$

For the tenth harmonic (N = 10), the average power is:

$$P_{T10T} = (30 - 60 \log 10) \text{ dBm} = -30 \text{ dBm} \qquad (3.22)$$

The harmonic average output relationship for the illustrative example is shown in Fig. 3.35. The constant B corresponds to the amplitude intercept of the function when extended to the fundamental (N = 1), and A corresponds to the slope of the line.

If the average output of a normally distributed function is increased by $\sigma_T(f_{NT})$ (10 dB) as shown in Fig. 3.35, it is then 16 percent probable that the resulting level will be exceeded. Conversely, if the average level is decreased by $\sigma_T(f_{NT})$, it is 84 percent probable that the resulting level will be exceeded. These $\pm \sigma_T(f_{NT})$ levels are also illustrated in Fig. 3.35.

3.3.1.2 Harmonic Amplitude Models Based on MIL-STD-461C

One source of information regarding transmitter spurious output levels is the specification or standards associated with the particular CE equipment. Transmitter specifications impose a limit on spurious outputs, and for certain types of problems it may be desirable to use these levels in performing an EMI prediction. If this approach is used, the resulting transmitter harmonic amplitude models would be obtained by setting A and σ to zero, and B to the specification limit. Thus, for example, if transmitter harmonic amplitude models were based on MIL-STD-461C,[8] the constants for the model would be A = 0, B = -80 dB, except as indicated below, and $\sigma_T(f_{NT}) = 0$.

For transmitters with fundamental power outputs less than 10 kW, the value of B for the second and third harmonics will be $-(50 + 10 \log P)$, where P is the peak power in watts. Transmitters with peak powers less than or equal to 0.1 W are not covered by MIL-STD-461C.

3.43

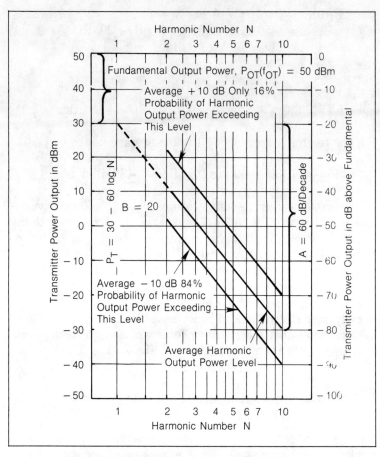

Figure 3.35—Math Model of Transmitter Spurious Output

3.3.1.3 Statistical Summary Harmonic Amplitudes

If data on transmitter harmonic emission outputs are available from spectrum signature measurements or other information sources, they should be used to determine specific harmonic output models. Conversely, in many instances, specific data are not available. Thus, it is necessary to employ other techniques for determining specific models to be used in EMC analysis.

In order to provide transmitter harmonic amplitude models that may be used in the absence of specific measured data, statistical summary models have been derived from available spectrum signature data.[9] The results obtained by summarizing data for approximately 100 different transmitter nomenclatures are presented in Table 3.2.

Table 3.2—Constants for Transmitter Harmonic Models Obtained from Statistical Summary of Available Data (See Fig. 3.5)

Transmitter Category on Fundamental Frequency	Summary Values for Constants in Harmonic Amplitude Model		
	A (dB/Decade)	B (dB above Fundamental)	$\sigma_T(f_{NT})$ (dB)
All Transmitters Combined	−70	−30	20
Below 30 MHz	−70	−20	10
Between 30 MHz and 300 MHz	−80	−30	15
Above 300 MHz	−60	−40	20

The first line in the table presents values for A, B and $\sigma_T(f_{NT})$ derived from the data for all transmitters combined. The second, third and fourth lines provide values for A, B and $\sigma_T(f_{NT})$ obtained by grouping transmitter data on the basis of fundamental frequency. The appropriate set of values for A, B and $\sigma_T(f_{NT})$ may be used in Eq. (3.18) to model transmitter harmonic amplitudes. The resulting average harmonic output levels for transmitters within each of the indicated frequency ranges are presented in Table 3.3.

Table 3.3—Summary of Harmonic Average Emission Levels

Harmonic Average Emission Level (dB above Fundamental)				
Harmonic Number	All Transmitters Combined	Transmitters Categorized According to Radio Frequency		
		Below 30 MHz	30 MHz to 300 MHz	Above 300 MHz
	$\sigma = 20$ dB	$(\sigma = 10$ dB)	$(\sigma = 15$ dB)	$(\sigma = 20$ dB
2	−51	−41	−54	−55
3	−64	−53	−68	−64
4	−72	−62	−78	−70
5	−79	−69	−86	−75
6	−85	−74	−92	−79
·7	−90	−79	−97	−82
8	−94	−83	−102	−85
9	−97	−87	−106	−88
10	−100	−90	−110	−90

3.3.1.4 Harmonic Amplitude Models Based on Measured Data

When measured data are available on transmitter harmonic emissions, they may be used directly to determine the constants A, B, and σ for harmonic amplitude models described in Section 3.3.1.1. This section describes how the constants may be determined from measure data for a specific transmitter. Transmitter harmonic amplitude measurements are sometimes performed on the basis of radiated levels. In this case, transmitter harmonic emission models derived from the data will include the combined effects of both transmitter harmonic power and antenna gain changes at the harmonics.

Constants for the harmonic emission function are determined by standard curve fitting techniques.[10] This is performed in the following manner. First, assume that there are M samples of data, each of which was taken out to some maximum harmonic N_{max} with a corresponding power output P_N. From these data the following constants are computed:

$$C_1 = \sum_{N=2}^{N_{max}} \sum_{i=1}^{M} P_{N_i}^2 \qquad (3.23)$$

$$C_2 = M \sum_{N=2}^{N_{max}} (\log N)^2$$

$$C_3 = \sum_{N=2}^{N_{max}} \sum_{i=1}^{M} (P_{N_i} \log N_i)$$

$$C_4 = \sum_{N=2}^{N_{max}} \sum_{i=1}^{M} P_{N_i}$$

$$C_5 = M \sum_{N=2}^{N_{max}} \log N$$

After computing these constants, the required transmitter parameters are evaluated from the following relationships:

$$A = \frac{MN_{max}\, C_3 - C_4 C_5}{MN_{max}\, C_2 - C_5{}^2} \qquad (3.24)$$

$$B = \frac{C_4 - AC_5}{MN_{max}}$$

$$\sigma_T(f_{NT}) = \left[\frac{C_1 - BC_4 - AC_3}{MN_{max} - 1} \right]^{1/2}$$

Illustrative Example 3.8

Assume that measured data are available for 10 harmonic outputs (N_{max} = 10) representing a given transmitter at each of three tuned frequencies (M = 3). Also assume that resulting measured data are presented in Table 3.4 and summarized in Fig. 3.36. From Table 3.4 there are three measured values at each harmonic (i = 1, 2, 3) corresponding to the three different tuned frequencies.

A, B and $\sigma_T(f_{NT})$ are determined in the following manner. The quantities P_{Ni}, $P_{NI}{}^2$, log N, (log N)^2 and P_{Ni} log Ni are given in the third through the seventh columns of the table. The constants C_1 through C_5 are determined as follows. Note that it is necessary to round off the constants so that only the significant digits are retained.

C_1 is obtained by summing all $P_{Ni}{}^2$ values in column 4. The result is C_1 = 37,969 ≈ 38,000

C_2 is obtained by summing all (log N)^2 values in column 6 and multiplying by M = 3. The result is C_2 = 15.63 ≈ 16

C_3 is obtained by summing all values in column 7. The result is C_3 = − 763.9 ≈ − 760

C_4 is obtained by summing all values in column 3. The result is C_4 = − 985 ≈ − 980

C_5 is obtained by summing all values in column 5 and multiplying by $M = 3$.

The result is $C_5 = 19.68 \approx 20$

With the five computed constants, A, B and $\sigma_T(f_{NT})$ are obtained from Eq. (3.24):

$$(3.25)$$

$$A = \frac{MN_{max}\ C_3 - C_4 C_5}{MN_{max}\ C_2 - C_5{}^2} = \frac{(3)(10)(-760) - (-980)(20)}{(3)(10)(16) - (20)^2}$$

$$= \frac{-23.000 + 20,000}{480 - 400} = -38 \text{ dB/octave}$$

$$B = \frac{C_4 - AC_5}{MN_{max}} = \frac{-980 - (-38)(20)}{(3)(10)} = \frac{-220}{30} = -7.3 \text{ dB}$$

$$\sigma_T(f_{NT}) = \left[\frac{C_1 - BC_4 - AC_3}{MN_{max} - 1} \right]^{1/2}$$

$$= \left[\frac{38,000\ (-7)(-980) - (-38)(-760)}{(3)(10) - 1} \right]^{1/2}$$

$$= \left[\frac{38,000 - 6,900 - 28,000}{29} \right]^{1/2}$$

$$= [100]^{1/2} = 10 \text{ dB}$$

3.3.1.5 Accuracy of the Spurious Output Model

A discussion of the accuracy of the model for the transmitter harmonic emission outputs involves an analysis of the basic assumptions concerning the distribution of the harmonics. After the validity of these assumptions is accepted, the question of accuracy is then primarily one of determining the error of estimate obtained when deriving the statistics from a limited number of samples. The validity of the transmitter harmonic assumptions has been supported by testing numerous sets of harmonic data.[11]

Table 3.4—Determination of Transmitter Constants from Measured Data

(1) Harmonic Number (N)	(2) Data Set (i)	(3) P_{Ni}*	(4) P_{Ni}^2	(5) $\log_{10}N$	(6) $(\log_{10}N)^2$	(7) $P_{Ni}\log_{10}N_i$
2	1	− 25	625			− 7.5
	2	− 26	676	0.30	0.09	− 7.8
	3	− 22	484			− 6.6
3	1	− 33	1,089			− 16
	2	− 23	529	0.48	0.23	− 11
	3	− 28	784			− 13
4	1	− 26	676			− 16
	2	− 35	1,215	0.60	0.36	− 22
	3	− 24	576			− 14
5	1	− 33	1,089			− 23
	2	− 36	1,296	0.70	0.49	− 25
	3	− 40	1,600			− 28
6	1	− 28	784			− 22
	2	− 34	1,156	0.78	0.61	− 27
	3	− 41	1,681			− 32
7	1	− 40	1,600			− 34
	2	− 35	1,215	0.85	0.72	− 30
	3	− 43	1,849			− 37
8	1	− 51	2,601			− 46
	2	− 48	2,304	0.90	0.81	− 43
	3	− 45	2,025			− 40
9	1	− 40	1,600			− 38
	2	− 45	2,025	0.95	0.90	− 43
	3	− 42	1,764			− 40
10	1	− 47	2,209			− 47
	2	− 46	2,116	1.0	1.0	− 46
	3	− 49	2,401			− 49
Total		− 985	37,969	6.56	5.21	− 763.9

*Measured Harmonic Amplitude in dB above Fundamental

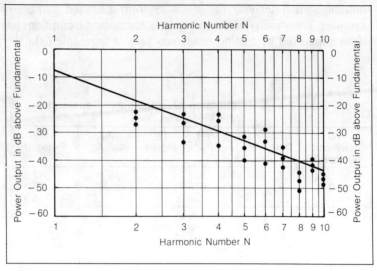

Figure 3.36—Least Squares Fit to Harmonics of the Tuned Frequency

When statistics for a particular type of transmitter are obtained from spectrum signature data, a minimum of three sample points at each harmonic are usually available. The question of accuracy then is a function of the number of samples. The estimate of $P_T(f_{NT})$ is normally distributed about the true values with a standard deviation, $\sigma_E(N)$ given by:[12]

$$(3.26)$$

$$\sigma_E(N) = \sigma_T(f_{NT}) \left[\frac{1}{MN_{max}} + \frac{[\log N - E(\log N)]^2}{M \sum\limits_{N=2}^{N_{max}} [\log N - E(\log N)]^2} \right]^{1/2}$$

where, $\sigma_T(f_{NT})$ = standard deviation associated with harmonic variations

M = the number of samples at each harmonic

N = harmonic number

N_{max} = the maximum harmonic measured

$E(\log N)$ = expected or mean value for log N averaged over all N from 2 to N_{max}

3.50

The uncertainty in the estimate indicated in Eq. (3.26) is minimum at the harmonic where log N is equal to the mean of log N, and the uncertainty increases for harmonics removed from the mean.

Note that the rate of improvement in the error of estimate diminishes rapidly with increasing sample size. This trend is illustrated in Fig. 3.37, which is a graph of maximum and minimum errors of estimate versus sample size (assuming a standard deviation $\sigma_T(f_{NT})$ of 10 dB). Measurements on a small number of equipment samples will produce relatively accurate results. Beyond this point, there is a diminishing return in the relationship between accuracy and the number of equipments measured.

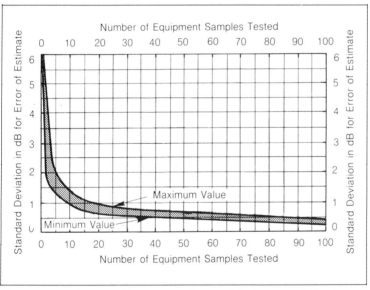

Figure 3.37—Relationship between Error of Estimate and Number of Equipment Samples (20 Harmonics)

3.3.2 Harmonic Emission Frequency Characteristics

For all types of transmitters, the relationship between the frequencies of the harmonics and fundamental emission outputs are described by:

$$f_{NT} = Nf_{OT} \tag{3.27}$$

3.51

where, f_{NT} = harmonic frequency

N = harmonic number

f_{OT} = fundamental frequency

In general, outputs that are harmonically related to frequencies other than the transmitter fundamental (harmonics of a master oscillator or clock, for example) are significantly lower in amplitude than harmonics of the fundamental. They may be ignored except in situations where large interference margins are present. If emission outputs which are harmonically related to frequencies other than the fundamental are considered, then the interference margin obtained from the amplitude cull should be reduced by 20 dB for those outputs.

For transmitters having a master oscillator frequency below the fundamental, frequencies associated with harmonics of the master oscillator can be described like that in Eq. (3.27). Here the fundamental frequency f_{OT} in the equation is replaced by the master oscillator frequency f_{MOT}.

Some transmitters use a mixing scheme for frequency generation. The process by which these transmitters generate the fundamental frequency depends on nonlinear signal combination, such that the final output may contain signals at all frequencies corresponding to the sum and difference of the input signals and their harmonics. This relationship is:

$$f_{pq} \pm = |pf_1 \pm qf_2| \qquad (3.28)$$

where, f_{pq} = output emission frequencies

p, q = positive integers

f_1, f_2 = input signals

One of these outputs is the fundamental frequency of the transmitter. Even though the other undesired outputs may be attenuated by filters or band-limiting amplifiers within the transmitter, some are significant in amplitude. They are considered when performing an EMI analysis.

The modulation envelopes associated with harmonic outputs are directly related to the baseband modulation envelopes used for developing the fundamental output. However, for some pulse-modulated transmitters, the modulation envelope associated with the Nth harmonic is assumed to have the same shape as the envelope used for the fundamental but the bandwidths are assumed to be proportional to the harmonic number.

3.4 Nonharmonic Emission

Transmitters produce spurious emissions in addition to harmonics. These spurious emissions usually result from the nonlinear operation of some stage of the transmitter. Although their amplitudes are usually less than those associated with harmonic emissions, it is still sometimes necessary to consider these emissions in EMI prediction. This is particularly true for frequencies below the transmitter fundamental frequency because harmonics of the fundamental emission do not exist in this region.

3.4.1 Nonharmonic Emission Amplitude

A general mathematical model for spurious emission levels (excluding harmonics) may be expressed similar to that given by Eq. (3.19). The main difference is that integer values of N are replaced by a continuous frequency variable. Thus, the spurious emission amplitude model is:

$$P_T(f) = P_T(f_{OT}) + A' \log f/f_{OT} + B' \qquad (3.29)$$

where, $P_T(f_{OT})$ = fundamental power in dBm
   $P_T(f)$ = average power in dBm at frequency, f, within bandwidth B_T
   A' and B' = constants for specific transmitters (A' corresponds to slope in dB/decade and B' corresponds to the intercept with f_{OT} in dB above fundamental output)

The amplitude variations observed in harmonic emissions also occur for other spurious emissions. These variations are modeled by a normal distribution with a standard deviation $\sigma_T(f)$.

One of the main problems that arises in attempting to model spurious emissions is that specific data are not usually available.

In this case the spurious amplitude models should be based on MIL-STD-461C which means that A', B' and $\sigma_T(f)$ would be as given in Section 3.3.1.2. If measured data are available, the techniques described in Section 3.3.1.4 may be used to determine A', B' and $\sigma_T(f)$.

3.4.2 Nonharmonic Emission Frequency

Although most transmitter spurious outputs occur at harmonic related frequencies, certain types of high-power microwave transmitters have significant emissions at frequencies which are not harmonically related to the fundamental frequency. It is necessary then to use statistics to describe the probability that an emission output will occur within any given frequency range.

Unless the receiver being considered has a relatively wide bandwidth, the probability is small of a nonharmonically related transmitter output being close enough in frequency to produce interference. These emission outputs are neglected in most EMC analysis.

The mathematical model that is used to describe the cumulative probability that an output will occur within a bandwidth B at a specified frequency separation (Δf) from any given transmitter frequency (f_{OT}) is:

$$\text{Probability} = H\ \frac{B}{f_{OT}} \qquad (3.30)$$

where,   H = constant that is determined for specific transmitters

B = bandwidth of interest

f_{OT} = transmitter fundamental frequency

Equation (3.30) is the expression for the cumulative probability distribution function associated with a uniform distribution. Several different values of H may be required to describe the statistics over the entire frequency range for which significant spurious outputs occur. Each individual value of the parameter H applies within a specific frequency range.

If specific measured data on nonharmonically related outputs are available, they are used to define the probability that those outputs will occur in a given frequency range. Figure 3.38 presents relationships that are used to represent the frequency function for nonharmonic outputs for which specific data are not available. The functions in Fig. 3.38 were derived from composite data on several transmitters. The function with a value H = 18.5 should be used for frequencies (f_{OR}/f_{OT}) between the transmitter fundamental and 1.5 times the fundamental. The other function (i.e., H = 6) is used for frequencies between 1.5 times and four times the fundamental. It is not necessary to consider these outputs for frequencies above the fourth harmonic.

The energy content in the sidebands surrounding the nonharmonic spurious outputs is described in the same way as the modulation envelopes for the fundamental and harmonic outputs.

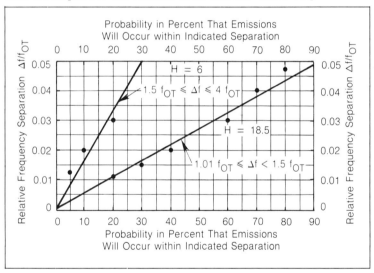

Figure 3.38—Typical Probability Distribution for Magnetron Nonharmonic Frequency Functions

Illustrative Example 3.9

To illustrate how the relationships in Fig. 3.38 are used to determine the probability that a nonharmonically related spurious output will occur in a receiver passband, consider a surveillance radar-transmitter operating at 1.0 GHz and a microwave communication receiver operating at 2.3 GHz. Calculate the probability that a nonharmonically related spurious output from the radar will fall within the receiver 60 dB passband of 10 MHz.

Since f_{OR}/f_{OT} = 2.3 (is greater than 1.5), the H = 6 graph in Fig. 3.38 is selected. With B = 10 MHz and f_{OT} = 1.0 GHz, the probability of a transmitter nonharmonically related spurious output occurring in the receiver passband is obtained from Eq. (3.30):

$$\text{Probability} = 6 \; \frac{10 \times 10^6 \; \text{Hz}}{10^6 \; \text{Hz}} = 60 \times 10^{-3}$$

$$= .06 \text{ or } 6 \text{ percent}$$

In general, the probability of a nonharmonically related spurious output occurring in a relatively narrow frequency band is small. However, these outputs may result in significant probabilities of interference in the case of broadband receivers.

3.5 Transmitter Emission Noise

Because of the relatively low power level (power spectral intensity) associated with this noise, it is generally insignificant in comparison with other interfering signals that are present in a given electromagnetic environment. With the exception of high-power transmitters, this broadband noise is generally not considered in EMC analysis.

For those cases where it is necessary to consider the broadband noise generated by transmitters, the mean amplitude of the noise may be considered to be included in the modulation envelope for frequencies close to the transmitter fundamental, i.e., within ± 10 percent of the fundamental frequency. For frequencies that are further removed, the amplitude of the noise may be represented in the manner described for nonharmonic emissions. If specific measured data are not available to represent transmitter noise levels (which is usually the case) it is suggested that the levels be based on MIL-STD-461C as given in Section 3.3.1.2.

3.6 Composite Examples

This section summarizes much of the material already presented in this chapter and some material from Chapters 1 and 2. Two illustrative examples are provided, one involving an aircraft TACAN receiver and the second involving an S-band radar.

Illustrative Example 3.10

Predict the potential EMI which may exist between an aircraft TACAN receiver operated at 1,090 MHz and a P-band radar transmitting at 220 MHz. The closest approach of the aircraft to the air-search radar is 12.9 km (8 mi), corresponding to a situation when the TACAN TX-RX pair are separated by 66 km (41 mi). The rated nominal TX-RX characteristics are:

Parameter	P-Band Radar	Aircraft TACAN RX	Airport TACAN TX
Operating frequency (f_o)	220 MHz	1,090 MHz	1,090 MHz
Peak power output	2 MW		3 kW
Antenna gain (in-band)	25 dB	3 dB	3 dB
Receiver bandwidth	N/A	165 kHz	N/A
Receiver sensitivity (S = N)	N/A	−80 dBm	N/A

The receiver power P_A, due to the intentional TACAN transmitter (s subscript = signal of interest), is [see Eq. (1.2)]:

$$P_{As} = P_{Ts} + C_{TRs} \qquad (3.31)$$

$$= P_{Ts} + G_{Ts} - L_{dBs} + G_{Rs}$$

$$= +65 \text{ dBm} + 3 \text{ dB} - 130 \text{ dB} + 3 \text{ dB}$$

$$= -59 \text{ dBm}$$

where, P_{Ts} = TACAN TX power (3 kW) = +65 dBM

G_{Ts} = TACAN TX antenna gain = 3 dB

G_{Rs} = TACAN RX antenna gain = 3 dB

L_{dBs} = transmission space loss $(4\pi R/\lambda)^2$ = 130 dB for a 66 km TX-RX separation at λ = 0.275 m (f_o = 1,090 MHz; see Fig. 2.7)

This −59 dBm level corresponds to a S/N ratio of 21 dB.

In the first step of performing an EMC analysis, it is assumed that TX-RX frequency alignment exists. This was identified as RIM (Receiver Interference Margin) in Section 2.6. From the above nominal characteristic list, the fifth harmonic of the radar (5 × 220 MHz = 1,100 MHz) exists near the 1,090 MHz TACAN receiver.

For the search radar transmitter (i subscript = interfering emitter) to TACAN receiver situation, Eqs. (3.31) and (3.32) become:

$$P_{Ai} = P_{Ti} + C_{TRi} \tag{3.32}$$

$$= P_{Ti}(f_{5T}) + G_{Ti}(f_{5T}) - L_{dBi} + G_{Ri}$$

$$= +7 \text{ dBm} + 12 \text{ dB} - 116 \text{ dB} + 3 \text{ dB}$$

$$= -94 \text{ dBm}$$

where, $\quad P_{Ti}(f_{5T})$ = radar fundamental TX power (2 MW = +93 dBm) + relative level of radar fifth harmonic (-86 dB, see Table 3.3, third column)

$$= (93 \text{ dBm} - 86 \text{ dB}) = +7 \text{ dBm}$$

$G_T(f_{5T})$ = radar antenna gain at fifth harmonic (gain $- 13$ dB = 12 dB; see Chapter 5)

L_{dBi} = transmission space loss at 12.9 km separation

At -94 dBm, the average available power P_A from the potentially interfering radar is 14 dB below the TACAN receiver sensitivity (-80 dBm). It is 35 dB below the signal level (-59 dBm) from the TACAN TX at the RX input terminals. In other words, the S/I ratio at the TACAN RC is 35 dB. Considering that $\sigma = 15$ dB (see Tables 3.2 and 3.3), there is less than a one-percent probability of an EMI problem. Thus, it is not necessary to proceed further from the first step amplitude analysis to the second step frequency analysis since the latter serves to reduce the EMI margins even further (see Sections 2.6.1 and 2.6.2).

Illustrative Example 3.11:

Predict the potential EMI situation which may exist between a tropospheric scatter communication transmitter operated at 1,175 MHz and an L-band radar receiver tuned to 1,280 MHz. This is a fundamental interference margin (FIM) problem (see Chapter 2). While the tropo transmitter is located 160 km (100 mi) away and beyond the line of sight, the associated scatter volume is seen by the radar antenna as it scans by. The free space and forward scatter loss, computed from Chapter 6, is 155 dB. Since the short-form EMI analysis of Section 2.7 will be used for this example, the rated nominal TX-RX characteristics are simply listed.

Parameter	Tropo TX	Use Lines	Radar TX	Use Lines
Operating frequency	1,175 MHz	1	1,290 MHz	4
Peak power output	1 kW (60 dBm)	8	NA	
Antenna gain	45 dB	10	35 dB	11
Transmitter pulse width	1 μs	18	NA	
Transmitter bandwidth	640 kHz	18	NA	
Receiver bandwidth	NA		350 kHz	19
Receiver sensitivity (S = N)	NA		-105 dBm	14

The reverse EMI problem (radar TX to tropo RX) could also exist, but this is not considered here. Applying lines 1, 4 and 7 of the short-form EMI analysis, it is confirmed that this is an FIM situation.

Short Form EMI Analysis

Transmitter and Receiver Frequency Limits

Frequency:
☐ kHz; ☐ MHz

1. TX Fundamental Frequency (f_{OT})
2. TX Minimum Spurious Frequency ($f_{ST})_{min}$ or $0.1f_{OT}$
3. TX Maximum Spurious Frequency ($f_{ST})_{max}$ or $10f_{OT}$
4. RX Fundamental Frequency (f_{OR})
5. RX Minimum Spurious Frequency ($f_{SR})_{min}$ or $0.1f_{OR}$
6. RX Maximum Spurious Frequency ($f_{SR})_{max}$ or $10f_{OR}$
7. TX-RX Maximum Allowable Frequency Separation for Fundamental EMI, Δf_{max} or $0.2f_{OR}$

Applicability of Four EMI Prediction Cases:

SIM = TX Harmonic & RX Spurious
    Is (2) _____ < (6) _____ ?   ☐ Yes, ☐ No
    Is (3) _____ > (5) _____ ?   ☐ Yes, ☐ No
    If either is No, there is no EMI Problem—Stop.

RIM = TX Harmonic & RX Fundamental
    Is (2) _____ < (4) _____ ?   ☐ Yes, ☐ No
    Is (3) _____ > (4) _____ ?   ☐ Yes, ☐ No
    If either is No, skip RIM and enter N/A on line 38.

TIM = TX Fundamental & RX Spurious
    Is (1) _____ < (6) _____ ?   ☐ Yes, ☐ No
    Is (1) _____ > (5) _____ ?   ☐ Yes, ☐ No
    If either is No, skip TIM and enter N/A on line 38.
    If both RIM and TIM were N/A, skip FIM and enter N/A on line 38.

FIM = TX Fundamental & RX Fundamental
Is $|(1)$ _____ $- (4)$ _____ $| <$
(7) _____ ?   ☐Yes, ☐No
If No, skip FIM and enter N/A on line 38.

Surviving cases   ☐SIM, ☐RIM, ☐TIM, ☐FIM
        ☐No cases survived—No EMI problem.

Amplitude Analysis

	FIM	TIM	RIM	SIM
8. TX Power, $P_T(f_{OT})$, (peak power if pulsed)				
9. TX Spurious Power Output: $P_T(f_{ST})$ or $P_T(f_{OT}) - 60$ dB				
10. TX Antenna Gain in RX Direction: $G_{TR}(f)$ or 0 dB				
11. RX Antenna Gain in TX Direction: $G_{RT}(f)$ or 0 dB				
12. Propagation Loss, L Using Frequency No.	(1)	(1)	(4)	(2)
Loss in dB from Fig. No. 2.7	-	-	-	-
13. Unintentional Power Available $P_A(f)$ Add 8 to 12				
14. RX Fundamental Susceptibility $P_R(f_{OR})$				
15. RX Spurious Suscept.: $P_R(f_{SR})$ or $P_R(f_{OR}) + 80$ dB				
16. Preliminary EMI Prediction: Line 13-14 or 13-15				

16. Preliminary EMI Prediction: Line 13-14 or 13-15
    If EMI margin < -10 dB, EMI Highly Improbable
    —Stop
    If EMI margin > -10 dB, Start Frequency Culling

Frequency Analysis

Bandwidth Correction

Frequency:
☐kHz; ☐MHz

17. TX PRF (if pulse)   pps
18. TX Bandwidth ($B_T = 2/\pi\tau$ if pulse; τ = width
19. RX Bandwidth B_R
20. Adjustment (from lines 17 to 19, use Fig. 2.8
    and 2.9)   dB
21. Bandwidth Corrected, EMI Margin = lines 16
    + 20   dB
        If EMI Margin ≤ -10 dB, EMI Highly Improbable—Stop

Frequency Correction

Frequency:
☐kHz; ☐MHz

22. RX Local Oscillator Frequency f_{LO}
23. RX Intermediate Frequency f_{IF}

	FIM	TIM	RIM	SIM
24. TX-RX Frequency Separation: $\Delta f = |(1) - (4)|$				
25. $\Delta f > (B_T + B_R)/2$ (from line 24, use Fig. 2.10)				

26. Calculate $f_{OT}/f_{LO} \pm f_{IF}$ to nearest integer

27. Multiply lines 22 × 26   MHz
28. $\Delta f = |1 - 23 - 27| = $ _____: $| + 23 - 27| = $ _____
29. Select smaller Δf from line 28   MHz
30. $\Delta f > (B_T + B_R)/2$ (from line 29, use Fig. 2.10)   dB

31. Calculate f_{OR}/f_{OT} to nearest integer

32. Multiply lines 1 × 31   MHz
33. $\Delta f = |(4) - (32)|$ MHz
34. $\Delta f > (B_T + B_R)/2$ (from line 33 use Fig. 2.10)   dB

35. Calculate Minimum Δf (see Form A)   MHz
36. If $\Delta f > (B_T + B_R)/2$ (from line 35 use Fig. 2.10)   dB

EMI Frequency Corrected Summary

37. Add line 21 to line

25	30	34	36

38. Total here   dB

If EMI Margin < − 10 dB, EMI Highly Improbable

Detailed Analysis
Harmonic or Spurious Response Correction*

          FIM TIM RIM SIM

39. Correction from Form B   dB
40. Corrected EMI add line 38 to line 39*   dB

Modulation Correction

41. Correction from Form C   dB
42. Corrected EMI Add line 40 to line 41   dB

Polarization Correction

43. Correction from Form D   dB
44. Corrected EMI Add line 42 to line 44   dB

Propagation Loss Correction

45. Correction from Form E   dB
46. Corrected EMI Add line 44 to line 46   dB

If EMI < − 10 dB EMI Highly Improbable
− 10 dB ≤ EMI ≤ 10 dB EMI Marginal
EMI > 10 dB EMI Probable

*Apply corrections only if nominal − 60 dB TX (line 9) and/or + 80 dB RX (line 15) corrections were used.

© Copyright 1987, Interference Control Technologies, Inc.

3.61

Step 1: Amplitude Analysis

Frequency alignment is assumed for the first step in EMC analysis. Thus, the full 60 dBm TX power is entered on line 8. Since both TX and RX antennas are momentarily looking at each other via the common scatter volume in space, their full gains are entered on lines 10 and 11. The associated propagation loss, 155 dB, is entered on line 12. Adding these up yields an available power of -15 dBm. Finally, based on a radar receiver sensitivity of -105 dBm (line 14), the available power is 90 dB greater (line 16). Since EMI would be severe, it is necessary to go to the second step (frequency analysis).

Step 2: Frequency Analysis

Assume that the tropospheric link is transmitting pulse code modulation (PCM) data at a basic clock rate of 500 kbps (line 17). For a 50 percent duty cycle, the nominal pulse width is $\tau = 1/2$ bps $= 1$ μs. The rise time is assumed to be 10 percent of the width. The associated transmitter bandwidth is 0.64 MHz (line 18) and the listed receiver bandwidth is 350 kHz (line 19). Thus, using either Eq. (2.9) or Fig. 2.8, the bandwidth adjustment is -3 dB (use K = 10 since PRF $>$ B_r) shown in line 20. The corrected bandwidth (line 21) yields an EMI ratio of 87 dB, still indicating a substantial EMI situation.

To correct for frequency misalignment, the TX and RX frequencies listed in lines 1 and 4 correspond to a Δf of 105 MHz (line 24). Using either Fig 3.30 or Fig. 2.10, the misalignment correction corresponds to -81 dB (line 25). Thus, the final EMI margin (I/N ratio) is 6 dB (line 38), a potential EMI situation.

Since the above EMI situation is a worst case, corresponding to when the scanning radar antenna is looking at the common scatter volume, this would exist only about 1 percent of the time for a 3° horizontal beamwidth (see Chapter 5).

If the radar receiver is tuned up in frequency from 1,280 MHz, the EMI situation will improve. Based on a desired EMI margin of -10 dB and an existing margin of $+6$ dB (line 38), an added improvement of 16 dB is sought. This requires that the -81 dB frequency misalignment correction (line 25) be increased to -97 dB. From Fig. 3.30, the frequency separation for $\tau = 1$ μs and $\Delta \tau = 0.1$ us, and for a -97 dB relative power, is 250 MHz. Thus, for a $f_{OT} = 1,175$ MHz, f_{OR} should be $f_{OT} + \Delta f = 1,175 + 250$

= 1,425 MHz. Since the L-band radar can only tune up to 1,350 MHz (Δf = 175 MHz) the best rejection due to frequency assignment would be -89 dB to yield an I/N margin of -2 dB, which is probably satisfactory here.

3.7 Transmitter Intermodulation

In general, intermodulation may occur in both transmitters and receivers. To determine which type intermodulation is predominant for a given EMI situation, calculate the equivalent interference level which results from both transmitter and receiver intermodulation and consider the case which results in the largest potential interference.

The transmitter intermodulation problem is illustrated in Fig. 3.39. The figure indicates that intermodulation will occur in both of the two transmitters. The predominant transmitter intermodulation situation depends on the geometry, power levels and frequencies of the two transmitters. In general, it will be necessary to consider both transmitter intermodulation situations to determine which one produces the largest signal at the receiver.

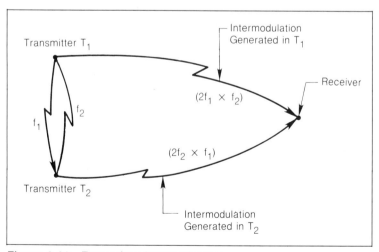

Figure 3.39—Transmitter Intermodulation

For cases where the frequency separation (Δf) between the transmitters is less than or equal to one percent of the transmitter frequency, the equivalent transmitter intermodulation power (P_E) is given by the equation:

$$P_E(\text{dBm}) = P_I(\text{dBm}) - 10 \text{ dB} \qquad (3.33)$$

where, $P_I(\text{dBm})$ = interfering power available at the transmitter where the intermodulation occurs.

For cases where the frequency separation is greater than 1 percent, P_E is given by the equation:

$$P_E(\text{dBm}) = P_I(\text{dBm}) - 10 \text{ dB} - 30 \log \Delta f \text{ percent} \qquad (3.34)$$

It should be noted that P_E is the intermodulation signal level at the transmitter where the intermodulation occurs. To determine the level at a receiver, it is necessary to include the effects of propagation loss.

3.8 References

1. Babcock, L.F., "Equipment Operational Parameter Variability," *Proceedings of the Tenth Tri-Service Conference on EMC*, November 1964.
2. Rome Air Development Center, Contract No. AF30(602)-3118, 1966, pp. 2-17, Interference Notebook, RADC-TR-66-1.
3. *Reference Data for Radio Engineers* (New York: Howard W. Sams & Company, Inc., 5th Edition, 1968).
4. Ports, D.C.; Howland, Jr., A.R.; and Moore, R.M, "Analysis of RFI in Transmission Lines and Filters," *Electronic Industries*, July 1960.
5. Heisler, Jr., "Preparation of Statistical Input Functions for Interference Prediction," 7th Armour Research Foundation Conference, Chicago, 1961.
6. MIL-STD-499D.
7. Heisler.

8. MIL-STD-461, "Electromagnetic Interference Characteristics Requirements for Equipment."
9. Duff, W.G. and Edwards, J.H., "Summary of Equipment EMC Characteristics," *1970 Regional EMC Symposium Record*, San Antonio.
10. Acton, F.S., *Analysis of Straight-Line Data* (New York: John Wiley & Sons, 1953).
11. Heisler.
12. Hald, A., *Statistical Theory with Engineering Applications* (New York: John Wiley & Sons, 1952).

3.9 Bibliography

1. Acton, F.S., *Analysis of Straight Line Data*, (New York: John Wiley & Sons, Inc., 1953).
2. Babcock, L.F., "Equipment Operational Variability," *Proceedings of the Tenth Tri-Service Conference on EMC*, November 1964.
3. Blakely, C.E., and Bailey, R.N., "The Distribution and Correlation of Transmitter Interference," *Proceedings of the Sixth Conference on Radio Interference Reduction* (Armour Research Foundation, October 1960).
4. "Characteristics of USAF Electronic Equipment for Ground Use," RADC Technical Report 52-14, RADC, USAF Griffiss AFB, Electronic Development Div., New York, 1952.
5. Duff, W.G., et. al., "Transmitter and Receiver FOM Scoring," *1974 IEEE EMC Symposium Record*, (New York: IEEE, 1974).
6. Duff, W.G., et. al., "The Application of Spectrum Signature Data to Interference Analysis," *1966 IEEE EMC Symposium Record* (New York: IEEE, 1966).
7. Duff, W.G., and Edwards, J.H., "Summary of Equipment EMC Characteristics," *1970 IEEE Regional EMC Symposium Record* (New York: IEEE, 1970).
8. Duff, W.G., et. al., "EMC Design Criteria," *Southeastern Regional EMC Symposium Record* (New York: IEEE, 1969).
9. Duff, W.G., and Moore, R.M., "Graphical-Numerical Prediction of Tuned RF Amplifier Output Spectrum: IRE Convention," 1961.
10. Duff, W.G., et. al., "Compatibility Prediction Accuracy as a Function of Spectrum Signature Data Inputs," *1966 IEEE EMC Symposium Record* (New York: IEEE, 1966).

11. "Electromagnetic Interference Characteristics Requirements for Equipment," MIL-STD-461A, August 1968.
12. Hald, A., *Statistical Theory with Engineering Applications* (New York: John Wiley & Sons, 1952).
13. Hebrand, F.B., *Introduction to Numerical Analysis* (New York: McGraw-Hill Book Co., Inc., 1961).
14. Heisler, K.G., Jr., "Preparation of Statistical Input Functions for Interference Prediction," *Proceedings of the Seventh Armour Research Foundation Conference*, 1961.
15. "Military Standard Radio Frequency Spectrum Characteristics, Measurement of," MIL-STD-449C.
16. Paul, D.; Clayton, R; and Weiner, D.D., "Summary of Required Input Parameters for Emitter Models in IEMCAP," RADC-TR-78-140, Final Technical Report, June 1978.
17. Swisher, G.M., and Doebelin, E.C., "Digital Computer Study of Fourier Transform Techniques for System Modeling by Pulse Testing," *Proceedings of the Thirteenth Midwest Symposium on Circuit Theory*, 70C(-Ct, 1970, pp. XIV.1.1, XIV.1.10.

Chapter 4

Receiver Considerations for EMC Design

The previous chapter discussed transmitter characteristics that must be considered in the design of telecommunications systems. This chapter identifies receiver characteristics that must be considered and presents methods and mathematical models for representing these characteristics. Techniques for selecting applicable models for a particular receiver are described. The methods and techniques in this chapter permit representing receiver responses to potentially interfering signals over a wide range of frequencies and power levels.

Receivers are designed to respond to certain types of electromagnetic signals within predetermined frequency bands. However, receivers also respond to undesired signals having various modulation and frequency characteristics. It is necessary, therefore, to treat a receiver as potentially susceptible to all transmitter emissions considered in an analysis.

When performing an EMC design of a telecommunications system, it is necessary to describe receiver susceptibility to different types of emission sources. What is required is a composite susceptibility function which represents the maximum interfering signal level that can be tolerated as a function of both the frequency and the type of interfering signal. Many problems, however, are involved in determining susceptibility of a particular receiver to a specific type of interference. The next section briefly describes receiver susceptibility effects that are considered. It discusses the type of information required and the problems involved in specifying each of these effects.

4.1   Receiver EMC Characteristics

There are a number of interference effects that an undesired signal can produce in a receiver. In order to represent receiver composite susceptibility, it is necessary to consider these effects and to determine which effects dominate within a given range of frequencies.

Figure 4.1 is a functional diagram useful in discussing various receiver EMI effects. A superheterodyne receiver generally employs radio-frequency (RF) stages which provide frequency selectivity and/or amplification and one or more mixers which translate the RF signal to intermediate frequencies (IF). It also contains IF stages which provide further frequency selectivity and amplification; a detector which recovers the modulation and post-detection stages that process the signal and drive one or more output devices. Since tuned-radio-frequency (TRF) and crystal-video receivers do not use the superheterodyne principle, they do not contain mixers and IF amplifiers. In specifying receiver susceptibility it is necessary to consider the effects of an interfering signal on each of these stages. The resulting susceptibility function then represents a composite of the most significant effects.

For the purpose of EMC analysis, potentially interfering signals are considered to be in one of three basic categories: (1) co-channel, (2) adjacent signal and (3) out-of-band. These three categories are defined as follows (see Fig. 4.2).

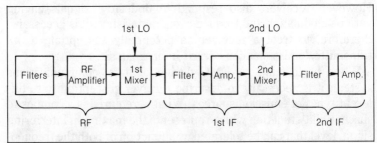

Figure 4.1—General Predetection Representation for Superheterodyne Receiver

Co-channel interference refers to signals having frequencies that exist within the narrowest passband of the receiver. For superheterodyne receivers, the culprit frequency of co-channel interference must be such that the interference is translated to the IF passband in the same way as the desired signal. This requires that the frequency of a co-channel interfering signal equals the tuned radio frequency plus one-half the narrowest IF bandwidth for superheterodyne receivers. In the case of either TRF or crystal-video receivers, selectivity is provided at RF, and the RF passband determines the applicable frequency range for co-channel signals.

Adjacent-signal interference refers to emissions having frequency components that exist within or near the widest receiver passband. They may be sufficiently separated from the receiver-tuned frequency such that they do not fall within the narrowest receiver passband. For example, in the case of a superheterodyne receiver, adjacent-signal interference falls within or near the RF passband but after conversion will fall outside the IF passband. For TRF receivers, adjacent-signal interference refers to signals that are outside of the RF passband but are still close enough to the receiver-tuned frequency so that they are attenuated by less than 60 dB.

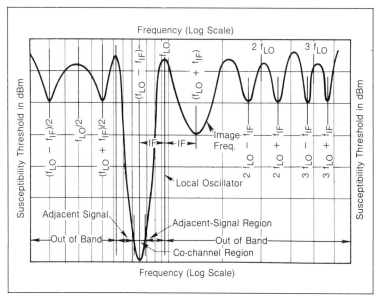

Figure 4.2—Receiver Susceptibility Characteristics

The adjacent-signal interference region may extend over a number of channels on each side of the receiver-tuned frequency. For example, for a typical UHF communication receiver having 50 kHz channel spacing, the adjacent-signal interference region may include 200 channels (10 MHz) on each side of the desired channel.

Out-of-band interference refers to signals having frequency components which are significantly outside of the widest receiver passband. These are identified above and below the adjacent-signal regions in Fig. 4.2.

The following sections describe EMI considerations associated with each category of receiver susceptibility. They show how to represent receiver characteristics for EMC analysis and design.

4.1.1   Co-channel Interference

Co-channel interference includes those potentially interfering emissions that exist within the narrowest predetection passband of the receiver. Because co-channel interfering signals are amplified, processed and detected in the same way as the desired signal, the receiver is particularly vulnerable to these emissions. Thus, co-channel EMI may either desensitize the receiver or override or mask the desired signal. It may also combine with the desired signal to cause serious distortion in the detected output or cause the automatic-frequency control circuitry to retune to the frequency of the interference, if this applies.

In Chapter 2 it was shown that the first phase of EMC analysis should be based primarily on the amplitude of the various potential interference functions. These include transmitter emission output, receiver susceptibility threshold, antenna gains and propagation loss. The purpose of amplitude analysis is for making a quick look at the total EMI problem to eliminate obvious noninterfering cases from further consideration. This defines the range of parameters that must be considered for surviving EMI cases. In performing amplitude analysis, relatively conservative assumptions are used for various interference functions. The variables of frequency, time and direction are considered only in a rather general manner.

For amplitude analysis, it is necessary to specify the receiver susceptibility threshold to co-channel signals. The receiver noise level $(S = N)$ is used for the co-channel susceptibility threshold.

Receiver noise level is related to the sensitivity, which may be obtained from the receiver technical manual, spectrum signature data or design specifications. See Vol. 1, Chapter 8 for a discussion of MIL-STD-449D which identifies measurement procedures and techniques used in the spectrum signature data collection program. For example, receiver sensitivity is often specified for a 3 dB signal-plus-noise-to-noise (S = N). Therefore, receiver noise (and thus the co-channel susceptibility threshold) is equal to the receiver sensitivity. Receiver co-channel susceptibility levels are used in the EMC amplitude analysis to calculate the Fundamental Interference Margin (FIM) and the Receiver Interference Margin (RIM). The FIM is the interference level that will exist if the transmitter and receiver are tuned to the same frequency, viz, a co-channel or adjacent channel. The RIM is the interference level that will exist if the receiver is tuned to a transmitter spurious emission (see Section 2.6).

The second phase of the EMC analysis as described in Chapter 2 is **frequency analysis**. During this phase, surviving potential EMI situations obtained from the amplitude analysis are refined by a more complete consideration of the frequency variable. Specifically, amplitude analysis results are modified to account for transmitter and receiver bandwidths and frequency misalignment.

For the second-step frequency analysis, receiver-tuned frequency and IF bandwidth must be specified. **Receiver-tuned frequency** is usually defined for each receiver to be included in the analysis, except for special situations such as those encountered in frequency assignment problems. For these situations, one important consideration is whether interference will exist if a receiver is tuned exactly to a transmitter output; this information is available as an output from the amplitude analysis. Information on the IF bandwidth is found in the receiver technical manual, specification or spectrum signature data.

Two final phases of the EMI analysis process described in Chapter 2 are the detailed analysis and the performance analysis. In the former, results derived from the frequency analysis are further modified to include effects of time and direction variables. Also, the combined and simultaneous effects of multiple interfering signals are considered. Performance analysis involves a consideration of operational performance and effectiveness factors to determine the resulting impact on overall system operational requirements.

Co-channel interfering signals do not require any special consideration in the detailed analysis. However, in the performance analysis it is necessary to consider modulation characteristics of both the desired and interfering signals, signal-to-noise and signal-to-interference ratios and detector characteristics as they affect these ratios.

4.1.2   Adjacent-Signal Interference

Adjacent-signal interference can produce any one of several effects in a receiver. For example, interference may be translated through the receiver together with the desired signal and both appear at the input to an IF stage. In this case, the IF selectivity and the adjacent-channel emission spectrum will both influence the relative level of the interfering signal appearing at the input to the detector. Alternately, one or more adjacent interfering emissions may produce nonlinear effects in the RF amplifier or mixer. Major nonlinear effects include desensitization, cross modulation and intermodulation.

Desensitization is reduction in the receiver gain to the desired signal as a result of an interfering emission producing automatic-gain control (AGC) action or causing one or more stages of the receiver to operate nonlinearly due to saturation. **Cross modulation** is the transfer of the modulation from an undesired emission to the desired signal as a result of the former causing one or more stages of the receiver to operate nonlinearly. **Intermodulation** is the generation of undesired signals from the nonlinear combination of two or more input signals which produce frequencies existing at the sum or difference of the input frequencies or their harmonics.

Adjacent-signal effects are not considered separately in the initial amplitude analysis. Results of the co-channel amplitude analysis form the basis for the adjacent-signal EMC analysis.   For the second-step frequency analysis, it is necessary to consider the frequency separation between receiver-tuned frequency and interfering emissions. This includes combined effects of signal and receiver bandwidths, emission spectrum and receiver selectivity. It identifies emissions that are within the receiver RF passband which have sufficient amplitude to produce nonlinear effects.

In the third-step detailed analysis it is necessary to consider strong, adjacent-signal interfering emissions both singly and collectively to evaluate effects of nonlinear interactions in the receiver front end. For the final-stage performance analysis, considerations for adjacent-signal interfering signals are the same as those that apply to co-channel interference.

4.1.3   Out-of-Band Interference

Strong **out-of-band interference** may produce spurious responses in a receiver. The superheterodyne receiver is most susceptible to those out-of-band signals that mix with local oscillator harmonics to produce a signal at the IF. Spurious responses in such a receiver usually occur at specific frequencies, and other out-of-band frequencies are attenuated by the receiver IF selectivity.

For a tuned-radio-frequency or crystal-video receiver, the receiver will be susceptible to those out-of-band interfering signals that are not adequately rejected by the RF selectivity.

For amplitude analysis it is necessary to describe the receiver susceptibility threshold to spurious responses. In general, the comments in Chapter 3 regarding transmitter harmonic emission amplitudes apply to receiver spurious responses amplitudes. For example, spurious responses are subject to random serial-number-to-serial-number variations. Thus, receiver spurious response susceptibility is represented statistically.

Frequencies associated with spurious responses are calculated in the second-step frequency analysis, and the separation between an interfering emission and a spurious response frequency is considered in the same way as for co-channel interference. Similarly, considerations that apply to the detailed and performance analyses are the same as those described for co-channel signals.

4.2   Fundamental Susceptibility Models

For the first-step amplitude analysis, it is necessary to represent the receiver susceptibility threshold in a manner that is consistent with other models (like transmitters, antennas and propagation) used in the EMC analysis process. See Chapter 2 for the 4 stages of EMI analysis: (1) amplitude analysis, (2) frequency analysis, (3) detailed analysis and (4) performance analysis. This section discusses considerations that apply to modeling susceptibility to various EMI effects and presents the models that are used. It also describes techniques for determining models for specific receivers from measured data. It presents statistical summary models that are used when specific data are not available or when all else fails.

4.2.1 Co-channel Susceptibility Threshold Models

Co-channel interference results from emissions at or near the operating frequency of the receiver, i.e., within the narrowest predetector passband of the receiver. Because co-channel signals are amplified, processed and detected in the same way as the desired signal, receivers are susceptible to relatively low-level co-channel emissions. Such emissions may produce interference by masking the desired signal, combining with the desired signal to produce distortion in the detected output, desensitize the receiver or create other effects.

Receiver noise level is used in amplitude analysis to represent the threshold of co-channel susceptibility. This level is chosen because it represents the minimum interfering signal level that must be considered. Thus, if an undesired signal is present at the tuned frequency of a receiver, it will not cause an EMI problem if its level at the input terminals of the receiver is below the receiver noise level. For EMI analysis, receiver co-channel susceptibility is represented as a statistical parameter which has a mean value $P_R(f_{OR})$ equal to the nominal noise level of the receiver.

Equipment-to-equipment variations in receiver co-channel susceptibility have been observed experimentally as shown in Fig. 4.3.[1] When performing an EMI analysis it is assumed that variations in receiver co-channel susceptibility are normally distributed random variables, and the standard deviation is either derived from measured data in the manner described in Chapter 3 for transmitters or a nominal value. Unless otherwise known, a standard deviation of 2 dB, which represents a statistical summary of available data is used. This variation in receiver co-channel susceptibility threshold implies a 16 percent probability that the receiver co-channel susceptibility threshold will exceed the average value by 2 dB or more.

Similarly, there is a 16 percent probability that the receiver co-channel susceptibility threshold will be 2 dB or more below the average value. The data presented in Fig. 4.3 are in general agreement with these observations.

If data regarding receiver co-channel susceptibility threshold $P_R(f_{OR})$ (receiver noise) are not immediately available, they can be calculated from a consideration of receiver bandwidth and noise figure F as follows:

$$P_R(f_{OR}) = FkTB_R \text{ Watts} \qquad (4.1)$$

where,
$$k = \text{Boltzman's Constant,} = 1.38 \times 10^{-23} \text{ W/°K/Hz}$$

$$T = \text{temperature in °K}$$

$$B_R = \text{receiver bandwidth in Hz}$$

Assuming operation at 290°K (approximately room temperature) and converting the expression for co-channel susceptibility threshold to dBm, Eq. (4.1) becomes:

$$P_R(f_{OR}) \text{ in dBm} = 10 \log [(4 \times 10^{-21})B_R(F) \times 10^{+3}]$$

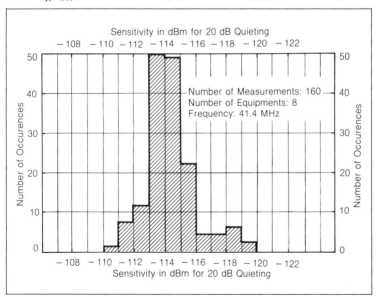

Figure 4.3—Histogram Showing Probability Distribution of co-Channel Receiver Sensitivity

$$= 10 \log (4 \times 10^{-18} B_R F)$$

$$= [-174 + 10 \log (B_R) + F_{dB}] \text{ dBm}$$

Figure 4.4 is a plot of Eq. (4.2) for different bandwidths and noise figures. Figure 4.5 shows the noise figure for typical RF amplifiers as a function of frequency.

Illustrative Example 4.1

To illustrate how Eq. (4.2) and Figs. 4.4 and 4.5 may be used to calculate the receiver co-channel susceptibility threshold, consider a typical radar receiver with a crystal mixer. Assume that the radar operates at L-band (1.3 GHz) and has a nominal IF bandwidth of 2 MHz. Referring to Fig. 4.5, the noise figure is approximately 8 dB. The co-channel susceptibility threshold (receiver S = N sensitivity) may be computed from Eq. (4.2) or Fig. 4.4:

$$
\begin{aligned}
P_R(f_{OR}) &= [-174 + 10 \log B_R + F_{dB}] \text{ dBm} \\
&= [-174 + 10 \log (2 \times 10^6) + 8] \text{ dBm} = \\
&-103 \text{ dBm}
\end{aligned}
$$

4.2.2 Co-channel Interference Frequency Models

Co-channel interference refers to a situation in which the interfering emission is at or near (within the narrowest receiver passband) the receiver operating frequency. In this case, emissions are translated into the IF passband along with the desired signal. Receiver parameters used for evaluating co-channel interference in the frequency analysis process are the fundamental frequency and narrowest bandwidth (the IF bandwidth for a superheterodyne receiver and the RF bandwidth for a TRF or crystal-video receiver). In performing the frequency analysis, nominal values are used for these parameters. These characteristics may usually be obtained from equipment operational plans and equipment technical specifications.

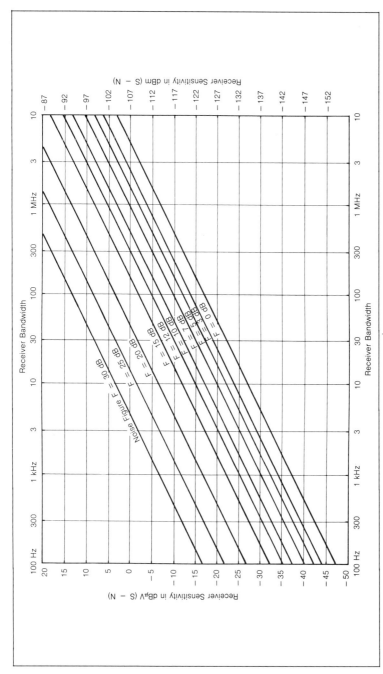

Figure 4.4—Receiver Narrowband Sensitivity vs. Bandwidth and Noise Figure

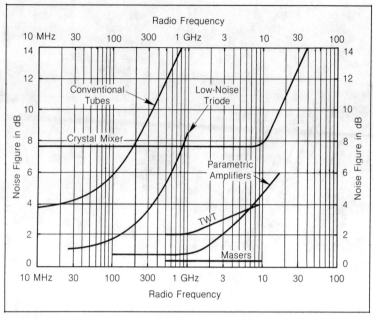

Figure 4.5—Realizable Noise Figure for RF Amplifiers

4.3 Adjacent-Signal Susceptibility Models

As mentioned previously, the term **adjacent-signal interference** refers to those potentially interfering emissions that are outside of the co-channel interference region but exist in the immediate vicinity of the receiver-tuned frequency, i.e., within the widest passband of the receiver.

Adjacent-signal emissions may produce any one of several interference effects in a receiver. The primary ones which must be considered in EMC design result from emissions being translated through the receiver with the desired signal and emissions causing nonlinear interactions in the receiver front end. The adjacent-signal characteristics that must be considered in an EMC analysis are selectivity and the various nonlinear interactions which include desensitization, intermodulation and cross modulation.

4.3.1 Receiver Selectivity

For superheterodyne receivers, the receiver IF selectivity determines the ability of the receiver to reject interfering emissions in the channels that are close to the tuned frequency of the receiver. If the receiver selectivity does not provide adequate rejection for adjacent channel signals, they will be transferred through the receiver with the desired signal and will produce interference in the receiver. In performing an EMC analysis, it is necessary to incorporate the effects of receiver selectivity to determine the resulting impact on interference.

4.3.1.1 General IF Selectivity Models

For superheterodyne receivers, IF selectivity characteristics are important in determining receiver ability to discriminate against adjacent-channel interference. The mathematical model used to represent receiver IF selectivity $S(\Delta f)$ is expressed as a piecewise linear function of the logarithm of frequency separation Δf:

$$S(\Delta f) = S(\Delta f_i) + S_i \log (\Delta f/\Delta f_i)$$

$$\text{for } \Delta f_i < \Delta f < \Delta f_i + 1 \qquad (4.3)$$

where,

S_i = slope of selectivity curve for applicable region

Δf_i = related to bandwidth of applicable region

$\Delta f = |f - f_{OR}|$

When spectrum signature data or other measured data are available, the above model can be used by specifying the frequency deviations associated with the 3 dB, 20 dB and 60 dB selectivity levels. The resulting selectivity model is shown in Fig. 4.6. Notice that a maximum value of 100 dB is assumed for receiver selectivity. This implies that any emission source greater than 100 dB above receiver sensitivity may penetrate and become a source of EMI.

Illustrative Example 4.2

It is required to mathematically model the IF selectivity characteristics for an X-band radar receiver used for Ground-Controlled Approach (GCA) landing of aircraft. Suppose that the 3 dB, 20 dB and 60 dB (IF selectivity) bandwidths are given as 2 MHz, 4 MHz and 8 MHz respectively. The selectivity is given by Eq. (4.3). From Fig. 4.6, the relative selectivity $S(\Delta f)$ is zero for all values of Δf less than one-half the 3 dB bandwidth or 1 MHz. Thus:

$$S(\Delta f) = 0 \text{ dB for } \Delta f \leqslant \Delta f_1 \text{ (1 MHz)}$$

The selectivity is 20 dB at $\Delta f = \Delta f_2$ which is equal to one-half the 20 dB bandwidth or 2 MHz. Thus:

$$20 \text{ dB} = S(\Delta f_1) + S_1 \log(\Delta f_2/\Delta f_1)$$

$$= S(\Delta f_1) + S_1 \log(2 \text{ MHz}/1 \text{ MHz})$$

$$20 \text{ dB} = 0 + S_1 \log 2$$

Thus, $$S_1 = 67 \text{ dB/decade}$$

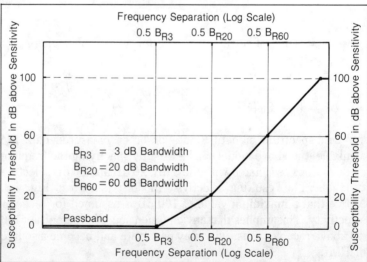

Figure 4.6—Receiver Selectivity Model Susceptibility Threshold in dB above Sensitivity

and, $S(\Delta f) = 67 \log(\Delta f/\Delta f_1)$ for 1 MHz $\leqslant \Delta f \leqslant 2$ MHz

$$\text{and } \Delta f_1 = 1 \text{ MHz}$$

Finally, the selectivity is 60 dB at $\Delta f = \Delta f_3$ which is equal to one-half the 60 dB bandwidth or 4 MHz. Thus:

$$60 \text{ dB} = S(\Delta f_2) + S_2 \log(\Delta f_3/\Delta f_2)$$

$$= S(\Delta f_2) + S_2 \log(4 \text{ MHz}/2 \text{ MHZ})$$

$$60 \text{ dB} = 20 + S_2 \log^2$$

Thus, $S_2 = 133$ dB/decade

and,
$$S(\Delta f) = 20 + 133 \log(\Delta f/\Delta f_2) \text{ for } \Delta f_2 = 2 \text{ MHz} \leqslant \Delta f$$

For example, the rejection to a potentially interfering signal 3 MHz away from the center of the receiver passband is:

$$S(3 \text{ MHz}) = 20 \text{ dB} + 133 \log (3 \text{ MHz}/2 \text{ MHZ})$$

$$= 20 \text{ dB} + 23 \text{ dB} = 43 \text{ dB}$$

To a signal 20 MHz away, rejection is:

$$S(20 \text{ MHz}) = 20 \text{ dB} + 133 \log(20 \text{ MHz}/2\text{MHz})$$

$$= 20 \text{ dB} + 133 \text{ dB} = 153 \text{ dB}$$

Since this is greater than 100 dB, the 100 dB rejection limit is used.

4.3.1.2 Summary IF Selectivity Models

For situations where no measured data are available, trends have been established by analyzing selective aspects of receivers belonging to similar groups. One good indicator for the selectivity characteristics is given by the shape factor: the ratio of the 60 dB bandwidth to the 3 dB bandwidth. Analysis of spectrum signature data for approximately 100 different receiver nomenclatures reveals that shape factor statistics are not significantly different for the various frequency bands. Of the receivers examined, approximately 90 percent have shape factors greater than two, 50 percent have shape factors greater than four and 20 percent have shape factors greater than eight. These results indicate that a receiver with good selectivity should have a shape factor of about two, whereas receivers with poor selectivity may have shape factors greater than eight.

One possible adverse characteristic of low shape factors is a poor phase response to the desired signal in the passband. Bode minimum-phase functions relate the phase response with the derivative of the attenuation function. Thus, a sharp change in attenuation at band edge is accompanied by pulse overshoot and ringing.

Applying the shape factor (SF) concept to Eq. 4.3, the IF selectivity relation yields:

$$S(\Delta f)_{dB} = 60 \; \frac{\log(\Delta f/\Delta f_1)}{\log \text{SF}} \; dB \tag{4.4}$$

When $\Delta f/\Delta f_1$ is chosen to equal the shape factor, Eq. (4.4) yields 60 dB.

Illustrative Example 4.3

Consider a typical HF, point-to-point communication receiver having an IF bandwidth of 10 kHz. Assuming a shape factor of four, the receiver selectivity model from Eq. (4.4) would become:

$$S(\Delta f) = 0 \text{ for } \Delta f \leqslant 5 \text{ kHz}$$

$$S(\Delta f) = 100 \log \frac{\Delta f(kHz)}{5} \text{ for } \Delta f \geqslant 5 \text{ kHz}$$

Similar models can be derived for other assumed values of the shape factor.

4.3.2 Nonlinear Adjacent-Signal Effects

When receivers are subjected to strong adjacent interfering signals, nonlinear interactions can occur in the RF stages of the receiver and these interactions can result in interference as a result of desensitization, intermodulation or cross modulation. In order to provide proper consideration to receiver adjacent-signal EMI effects during system planning and design, it is necessary to be able to describe the receiver adjacent-signal susceptibility in a quantitative manner. This section presents models that may be used to describe receiver susceptibility to desensitization, intermodulation and cross modulations. MIL-STD-461C, statistical summaries of spectrum signature data or specific measured data on a particular receiver type may be used as the basis for the receiver adjacent-signal EMI models.

For EMI situations for which mild nonlinearities result, a nonlinear transfer function may be used to analyze the interference. The nonlinear transfer function is based on the theory of functionals and functional expansions which was first proposed by Vito Volterra in 1930.[2] He established a working definition of a functional by noting that, just as a function operates on a set of variables to produce a new set of variables, a functional operates on a set of functions to produce a new set of functions. Using this definition, Volterra observed that an arbitrary functional could be expanded in what is now called a **Volterra Series**, in a way similar to the power series expansion of a function. He showed that every homogeneous functional of degree n, acting on an arbitrary function, x(t), could be written:

$$F_n[x(t)] = \int_a^b \cdots \int_a^b k_n(\zeta_1, \zeta_2, \zeta_3 \cdots \zeta_n)$$

$$x(\zeta_1) \cdots (\zeta_n) \, d\zeta_1 \, d\zeta_2 \cdots d\zeta_n \qquad (4.5)$$

where [a, b] is the interval appropriate for the problem being considered. Observing that Eq. (4.5) holds, the Volterra series expansion of any arbitrary functional G[x[t]] may be written:

$$G[x(t)] = \sum_{n=0}^{\infty} F_n[x(t)] \qquad (4.6)$$

The first important application of this Volterra series expansion to the analysis of nonlinear circuits was by Wiener in 1942, who related the output of a system, y(t), to the input, x(t), by a Volterra series of the form:[3]

$$y(t)] = \sum_{n=1}^{\infty} y_n(t) \qquad (4.7)$$

where the y_n are given by:

$$y_n(t) = \int_{\infty}^{\infty} ... \int_{\infty}^{\infty} h_n\ (\tau_1,...,\tau_n)$$

$$x(t - \tau_1) ... x(t - \tau_n)d\tau_1 ... d\tau_n \qquad (4.8)$$

The simplification of Eq. (4.7) will provide the theoretical basis for this discussion of nonlinear interference effects.

Begin by noting that $h_n(\tau_1,...,\tau_n)$ has been defined as the nonlinear impulse response of order n, and that the Fourier transform of h_n:

$$H_n(f_1,...,f_n) = \int_{-\infty}^{\infty} ... \int_{-\infty}^{\infty} h_n(\tau_1,...,\tau_n)$$

$$\exp[-j2\pi(f_1\tau_1 + ... + f_n\tau_n)]d\tau_1 ... d\tau_n \qquad (4.9)$$

is defined as the nonlinear transfer function of order n.[4] It is apparent that the inverse Fourier transform:

$$h_n(\tau_1,...,\tau_n) = \int_{-\infty}^{\infty} ... \int_{-\infty}^{\infty} H_n(\phi_1,...,\phi_n)$$

$$\exp[j2\pi(f_1\tau_1 + ... + f_n\tau_n)]df_1 ... df_n \qquad (4.10)$$

will allow expression of Eq. (4.8) in terms of these $H_n(f)$. Therefore, if Eq. (4.10) is substituted into Eq. (4.7), and the integrations over τ_k are performed, $y(t)$ is found to be:

$$y(t) = \sum_{n=1}^{\infty} \int_{-\infty}^{\infty} ... \int_{-\infty}^{\infty} H_n(f_1,...,f_n)X(f_1)...X(f_n)$$

$$\exp[j2\pi(f_1 + f_2 + ... + f_n)t)]df_1 ... df_n \qquad (4.11)$$

The integrations over τ_k have produced $X(f_k)$, which is the frequency domain input signal spectrum. The assumptions which will be made to simplify Eq. (4.11) so that it may be used in developing system level nonlinear models are:

1. Inputs to the system of interest are assumed to be modulated sinusoidal voltages into a normalized impedance (1 Ω).
2. The system of interest is assumed to behave quasistatistically.
3. Only the lowest-order term contributing to a particular nonlinear effect will be used in the mathematical description of that effect.

Given the third assumption, Eq. (4.7) may be rewritten:

$$y(t) = y_1(t) + y_2(t) + \ldots + y_N(t) = \sum_{n=1}^{N} y_n(t) \qquad (4.12)$$

where $y_N(t)$ is the lowest order term contributing to the nonlinear effect being considered. To evaluate Eq. (4.12), the second simplifying assumption will be used, and the input to the system will be represented as the sum of Q sinusoids:

$$x(t) = \sum_{q=1}^{Q} E_q \cos(2\pi f_q t) \qquad (4.13)$$

where E_q is a complex modulated voltage. This may be represented in the complex plane by noting that:

$$\cos(Z) = \frac{e^{jZ} + e^{-jZ}}{2} \qquad (4.14)$$

Thus, if we define $f_{-q} = f_q$, and $\bar{E}_{-q} = \bar{E}_q$, Eq. (4.13) is written:

$$x(t) = 1/2 \sum_{q=-Q}^{Q} \bar{E}_q \exp(j2\pi f_q t) \qquad (4.15)$$

Using this form for the system input, and using Eq. (4.8) to find the form of the nth order response term yields the following result:

$$y_n(t) = 1/2^n \sum_{q_1=-Q}^{Q} \ldots \sum_{q_n=-Q}^{Q} E_{q1} \ldots E_{qn} H_n(f_{q1}, \ldots, f_{qn})$$

$$\exp[j2\pi(f_{q1} + \ldots + f_{qn})t] \qquad (4.16)$$

4.19

A combined analysis yields the result that, if the excitation of Eq. (4.16) consists of Q sinusoids, each $y_n(t)$ will contain:

$$M = \frac{(2Q + n - 1)!}{n!(2Q - 1)!} \tag{4.17}$$

output frequency mixes. Therefore, for a two-tone input (Q = 2), $M = (4 + N - 1)!$. Then $y_1(t)$ contains $4 = (4!)/6$ frequency mixes, $y_2(t)$ contains 10 mixes, $y_3(t)$ contains 20 mixes and so on.

Consider, then, a system where terms with $n > 3$ contributes negligibly to the output. There will then be 34 different frequency mixes arising from an input of the form:

$$x(t) = \bar{E}_1 \cos 2\pi f_1 t + \bar{E}_2 \cos 2\pi f_2 t \tag{4.18}$$

Substituting Eq. (4.18) into Eq. (4.12) yields Table 4.1 which gives the 34 responses which must be summed to obtain y(t).

Table 4.1 may be used to generate models for any nonlinear response where the major nonlinear effect is of order $N < 3$. If these models are to be of use in system level analysis, two assumptions are useful:
1. Voltages must be considered real.
2. The nonlinear transfer functions, which are arbitrary functions in the complex plane, must have their phase angles specified as inherent parts of each nonlinear model. This is because phase information is generally unavailable for system-level analyses.

Desensitization

Desensitization occurs when an interfering signal enters a receiver with sufficient magnitude to cause the receiver amplifiers to operate nonlinearly. Desensitization can be a serious problem in a complex electromagnetic environment because its effects are cumulative; i.e., all signals entering the receiver RF passband contribute to desensitization, and the resulting nonlinear operation may cause system degradation even if individual interfering signals cause no problems.

To consider the effects of a third-order desensitization, assume that $n > 3$ need not be considered. Assume that the desired signal and modulation may be represented by:

$$S_i(t) = S[1 + s(t)] \cos \omega_s t \qquad (4.19)$$

Table 4.1—Responses Which Must Be Summed to Obtain y(t) for N = 3, Q = 2

Combination No.	Frequency of Response	Amplitude of Response	Type of Response
n = 1			
1	f_1	$1/2\ E_1\ H_1\ (f_1)$	
2	f_2	$1/2\ E_2\ H_1\ (f_2)$	Linear
3	$-f_1$	$1/2\ E_1\ H_1\ (-f_1)$	
4	$-f_2$	$1/2\ E_2\ H_1\ (-f_2)$	
n = 2			
1	$f_1 + f_2$	$1/2\ E_1\ E_2\ H_2\ (f_1, f_2)$	
2	$f_2 - f_1$	$1/2\ E_2\ E_1\ H_2\ (f_2, -f_1)$	
3	$-f_1 - f_2$	$1/2\ E_1\ E_2\ H_2\ (-f_1, -f_2)$	Second-Order
4	$f_1 - f_2$	$1/2\ E_1\ E_2\ H_2\ (f_1, -f_2)$	Intermodulation
5	$f_1 - f_1 = 0$	$1/2|E_1|^2H_2(f_1, -f_1)$	
6	$f_2 - f_2 = 0$	$1/2|E_2|^2H_2(f_2, -f_2)$	
7	$2f_1$	$1/4\ E_1^2H_2\ (f_1, f_1)$	
8	$2f_2$	$1/4\ E_2^2H_2\ (f_2, f_2)$	Second
9	$-2f_1$	$1/4\ E_1^2H_2\ (-f_1, -f_1)$	Harmonic
10	$-2f_2$	$1/4\ E_2^2H_2\ (-f_2, -f_2)$	
n = 3			
1	$f_1 + f_2 - f_1 = f_2$	$3/4\ E_1^2E_2H_3\ (f_1, f_2, -f_1)$	
2	$f_2 - f_1 - f_1 = -f_1$	$3/4\ E_1E_2H_3\ (f_2, -f_1, -f_1)$	Third-Order
3	$f_1 - f_1 - f_2 = -f_2$	$3/4\ E_1E_2H_3\ (f_1, -f_1, -f_2)$	Desensitization
4	$f_1 + f_2 - f_2 = f_1$	$3/4\ E_1E_2H_3\ (f_1, f_2, -f_2)$	
5	$2f_1 + f_2$	$3/8\ E_1^2E_2H_3\ (f_1, f_1, f_2)$	
6	$2f_2 - f_1$	$3/8\ E_1E_2^2H_3\ (f_2, f_2, -f_1)$	Third-Order
7	$-2f_1 - f_2$	$3/8\ E_1^2E_2H_3\ (-f_1, -f_1, -f_2)$	Intermodulation
8	$f_1 - 2f_2$	$3/8\ E_1E_2^2H_3\ (f_1, -f_2, -f_2)$	
9	$2f_1 - f_1 = f_1$	$3/8\ E_1E_1^2H_3\ (f_1, f_1, -f_1)$	
10	$2f_2 - f_2 = f_2$	$3/8\ E_2E_2^2H_3\ (f_2, f_2, -f_2)$	Third-Order
11	$f_1 - 2f_1 = -f_1$	$3/8\ E_1E_1H_3\ (f_1, -f_1, -f_1)$	Compression
12	$f_2 - 2f_2 = -f_2$	$3/8\ E_2E_2H_3\ (f_2, -f_2, -f_2)$	
13	$2f_1 - f_2$	$3/8\ E_1^2E_2H_3\ (f_1, f_1, -f_2)$	
14	$f_1 + 2f_2$	$3/8\ E_1E_2^2H_3\ (f_1, f_2, f_2)$	Third-Order
15	$f_2 - 2f_1$	$3/8\ E_2E_1^2H_3\ (f_2, -f_1, -f_1)$	Intermodulation
16	$-f_1 - 2f_2$	$3/8\ E_1E_2^2H_3\ (-f_1, -f_2, -f_2)$	
17	$3f_1$	$1/8\ E_1^3H_3\ (f_1, f_1, f_1)$	
18	$3f_2$	$1/8\ E_2^3H_3\ (f_2, f_2, f_2)$	Third
19	$-3f_1$	$1/8\ E_1^3H_3\ (-f_1, -f_1, -f_1)$	Harmonic
20	$-3f_2$	$1/8\ E_2^3H_3\ (-f_2, -f_2, -f_2)$	

while the interfering signal may be written:

$$I_i(t) = I \cos \omega_i t \qquad (4.20)$$

The presence of s(t) in Eq. (4.19) indicates that the system behaves quasistatistically. If noise is negligible, the total input to the system is simply the sum of the two signals $S_i(t) + I_i(t)$. This is a two-tone cosinusoidal input of the form seen previously, and therefore the input/output voltage relationship may be derived from Table 4.1:

$$v_o(t) = [1 + s(t)]SH_1 (f_s) \cos \omega_s t$$

$$+ \frac{3}{2}I^2SH_3(f_s, f_i, -f_i)[1 + s(t)] \cos \omega_s t \qquad (4.21)$$

This equation represents the transfer functions as complex functions with arbitrary phase. To obtain Eq. (4.21) in a form useful for a system-level analysis requires that these arbitrary phase angles be specified. The following assumptions are made:

1. The linear (desired) portion of the response is entirely positive real, i.e., $\phi_1 = 0$.
2. The phase angle of H_3 will be limited to values of 0 or π.

Equation (4.21) is valid if only terms of order $n \leqslant 3$ must be considered to represent the transfer function of the nonlinear device. However, for any more than slight desensitization, higher-order terms must be considered. Higher-order terms could be added, but a series to represent this condition is slowly converging and computation of the coefficients generally is impractical. The effects of considering only third-order desensitization may be examined by considering Fig. 4.7, which shows the effect of phase angle on desensitization. This figure shows that higher-order terms and phase must be considered to accurately predict large desensitization.

If Eq. (4.21) is to represent desensitization, however, the actual system output will be less than the linear portion of the response. This leads to $\phi_3 = \pi$, which is equivalent to the statement that H_3 is an entirely real, negative quantity since $e^{j\pi} = -1$. Rewriting Eq. (4.21) using this requirement yields:

$$v_o(t) = S[H_1(f_s) + \frac{3}{2}I^2H_3(f_s,f_i,-f_i)]$$

$$[1 + s(t)] \cos \omega_s t \qquad (4.22)$$

Using Eq. (4.22), the effects of desensitization may be expressed as:

$$\frac{\Delta S_o}{S_o} = \frac{S_o(\text{volts}) - S'_o(\text{volts})}{S_o \ (\text{volts})} \qquad (4.23)$$

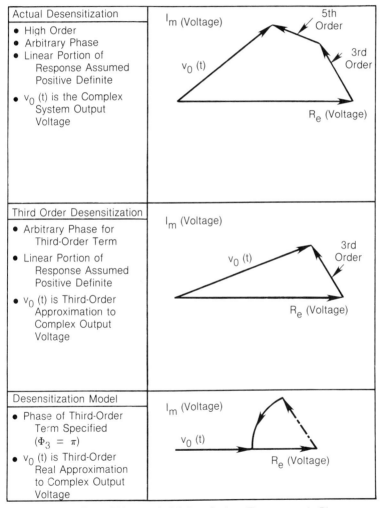

Figure 4.7—The Effect of Higher-Order Terms and Phase on Desensitization

where,

S_o (volts) = desired signal output without interference
S'_o (volts) = desired signal output with interference

Then,

$$\frac{\Delta S_o}{S_o} = \frac{3 \, I^2 H_3(f_s, f_i, -f_i)}{2 \, H_1(f_s)} \qquad (4.24)$$

$$\frac{\Delta S_o}{S_o} \, dB = 20 \log I^2 + 20 \log \frac{3}{2} \left| \frac{H_3(f_s, f_i, -f_i)}{H_1(f_s)} \right| \qquad (4.25)$$

$$= 2P_I \, dBm + F(f_s, f_i) \qquad (4.26)$$

where,

$P_I dBm$ = average interfering signal power in dBm
$F(f_s, f_i)$ = function that represents device characteristics

In order to use Eq. (4.26) to calculate the effects of desensitization resulting from a particular interfering signal power level, it is necessary to specify a value for the desensitization function $F(f_s, f_i)$ for the particular receiver type being considered. If the change in signal level is known for a specific interfering signal level, $P_i(f_I)$, the desensitization function may be calculated from:

$$F(f_s, \, f_i) = -2P_I^{\;*} (f_I) \, dBm + \left[\frac{\Delta S_o}{S_o} \right]^{*} \, dB \qquad (4.27)$$

Intermodulation

In this section, models used to describe nonlinear intermodulation effects will be discussed. Intermodulation is the process occurring when two or more signals mix in a nonlinear device to produce an output at a frequency which causes performance degradation. Effects which will be discussed in this section are second-, third- and fifth-order, two-signal receiver intermodulation products.

The assumptions used in the analysis of third-order intermodulation are the same as those used in the desensitization analyses with the exception of the representation used for the interfering signal. Here, it is assumed that there are two interfering signal components, $I_1(t)$ and $I_2(t)$, present at the input of the nonlinear device. The first interfering signal component is assumed to be an unmodulated carrier and the second is amplitude modulated. The total interfering signal is thus represented by:

$$I_i(t) = I_1 \cos \omega_1 t + I_2[1 + i(t)] \cos \omega_2 t \qquad (4.28)$$

This equation, together with the equations in Table (4.1), will be used to develop the models describing intermodulation effects. To simplify the discussion, there will be two assumptions made concerning the signals at frequencies f_1 and f_2:

1. The signal at f_1 is assumed to be nearer the center of the receiver passband than the signal at f_2.
2. Of the possible third-order responses:

    a. $2f_1 + f_2$
    b. $2f_1 - f_2$
    c. $2f_2 + f_1$
    d. $2f_2 - f_1$

the response (b) at $2f_1 - f_2$ is assumed to be the major interfering signal component. The others will be sufficiently attenuated by RF selectivity to be insignificant since they fall farther from the center of the RF passband than does (b).

Now, from Table 4.1 the intermodulation term at frequency $2f_1 - f_2$ may be written, given that $S_i(t)$ is again a modulated carrier:

$$v_o(t) = SH_1(f_s)[1 + s(t)] \cos \omega_s t$$

$$+ \frac{3}{4}I_1^2 I_2 H_3(f_1, f_1, -f_2)[1 + i(t)] \cos(2\omega_1 - \omega_2)t \qquad (4.29)$$

A general expression for the contribution of an nth degree term to a particular two-signal intermodulation product is given by:

$$\frac{n!}{2^{n-1}(\alpha - n_\alpha)!(\beta - n_\beta)!n_\alpha!n_\beta!} I_1^\alpha I_2^\beta \cos[(\alpha - 2n_\alpha)w_1 t \pm (\beta - 2n_\beta)w_{s2}t$$

For this case, $\alpha + \beta = n$, and n_a and n_b are zero/positive integers such that $n_a < 1/2a$ and $n_b < 1/2b$. If consideration is limited to contributions of nth degree terms to nth-order effects, n_a and n_b are zero and the above equation reduces to:

$$\frac{n!}{2^{n-1}\,\alpha!\,\beta!}\ \ \frac{I_1^\alpha\,I_2^\beta}{}\ \cos\,(\alpha\omega_1\,+\,\beta\omega_2)t \tag{4.30}$$

This equation is developed from a combined analysis in Ref. 5.

The second term in Eq. (4.29) is the third-order intermodulation term. Higher order terms may also be calculated from the relations in Eq. (4.30), which will lead to the equations which describe fifth-order intermodulation effects.

Returning to Eq. (4.29), it may be seen that the amplitude of the third-order intermodulation carrier is given by:

$$IMv_0(t)\ =\ +\frac{3}{4}I_1^2 I_2 H_3(f_1,\,f_1,\,-f_2)$$

while the intermodulation output power in dBm is given by:

$$P_{IM}\ =\ 2P_1\ dBm\ +\ P_2\ dBm\ +\ 20\ \log\ \frac{3}{\sqrt{2}}\ +\ H_3(f_1,\,f_1,\,-f_2)\ dB \tag{4.31}$$

For receivers, it is convenient to express the results in terms of an equivalent input power level (in terms of the desired signal level P_D) that is required to produce the same effects in the receiver as the intermodulation product. The output for the desired signal may be found from Eq. (4.29) and is just the magnitude of the desired signal carrier.

$$\text{Desired signal output power in dBm}\ =\ P_D\ dBm\ +\ H_1(f_s)\ dB \tag{4.32}$$

If this desired output power is assumed to be equal to the intermodulation output power, Eqs. (4.31) and (4.32) may be equated, resulting in:

$$P_D\ dBm\ =\ 2P_1\ dBm\ +\ P_2\ dBm\ +\ 20\ \log\ \frac{3}{\sqrt{2}}\ +$$

$$H_3(f_1,\,f_1,\,-f_2)\ dB\ -\ H_1(f_s)\ dB \tag{4.33}$$

$$= 2P_1 + P_2 + IMF(f_s, f_1, f_2) \qquad (4.34)$$

where,

$$IMF(f_s, f_1, f_2) = \text{the intermodulation function}$$

With reference to Eq. (4.33), the equivalent input signal for intermodulation is a function of the power levels of the two interfering signals, the nonlinearity factor $(20 \log 3/\sqrt{2} = k_3)$ and the transfer functions. The problem becomes how to evaluate the intermodulation function $[20 \log 3/\sqrt{2} + H_3 (f_1, f_1, -f_2) - H_1(f_s)]$ for a particular receiver. As was the case with desensitization, it will be convenient to use specific data to evaluate the function for a particular set of input conditions as discussed in Section 4.4.2.

Cross Modulation

Cross Modulation is the term used to describe degradation caused by the transfer of modulation from an interfering signal to the desired signal. Cross modulation is similar to desensitization (discussed earlier) in two ways which bear on the following discussion. The similarities are:

1. Cross modulation is treated as a third-order effect.
2. Cross modulation may be considered a nonlinear phenomenon which occurs at intervals corresponding to increased interfering signal levels which cause the receiver amplifiers to operate nonlinearly, causing desensitization in these intervals.

Based on the preceding similarities, the discussion of cross modulation will follow that of desensitization except for the representation of the interfering signal, which is assumed to be an amplitude-modulated carrier, with modulation such that i(t) is less than one.

$$I_i(t) = I[1 + i(t)]\cos \omega_i t$$

$$v_o(t) = S[H_1(f_s) + \frac{3}{2}I^2 H_3(f_s, -f_i, f_i)]$$

$$[1 + 2i(t) + i^2(t)][(1 + s(t)]\cos \omega_s t \qquad (4.35)$$

In Eq. (4.35), the term involving $i^2(t)$ is second order and is insignificant with respect to the remainder of the expression. Now carrying out the multiplications in Eq. (4.35), and eliminating terms with second order modulation gives:

$$v_o(t) = S[H_1(f_s) + \frac{3}{2}I^2H_3(f_s, -f_i, f_i)$$

$$\left[1 + s(t) + \frac{\frac{3}{2}H_3(f_s, f_i, -f_i)I^2}{H_1(f_s) + \frac{3}{2}H_3(f_s, f_i, -f_i)I^2} \; 2i(t) \right] \cos \omega_s t$$

$$(4.36)$$

Equation (4.36) is the expression for an amplitude-modulated signal where the modulation consists of a combination of the desired and interfering signal modulations, s(t) and i(t). If the modulation component resulting from the interfering signal modulation is restricted so that the maximum amplitude of the modulation signal is less than or equal to the amplitude of the carrier, overmodulation is avoided. In this case, the nonlinearity should not cause significant distortion of the modulation. In order to avoid overmodulation, it is necessary that:

$$m_s + \left| \frac{\frac{3}{2} I^2H_3(f_s, f_i, -f_i)}{H_1(f_s) + \frac{3}{2} I^2H_3(f_s, f_i, -f_i)} \right| 2 m_i \leqslant 1$$

where m_s and m_i represent the maximum values of s(t) and i(t).

One measure of the effect of cross modulation is provided by the ratio of the sideband component resulting from the desired signal to the sideband component resulting from the interfering signal. The resulting ratio, termed the "cross modulation ratio" (CMR), is expressed in terms of m_s and m_i:

$$CMR = \frac{[H_1(f_s) + \frac{3}{2}I^2H_3(f_s, f_i, - f_i)]m_s}{[\frac{3}{2} I^2H_3(f_s, f_i, - f_i)]2m_i} \tag{4.37}$$

If the desired and interfering signals are limited to "small-signal" conditions such that the third-order effect is much less than the linear response:

$$H_1(f_s) >> \frac{3}{2} I^2H_3(f_s, f_i, -f_i) \tag{4.38}$$

and the cross modulation ratio may be written:

$$CMR = \frac{H_1(f_s)m_s}{3I^2H_3(f_s,f_i,-f_i)m_i} \qquad (4.39)$$

or,

$$CMR\ dB = -2P_1\ dBm + H_1(f_s)\ dB - H_3(f_s,f_i,-f_i)\ dB -$$

$$20 \log \frac{2\ m_s}{3\ m_i} \qquad (4.40)$$

where,

$$P_I = \text{interfering signal power in dBm}$$

Equation (4.40) assumes that the major cross modulation is of the third order and results in an amplitude modulation effect. If both the desired and interfering signals have the same modulation characteristics ($m_s = m_i$), the last three terms of Eq. (4.40) are functions of the gain, selectivity and nonlinear characteristics of the device under consideration. For convenience, these terms may be represented by a single function, $CMF(f_i, f_s)$, which is referred to as the cross modulation function. Thus:

$$CMR\ dB = -2P_1\ dBm + CMF(f_i, f_s) \qquad (4.41)$$

In order to use the equations for cross modulation, it is necessary to specify a value for the cross modulation function. If the cross modulation effects are specified for a given interfering signal level $P_i^*(f_I)$ dBm the cross modulation function may be evaluated as follows:

$$CMF(f_I)\ dB = 2P_i^*\ (f_I)\ dBm + CMR^*\ dB \qquad (4.42)$$

where, CMR^* dB = cross modulation ratio resulting from reference interfering signal

4.3.2.1 Adjacent-Signal Frequency Limits

For all types of receivers, RF selectivity is important from the standpoint of adjacent-signal interference. The primary use of these data is to define the frequency region over which receiver front-end nonlinearities resulting in intermodulation, desensitization and cross modulation are important. If RF selectivity data are not available, which is usually the case, receiver intermodulation, desensitization or cross-modulation data may be used to provide an indication of the radio-frequency range over which adjacent-channel effects are significant.

For the frequency analysis, effects of RF selectivity are modeled by specifying Δf_{MAX} which represents the maximum frequency separation between the receiver and a potentially interfering transmitter emission for which adjacent-signal effects are significant. If a particular transmitter emission is separated from the receiver by more than Δf_{MAX}, it is not necessary to consider adjacent-signal emission effects in the detailed analysis. On the other hand, if the transmitter emission is separated from the receiver by less than Δf_{MAX} and the fundamental interference margin (FIM) from the amplitude analysis is large (on the order of 60 dB or larger, for example), adjacent-signal effects must be considered in the detailed analysis.

Table 4.2 provides values for Δf_{MAX} that may be used to define the adjacent-signal region when specific data are not available. The frequency separations presented in the table are obtained from statistical summaries of available receiver intermodulation data.

Figure 4.8 shows cumulative probability distribution functions for the maximum observed frequency separation between the nearest third-order intermodulation signal and the receiver-tuned frequency for all available data sets within the HF, VHF and UHF bands. For UHF receivers, only 25 percent of the measured third-order intermodulation characteristics involved near signal frequency separations greater than 10 percent of the tune frequency. This means that for a receiver operating at 300 MHz, there is only 25 percent probability that a measured third-order intermodulation response may result if the near signal is more than 30 MHz from the receiver-tuned frequency. Similar observations may be made for HF and VHF receivers.

Table 4.2—Frequency Limits for Adjacent-Signal Interference

*Receiver-Tuned Frequency	Maximum Adjacent-Channel Frequency Separation
Below 30 MHz	One-Half Receiver-Tuned Frequency
30 MHz to 300 MHz	One-Third Receiver-Tuned Frequency
above 300 MHz	One-Tenth Receiver-Tuned Frequency

*These frequency limits for adjacent-signal reference represent the 25 percent probability limits as illustrated in Fig. 4.15.

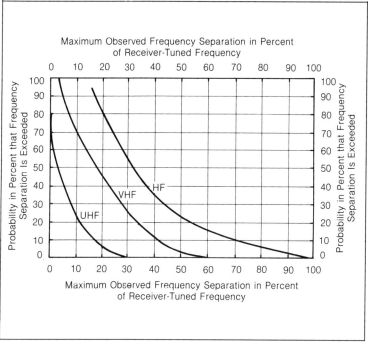

Figure 4.8—Maximum Observed Frequency Separation Between Nearest Intermodulation Signal and Receiver-Tuned Frequency

4.3.2.2 General Desensitization Models

When a receiver is subjected to one or more strong undesired signals in channels adjacent to the receiver-tuned frequency, nonlinearities in the receiver front end result in a reduction in gain for the desired signal. This effect is termed desensitization. Equation (4.26) expressed the gain change resulting from desensitization as a function of the interfering signal power and the desensitization functions as given below:

$$\frac{\Delta S_o}{S_o} \text{ dB} = 2 \, P_I \text{ dBm} + F(f_s, f_i)$$

The following sections present desensitization models that are based on MIL-STD-461, statistical summaries of measured data and specific measured data.

4.31

4.3.2.2.1 Desensitization Models Based on MIL-STD-461

The CS04 limits of MIL-STD-461 may be used with Eq. (4.26) to represent receiver desensitization effects. Equation (4.26) may be equated to an interference margin by expressing $\Delta S_o/S_o$ in terms of a reference level. This level will be assumed to be -20 dB (the minimum observable desensitization) and the interference margin will be the amount by which $\Delta S_o/S_o$ exceeds -20 dB. Expressed mathematically:

$$\text{Interference Margin} = \frac{\Delta S_o}{S_o} + 20 \text{ dB} \qquad (4.43)$$

In order to use Eq. (4.26) to calculate the effects of desensitization, it is first necessary to evaluate the function $F(f_s,f_i)$. If the change is signal level $(\Delta S_o/S_o)^*$ is known for some reference interfering signal level $(P_i)^*$, this may be substituted into Eq. (4.27) and $F(f_s, f_I)$ may be calculated. Thus:

$$F(f_s,f_i) = -2P_I{}^* (f_I) \text{ dBm} + \left[\frac{\Delta S_o}{S_o} \right]^* \text{dB} \qquad (4.44)$$

Once $F(f_s, f_i)$ has been evaluated for these specific conditions, the value may be substituted into Eq. (4.26) to give an expression for $F(f_s,f_i)$ for other interfering signal levels.

$$\frac{\Delta S_o}{S_o} \text{ dB} = 2P_I \text{ dBm} - 2P_I{}^*(f_i) \text{ dBm} + \left[\frac{\Delta S_o}{S_o} \right]^* \text{dB} \qquad (4.45)$$

If the CSO4 limits of MIL-STD-461 shown in Fig. 4.9 are used for the reference interfering signal level and $(\Delta S_o/S_o)^*$ is assumed to be -20 dB, default models are generated which will be used in the absence of a more complete user specification. The resulting default models are shown in Table 4.3.

4.3.2.2.2 Desensitization Models Based on Statistical Summary of Measured Data

Empirical data on receiver desensitization have been used to develop models to represent these effects. Figure 4.10 shows the general mathematical model for desensitization. The region of constant S/N (line segment 1 represents the signal-to-noise ratio when no interference is present. The signal-to-noise ratio without interference is:

$$S/N = P_D - P_{REF} + (S/N)_{REF} \qquad (4.46)$$

where,

P_D = desired signal level in dBm

P_{REF} = reference signal level in dBm

$(S/N)_{REF}$ = signal-to-noise ratio with reference signal level

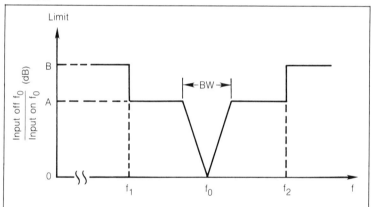

f_0 = Receiver-tuned frequency or band center for amplifiers

f_1 = Lowest tunable frequency of receiver band in use or the lowest frequency of amplifier passband

f_2 = Highest tunable frequency of receiver band in use or the highest frequency of amplifier passband

BW = Bandwidth between the 80 dB points of the receiver selectivity curve as defined in the test sample's technical requirements or the control plan

Limits:
1. The limit at A is 80 dB above the input level required to produce the standard reference output. (This limit shall not be used for amplifiers.)
2. The limit at B shall be set as follows:
   a. Receivers: 0 dBm applied directly to the receiver input terminals
   b. Amplifiers: The limit shall be as specified in the test sample's technical requirement or control plan. If no limit is defined in the above documents, the 0 dBm value shall be used.

Figure 4.9—Limits for CS04

Table 4.3—MIL-STD-461 Default Models for CW Desensitization (No AGC)

Amplifiers

For interfering signal frequencies outside of the amplifier passband; MIL-STD-461 specifies a limit of 0 dBm. Therefore, for:

$$f_I < f_L \text{ or } f_I > f_H$$

where, f_L = lowest operating frequency of amplifier

f_H = highest operating frequency of amplifier

$$P_I{}^* \text{ dBm} = 0 \text{ dBm}$$

$$\left[\frac{\Delta S_0}{S_0} \right]^* \text{ dB} = -20 \text{ dB}$$

therefore, $\dfrac{\Delta S_0}{S_0}$ dB = $2P_I$ dBm -20 dB

Receivers

For interfering signals within the receiver 80 dB bandwidth the default models are:

$$f_0 - \frac{BW}{2} \leqslant f_I \leqslant f_0 + \frac{BW}{2}$$

where, f_0 = receiver-tuned frequency

BW = receiver 80 dB bandwidth

$$P_I{}^* (f_I) \text{ dBm} = P_R \text{ dBm} + \frac{160}{BW} (f - f_0)$$

where, P_R dBm = receiver sensitivity

$$\left[\frac{\Delta S_0}{S_0} \right]^* \text{ dB} = -20 \text{ dB}$$

therefore,

$$\left[\frac{\Delta S_0}{S_0} \right] \text{ dB} = 2P_I \text{ dBm} - 2P_R \text{ dBm} - \frac{320}{BW} (f - f_0) - 20 \text{ dB}$$

For interfering signals outside of the receiver 80 dB bandwidth but within the overall tuning range of the receiver, models are:

$$f_L \leqslant f_I \leqslant f_0 + \frac{BW}{2} \text{ or } f_0 + \frac{BW}{2} \leqslant f_I \leqslant f_H$$

where, f_L = lowest operating frequency of receiver

f_H = highest operating frequency of receiver

Table 4.3—(continued)

P_{IZ}^* (f_I) dBm $= P_R$ dBm $+ 80$ dB

$\left[\dfrac{\Delta S_0}{S_0} \right]^* $ dB $= -20$ dB

therefore,

$\left[\dfrac{\Delta S_0}{S_0} \right]$ dB $= 2 \, P_I$ dBm $- 2P_R$ dBm $- 180$ dB

For interfering signals outside of the overall tuning range of the receiver the models are:

$$f_I < f_L \text{ or } f_I > f_H$$

where, P_I^* dBm $= 0$ dBm

$\left[\dfrac{\Delta S_0}{S_0} \right]^* $ dB $= -20$ dB

therefore,

$\left[\dfrac{\Delta S_0}{S_0} \right]$ dB $= 2P_I$ dBm $- 20$ dB

The breakpoint between line segments 1 and 2 is the receiver front-end saturation threshold. As the interfering signal power becomes larger than the threshold, the signal-to-noise begins to decrease. The rate of decrease with interfering signal power is mainly a function of signal-to-noise ratio before desensitization. Figure 4.11 shows the slope of the second line segment as a function of the desired signal level P_D in dBm relative to reference signal level P_{REF} in dBm. The desensitized signal-to-noise ratio may be computed:

$$(S/N)' = S/N - (P_A - P_{SAT})/R \qquad (4.47)$$

where, $(S/N)'$ = desensitized signal-to-noise ratio in dB
     S/N = signal-to-noise ratio in dB resulting from desired signal level without interference
     P_A = interfering signal power available are receiver input in dBm
     P_{SAT} = receiver front-end saturation level in dBm

4.35

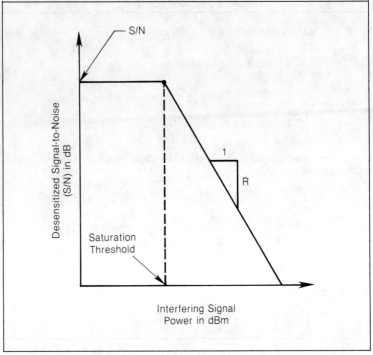

Figure 4.10—Desensitization Model

$$R = \text{desensitization rate (from Fig. 4.11)}$$

If more than one undesired signal is present at the receiver input, the composite signal should be considered in computing desensitization. In this case, the quantity in parentheses in Eq. (4.47) should be replaced by:

$$P_{EQ} = 10 \log \sum_{K}^{T} [\log^{-1}(P_{A_k} - P_{SAT_k})] \tag{4.48}$$

where,

P_{EQ} = composite effective interfering signal power in dBm

P_{A_k} = interfering signal power available at receiver input from kth transmitter in dBm (rms power)

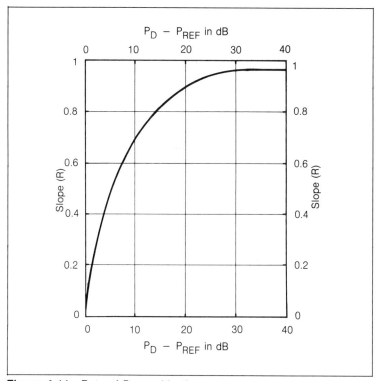

Figure 4.11—Rate of Desensitization

$$P_{SAT_k} = \text{receiver saturation level at the frequency of the kth transmitter in dBm}$$

$$T = \text{total number of undesired signals}$$

If the receiver saturation power level is not known from design considerations, then the following equation may be used to provide an estimate:

$$P_{SAT} = P_B + 10 \log (\Delta f/f_{OR}) \qquad (4.49)$$

$\Delta f/f_{OR}$ = interfering emission frequency separation relative to receiver-tuned frequency
P_B = reference value in dBm obtained from Fig. 4.12

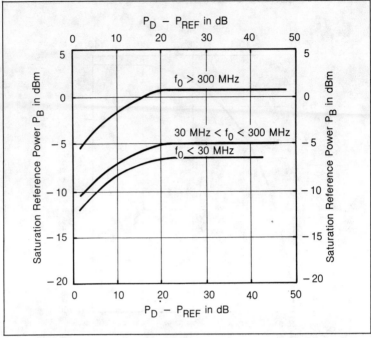

Figure 4.12—Saturation Reference Level

Illustrative Example 4.4

Consider a UHF communication receiver with a sensitivity P_{REF} of –110 dBm, for 6 dB (S + N)/N or 5 dB $(S/N)_{REF}$. Assume a desired signal level P_D of –90 dBm and an interfering signal P_i, power available P_A of –10 dBm, separated in frequency from the receiver by one percent of the receiver-tuned frequency. Calculate the resulting desensitized signal-to-noise ratio.

The signal-to-noise ratio without interference is given by Eq. (4.50):

$$S/N = P_D - P_{REF} + (S/N)_{REF} \tag{4.50}$$

$$= (-90 \text{ dBm}) - (-110 \text{ dBm}) + (5 \text{ dB}) = 25 \text{ dB}$$

The desensitized signal-to-noise ratio is given in Eq. (4.51):

$$\left(\frac{S}{N}\right)' = \frac{S}{N} - \frac{P_A - P_{SAT}}{R} \tag{4.51}$$

From Fig. 4.11, R = 0.9. The level for P_{SAT} is calculated from Eq. (4.52):

$$P_{SAT} = P_B + 10 \log (\Delta f/f_{OR}) \tag{4.52}$$

where,
$$P_B = +1 \text{ dBm from Fig. 4.12}$$

$$\Delta f/f_{OR} = 0.01 \text{ (statement of problem)}$$

$$\therefore P_{SAT} = -19 \text{ dBm}$$

Substituting into Eq. (4.51), the desensitized signal-to-noise ratio is:

$$\left(\frac{S}{N}\right)' = 25 \text{ dB} - \frac{(-10 \text{ dBm}) - (19 \text{ dBm})}{0.9}$$

$$= 25 \text{ dB} - \frac{9 \text{ dB}}{0.9}$$

$$= 15 \text{ dB}$$

Thus, an interfering signal of -10 dBm will reduce the gain of the receiver to the desired signal by 10 dB such that a S/N of 25 dB before EMI results in 15 dB after interference. This does not address other impacts of the interfering emissions.

4.3.2.3 Intermodulation Models

Because of nonlinearities within a superheterodyne receiver, two or more interfering signals may mix, i.e., intermodulate to produce signals at other frequencies. If these new frequencies are close enough to the receiver-tuned frequency, these signals may be amplified and detected by the same mechanism which processes the desired signal. Thus, possible degradation of performance may result.

The purpose of performing an intermodulation prediction is to identify pairs of transmitters within the electromagnetic environment which are emitting at frequencies that may cause such a disturbance in a particular receiver. The resulting signal-to-interference ratios are then computed. Intermodulation mixes which are considered in this section are second, third, fifth and seventh orders. (The order of an intermodulation product mix is determined by adding m and n of Eq. (4.53). Other than second-order (m = n = 1), the even-order products result in insignificant levels of EMI probabilities.) The seventh order is generally not considered to be a significant cause of interference.

4.3.2.3.1 Intermodulation Frequency Models

For an intermodulation product to cause interference, it must be transformed to a frequency within the IF passband for detection to occur. The method considered here is intermodulation in the RF amplifiers and first mixer which results in an intermodulation frequency at or near the receiver-tuned frequency f_{OR}.

Signals which are capable of producing intermodulation interference in a receiver must satisfy the following relationship:

$$|mf_1 \pm nf_2| = f_{OR} \pm B_R \qquad (4.53)$$

where, f_1 and f_2 = frequencies of two inferfering emission
$\qquad f_{OR}$ = receiver-tuned frequency
$\qquad B_R$ = IF bandwidth in which intermodulation products are significant
$\qquad$ m and n = integers

Equation (4.53) may be normalized to the receiver fundamental frequency and plotted to show the intermodulation relationship between two culprit signals:

$$\left| m\, \frac{f_1}{f_{OR}} \pm n\, \frac{f_2}{f_{OR}} \right| = \left| 1 \pm \frac{B_R}{f_{OR}} \right| \qquad (4.54)$$

Figure 4.13, obtained from Eq. (4.54), shows the resulting chart for second- and third-order intermodulation products. Intermodulation signal combinations falling on or near one of the lines are capable of generating an intermodulation product in the vicinity of the receiver-tuned frequency. For the purpose of EMC analysis,

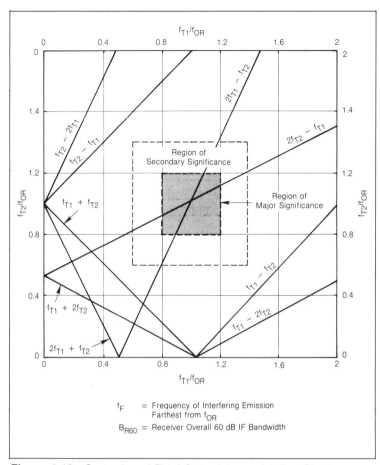

Figure 4.13—Second- and Third-Order Intermodulation Chart

the only signals that are considered to be potentially serious sources of intermodulation interference are those that are in the vicinity of the receiver frequency and produce intermodulation products which fall within the receiver overall 60 dB bandwidth around f_{OR}.

The following equations present the frequency criteria which two interfering signals must meet to offer potentially serious inter-modulation problems:

$$\left|\,|f_N \pm f_F| - f_{OR}\right| \leqslant B_{R60} \text{ (second order)}$$

$$\left|2f_N - f_F - f_{OR}\right| \leqslant B_{R60} \text{ (third order)}$$

$$\left|3f_N - 2f_F - f_{OR}\right| \leqslant B_{R60} \text{ (fifth order)}$$

$$\left|4f_N - 3f_F - f_{OR}\right| \leqslant B_{R60} \text{ (seventh order)}$$

Where, $\quad f_{OR}$ = receiver RF tuned frequency

$\qquad\quad f_N$ = frequency of interfering emission nearest to f_{OR}

$\qquad\quad f_F$ = frequency of interfering emission farthest from f_{OR}

The area on the chart marked region of major significance is particularly important because of the proximity of the signals to the receiver frequency. (RF bandwidths of superheterodyne receiver front ends are generally of low Q-factors (on the order of 10), whereas Q-factors of selectivity due to the IF transferred to the RF are typically on the order of 1,000.) Signals within this region will in general experience less RF selectivity (rejection) than will signals outside of the region. Thus, they are more likely to produce significant intermodulation products. The extent of this region is in general a function of RF selectivity, but the area indicated is representative of typical receivers.

Illustrative Example 4.5

Assume that an air-traffic control communication transmitter is tuned to 360 MHz. Determine other transmitter emission frequencies which may combine with the 360 MHz emission to produce second- and third-order intermodulation frequencies in a receiver used by the air-traffic controllers to intercept transmissions from pilots. The receiver is tuned to 300 MHz and co-located with the transmitter. For this situation, the transmitter frequency is 1.2 times the receiver frequency, i.e., $f_1/f_{OR} = 1.2$.

Referring to Fig. 4.13, potential second- and third-order intermodulation frequencies within $0 < f_2/f_{OR} < 2f_{OR}$ are:

$$\frac{f_2}{f_{OR}} = \begin{cases} 0.1 \text{ third order } (f_1 - 2f_2) \\ 0.2 \text{ second order } (f_1 - f_2) \\ 1.1 \text{ third order } (2f_2 - f_1) \\ 1.4 \text{ third order } (2f_1 - f_2) \end{cases}$$

4.42

The most significant frequencies from the standpoint of potential intermodulation interference for the specified situation are f_2/f_{OR} = 1.1 and 1.4. Thus, f_2 = 330 MHz and 420 MHz emission sources could be potentially hazardous to the air-to-ground receiver tuned to 300 MHz. This is especially true of the former emission. The frequencies corresponding to f_2/f_{OR} = 0.1 and 0.2 would be 30 MHz and 60 MHz respectively, and these frequencies should be sufficiently rejected by the RF front-end selectivity.

4.3.2.3.2 General Intermodulation Amplitude Models

It is convenient to express the intermodulation product in terms of an equivalent input power level, i.e., in terms of the input signal level at the tuned frequency required to produce an equivalent result in the receiver. Then IF selectivity protection can be applied to determine the resulting interference. The equivalent input signal P_E is a function of the power levels of the two interfering signals and an intermodulation factor (IMF) which depends on receiver nonlinearity, RF selectivity and gain. The resulting expression is:

$$P_E = mP_N + nP_F + IMF \qquad (4.56)$$

where,

P_E = equivalent input power in dBm
P_N and P_F = power in dBm at receiver input terminals resulting from interfering signals at frequencies f_N and f_F
f_N = frequency of emission nearest to f_{OR}
f_F = frequency of emission farthest from f_{OR}
m and n = constants associated with intermodulation order (m corresponds to the harmonic of the near signal and n corresponds to the harmonic of the far signal that are mixing to produce the intermodulation product)

In order to use Eq. (4.56), it is necessary to determine the intermodulation factor IMF for a specific receiver for the conditions of interest. MIL-STD-461 limits or spectrum signature data obtained under MIL-STD-449D provide information on intermodulation characteristics and may be used to determine the intermodulation factor as described in the following sections.

4.3.2.3.3 Intermodulation Models from MIL-STD-461

Intermodulation measurements made in accordance with MIL-STD-461 are performed so that the equivalent intermodulation signal is equal to the receiver sensitivity P_R ($P_D = P_R$) and the interfering signals are equal in amplitude. If this is the case, and if P_3^* (f_N, f_F) is defined as the power required for the signals at f_N and f_F to produce a standard response as a result of third-order intermodulation, then:

$$IMF(f_s, f_1, f_2) = P_R - 3P_3^*(F_N, f_F) \qquad (4.57)$$

Substituting Eq. (4.57) into Eq. (4.56) yields the result:

$$P_{IM} \text{ dBm} = 2P_N \text{ dBm} + P_F \text{ dBm} + P_R \text{ dBm} - 3P_3^*(f_N, f_F) \text{ dBm} \qquad (4.58)$$

The MIL-STD-461 CS03 limits for conducted susceptibility to intermodulation interference shown in Fig. 4.14 specify that no in-

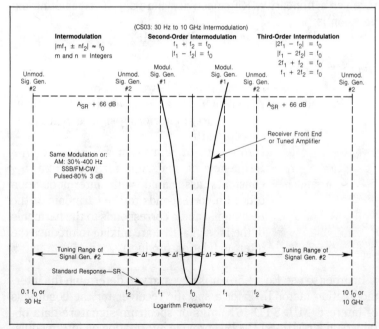

Figure 4.14—Intermodulation: Conducted Susceptibility Measurements

termodulation responses shall be observed when the interfering signals are 66 dB above the on-tune level required to produce a standard response.

$$P_3^*(f_1, f_2) = P_R \text{ dBm} + 66 \text{ dB} \qquad (4.59)$$

Substituting Eq. (4.59) into Eq. (4.58) leads to the third-order MIL-STD-461 default model:

$$P_{IM} \text{ dBm} = 2P_N \text{ dBm} + P_F \text{ dBm} - 2P_R \text{ dBm} - 198 \text{ dB} \qquad (4.60)$$

Equation (4.60) may be related to the interference margins by noting that:

$$\text{Interference margin} = P_{IM} \text{ dBm} - P_R$$

This will lead to the expression:

$$\text{Interference margin} = 2P_N \text{ dBm} + P_F \text{ dBm} - 3P_R \text{ dBm} - 198 \text{ dB} \qquad (4.61)$$

which is the default model used in the absence of complete user information.

The MIL-STD-461 CS03 limits may also be used to develop default models for second- and fifth-order intermodulation. The resulting default models are given below:

Second Order

$$P_{IM} \text{ dBm} = P_N \text{ dBm} + P_F \text{ dBm} - P_R \text{ dBm} - 132 \text{ dB} \qquad (4.62)$$

$$\text{Interference Margin} = P_N \text{ dBm} + P_F \text{ dBm} - 2 P_R \text{ dBm} - 132 \text{ dB} \qquad (4.63)$$

Fifth Order

$$P_{IM} \text{ dBm} = 3P_N \text{ dBm} + 2P_F \text{ dBm} - 4P_R \text{ dBm} - 330 \text{ dB} \qquad (4.64)$$

$$\text{Interference Margin} = 3P_N \text{ dBm} + 2P_F \text{ dBm} - 5P_R \text{ dBm} - 330 \text{ dB}$$

$$(4.65)$$

4.3.2.3.4 Intermodulation Models from Spectrum Signature Data

Intermodulation measurements made in accordance with MIL-STD-449D are performed so that the equivalent intermodulation signal is equal to the receiver sensitivity $P_R(f_{OR})$ ($P_E = P_R(f_{OR})$ when the two input interfering signals are equal in amplitude ($P_N = P_F$). $P^*(f_N, f_F)$ is defined as the power required for the two signals at f_N and f_F to cause a standard response (6dB signal-plus-noise-to-noise ratio at the output) as a result of intermodulation. The conditions for spectrum signature measurements are such that $P_N = P_F = P^*(f_N, f_F)$, and the intermodulation factor is given by:

$$\text{IMF} = P_R(f_{OR}) - (m + n)P^*(f_N, f_F) \qquad (4.66)$$

In order to use spectrum signature intermodulation data for EMI prediction, it is necessary to define what happens to the intermodulation factor as the input signals are changed to levels other than those for which spectrum signature measurements were performed.

As mentioned above, IMF is a function of receiver nonlinearity. It is essentially constant for signals below the saturation level and becomes a function of the signal level once the saturation level is exceeded.

For the purpose of calculating the equivalent input signal from spectrum signature data, intermodulation interference is divided into four separate cases.

Case I: situations where (1) the two signals producing intermodulation do not saturate the receiver front end, and (2) the desired signal and resulting intermodulation do not exceed the receiver AGC threshold. Many interfering situations fall into this category.

Case II: situations where the desired signal or the equivalent intermodulation input power exceeds the AGC threshold but the signals do not saturate the receiver front end

Case III: situations where the level of P_N exceeds the saturation level of the receiver front end

Case IV: situations where the level of P_F exceeds the saturation level of the receiver front end

Each of these cases is discussed below for third-order intermodulation. Within the region of signal levels that satisfy the conditions for Case I, the intermodulation factor is independent of the intermodulation input power levels. The resulting intermodulation factor then depends only on the frequency of the two intermodulation signals and may be determined from spectrum signature measurements by applying Eq. (4.66).

For third-order intermodulation situations that satisfy Case I conditions, the equivalent input signal is given by:

$$P_E = 2P_N + P_F + P_R(f_{OR}) - 3P^*(f_N, f_F) \qquad (4.67)$$

As the input power for either one or both intermodulation signals or the desired signal is increased, the resulting signal will exceed the receiver AGC threshold, and the receiver RF gain is reduced. For Case II situations, the reduction in RF gain is represented by a change in the intermodulation factor. The equivalent intermodulation input power is specified in terms of the Case I intermodulation equation and the RF gain change in dB (ΔG_{RF}) resulting from AGC:

$$P_E = 2\,P_N + P_F + P_R(f_{OR}) - 3P^*(f_N, F_F) + 2\Delta G_{RF} \qquad (4.68)$$

Intermodulation is defined by Eq. (4.68) for a Case II situation. However, to specify ΔG_{RF}, which is the AGC gain change preceding the nonlinearity, it is necessary to locate the major nonlinearity and define the method by which the AGC circuits distribute the gain control. Measurements on typical AM communication receivers in the HF, VHF and UHF bands indicate that approximately one half of the total AGC gain reduction (in dB) is applied to RF amplifiers.

For Case III, experimental observations indicate that as P_N is increased, a saturation level $P_{SAT}(f_N)$ is reached and that additional increases in P_N do not result in increases in the equivalent intermodulation input power. The condition ($P_N > P_{SAT}$) for equivalent intermodulation input power can be represented as a function of the Case I intermodulation equation and the amount by which P_N exceeds P_{SAT}:

$$P_E = 2P_N + P_F + P_R(f_{OR}) - 3P^*(f_N,f_F) - 2[P_N - P_{SAT}(f_N)] \tag{4.69}$$

The saturation level $P_{SAT}(f_N)$ was defined and discussed in Section 4.3.2.2.2.

Case IV is similar to Case III except that P_F is producing receiver saturation instead of P_N. For this case, the equivalent intermodulation input power is:

$$P_E = 2P_N + P_F + P_R(f_{OR}) - 3P^*(f_N,f_F) - (P_F - P_{SAT}(f_F)] \tag{4.70}$$

Again, the reader is referred to Section 4.3.2.2.2 for a discussion of the saturation level $P_{SAT}(f_F)$

If third-order intermodulation data are available, it should be used directly in Eqs. (4.67) through (4.70) to calculate the equivalent intermodulation input powers for specific interference conditions of interest. Interfering signal levels used in performing intermodulation measurements in accordance with MIL-STD-449D give $P^*(f_N, f_F)$ directly.

In general, $P_N \neq P_F$ in an EMI prediction situation; however, for MIL-STD-449D measurements, equal signal levels are used.

4.3.2.3.5 Statistical Summary Third-Order Intermodulation Models

The above discussion has described procedures for calculating third-order intermodulation levels when specific spectrum-signature measurements are available. Specific data will not always be available for every receiver included in a prediction problem. Therefore, in order to provide general information on receiver third-order intermodulation characteristics (which may be used in the absence of specific measured data), a summary of available intermodulation data is presented.

Figures 4.15, 4.16 and 4.17 show measured values of $P^*(f_N, f_F)$ as a function of frequency for available third-order intermodula-

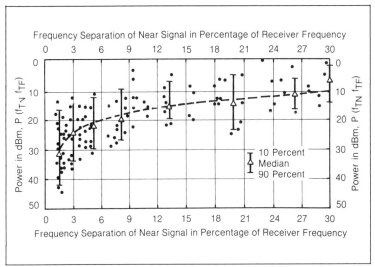

Figure 4.15—Summary of Third-Order Intermodulation Data, HF Receivers

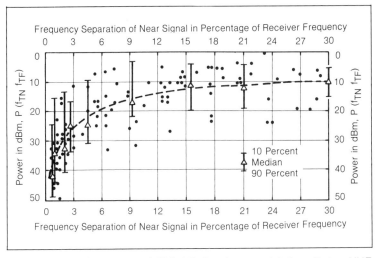

Figure 4.16—Summary of Third-Order Intermodulation Data, VHF Receivers

tion data for HF, VHF and UHF receivers. Measured values of $P^*(f_N, f_F)$ tend to exhibit a functional relationship with frequency, and in order to provide an indication of the range of observed $P^*(f_N, f_F)$ within each frequency band, the 10 percent, 50 percent

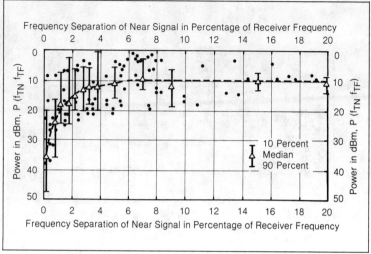

Figure 4.17—Summary of Third-Order Intermodulation Data, UHF Receivers

and 90 percent cumulative probability distribution values have been plotted. The percentages indicate the portion of the observed samples for which $P^*(f_N, f_F)$ exceeded the indicated value. For example, the 90 percent level represents the value of $P^*(f_N, f_F)$ such that 90 percent of the samples measured were above the indicated level. Therefore, if this level were used to specify intermodulation for a receiver, there is only a 10 percent probability that intermodulation EMI would result from signals below the specified value.

Equations 4.67 through 4.70 may be used to calculate equivalent intermodulation input power from spectrum signature data. If specific measurements are not available, an estimate of $P^*(f_N, f_F)$ may be found from the combined data plots shown in Figs. 4.15, 4.16 and 4.17.

Illustrative Example 4.6

To illustrate how Eqs. (4.67) through (4.70) may be used to calculate receiver intermodulation interference conditions, consider a typical UHF AM voice communications receiver. It has a sensitivity $P_R(f_{OR})$, of -110 dBm; an AGC threshold level of -80 dBm and a front-end saturation level of 0 dBm. Assume interfering signals at frequencies f_N and f_F, such that a third-order inter-modulation product is produced at the receiver-tuned frequency, e.g., $f_N/f_{OR} = 1.02$ and $f_F/f_{OR} = 1.04$. Calculate the equivalent input signal for the following interfering signal situations A through D:

Situation A: $P_N = -20$ dBm and $P_F = -15$ dBm

Both P_N and P_F are below the saturation level. Therefore, either a Case I or Case II condition exists as defined above. To determine whether Case I or Case II is applicable, it is assumed that Case I applies. If the resulting P_E is above the AGC threshold, Case II must be used. For Case I, the equivalent input signal is given by Eq. (4.67):

$$P_E = 2P_N + P_F + P_R(f_{OR}) - 3P^*(f_N,f_F)$$

The value of $P^*(f_N, f_F)$ can be found directly from receiver third-order intermodulation measurements or may be estimated from the summary of data presented in Fig. 4.16. For example, if 90 percent values (90 percent probability that the calculated interference condition will not be exceeded) are used, $P(f_N, f_F) = -20$ dBm for $f_N/f_{OR} = 1.02$ substituting into Eq. (4.67):

$$P_E = 2(-20 \text{ dBm}) + (-15 \text{ dBm}) + (-110 \text{ dBm}) - \\ 3(-20 \text{ dBm}) = -105 \text{ dBm}$$

This result means that the two interfering signals produce a third-order intermodulation response that is equivalent to a co-channel signal level of -105 dBm. This is 5 dB above the receiver sensitivity but still below the AGC threshold. Thus, Case I does apply.

Situation B: $P_N = -5$ dBm; $P_F = -10$ dBm

Again both P_N and P_F are below the saturation level. For Case I:

$$P_E = 2P_N + P_F + P_R(f_{OR}) - 3P^*(f_N, f_F)$$

$$= 2(-5 \text{ dBm}) + (-10 \text{ dBm}) + (-110 \text{ dBm}) - 3(-20 \text{ dBm})$$

$$= -70 \text{ dBm}$$

This is 10 dB above the AGC threshold and thus Case II applies. For Case II:

$$P_E = 2P_N + P_F + P_R(f_{OR}) - 3P^*(f_N,f_F) + 2\Delta GRF$$

In order to evaluate Eq. (4.68) it is necessary to determine the RF gain change, ΔG_{RF}, resulting from AGC. Typically, the AGC will reduce the total gain by the amount that the signal exceeds the AGC threshold. In this case the total gain would be decreased by 10 dB, i.e., $(-70\ dBm) - (-80\ dBm)$. Assuming that one-half of the total gain reduction (in dB) was applied to the RF amplifiers, then ΔG_{RF} is -5 dB. Therefore:

$$P_E = 2(-5\ dBm) + (-10\ dBm) + (-110\ dBm) - 3(-20\ dBm) + 2(-5\ dBm) = -80\ dBm$$

This means that the intermodulation response is equivalent to a co-channel signal of -80 dBm which is 30 dB above the receiver sensitivity.

Situation C: $P_N = +10\ dBm$; $P_F = -40\ dBm$

P_N is now above the saturation threshold, while P_F is not. Thus, a Case III situation exists and Eq. (4.69) applies:

$$\begin{aligned}
P_E &= 2P_N + P_F + P_R(f_{OR}) - 3^*P(f_N,f_F) - 2[P_N - P_{SAT}(f_N)] \\
&= 2(+10\ dBm) + (-40\ dBm) + (-110\ dBm) - \\
&\quad 3(-20\ dBm) - 2[(10\ dBm) - (0\ dBm)] \\
&= -90\ dBm
\end{aligned}$$

Therefore, the intermodulation response for this situation is equivalent to a co-channel signal of -90 dBm which is 20 dB above the receiver sensitivity.

Situation D: $P_N = -40\ dBm$; $P_F = +10\ dBm$

This is clearly a Case IV situation and thus Eq. (4.70) applies:

$$\begin{aligned}
P_E &= 2P_N + P_F + P_R(f_{OR}) - 3P^*(f_N,f_F) - [P_F - P_{SAT}(f_F)] \\
&= 2(-40\ dBm) + (+10\ dBm) + (-110\ dBm) -
\end{aligned}$$

3(−20 dBm) − [10 dBm − (0 dBm)]

= −130 dBm

Therefore, the intermodulation response for this situation is equivalent to a co-channel signal of −130 dBm. This is 20 dB below the receiver sensitivity and is inconsequential.

4.3.2.4 Cross-Modulation Models

Strong signals in a receiver adjacent-signal region may generate significant cross-modulation interference. In this type of EMI, modulation is transferred from the undesired signal to the desired one. Generation of cross modulation is a nonlinear effect and requires that the interfering source exhibit amplitude variations (modulation). Receivers whose desired intelligence is not transmitted by amplitude variations are not affected by nonlinear cross modulation.

Frequency requirements for formation of cross-modulation interference are not as restrictive as they are for intermodulation. A single interfering signal at any frequency in the adjacent-signal region may cause cross modulation resulting in degradation of performance. In this respect, cross modulation would seem to be the more serious problem. Fortunately, the effect of the desired signal on the amplitude of the cross-modulation product may limit the signal-to-interference ratio, making cross modulation less important than intermodulation.

Cross modulation resulting from AM, double-sideband interference is represented by:

$$CMR = -2P_A + CMF \qquad (4.71)$$

where,

CMR = cross-modulation ratio, which is a measure of the output signal-to-interference ratio in dB
P_A = interfering signal power available in dBm
CMF = cross-modulation factor

Equation (4.71) applies to a situation where both the desired and interfering signal are AM double sideband and have the same percent modulation. The equation applies primarily to S/I ratios of 6 dB or more. For S/I ratios of less than 6 dB it is important to realize that the interfering signal may overmodulate the carrier and thereby produce distortion products.

4.3.2.4.1 Cross-Modulation Models Based on MIL-STD-461

The limits for conducted susceptibility resulting from cross modulation are specified in MIL-STD-461 (CS05) as shown in Fig. 4.18. If these limits are used, the following default models result. From MIL-STD-461, the interfering signal power will be 66 dB above some standard reference, assumed to be the receiver sensitivity:

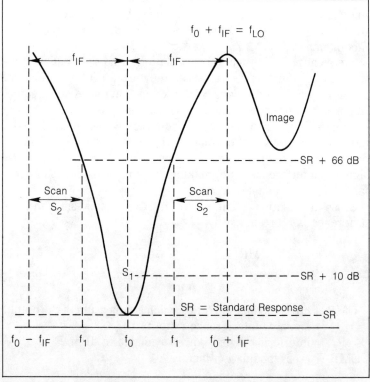

Figure 4.18—Cross Modulation (Conducted Susceptibility CS05)

$$P^*(f_I)dBm = P_R \text{ dBm} + 66 \text{ dB} \qquad (4.72)$$

and, $$CMR^* \text{ dB} = 0 \qquad (4.73)$$

Then the CMF may be written (see Eq. 4.42):

$$CMF \text{ dB} = 2P_R \text{ dBm} + 132 \text{ dB} \qquad (4.74)$$

and the default model is: (see Eq. 4.41)

$$CMR \text{ dB} = -2P_1 \text{ dBm} + 2P_R + 132 \text{ dB} \qquad (4.75)$$

It is possible to define an interference margin for cross modulation in much the same way as the desensitization interference margin was defined. The interference margin will be defined as the amount by which the CMR drops below a reference of 20 dB, the minimum observable cross modulation. Equation (4.76) may then be written using this criterion:

$$\text{Interference Margin} = CMR \text{ dB} - 20 \text{ dB} \qquad (4.76)$$

The equations just presented describe modulation of a desired AM signal by an interfering AM signal. Expressions similar to those given above may be derived for other types of cross modulation, although the derivation will not be repeated here.

4.3.2.4.2 Statistical Summary Cross-Modulation Models

Statistical analysis of measured data on typical receivers provides one source for the cross modulation parameter. Figure 4.19 shows the resulting cross-modulation parameter as a function of percent frequency separation for both desired and interfering signals and the operating frequency of the victim receiver.

Illustrative Example 4.7

For AM, double-sideband desired and interfering signals with equal percentages of modulation, consider an HF receiver and an interfering signal P_A of -30 dBm and a frequency separation of 1 percent. The cross-modulation factor CMF is found to be -40

from Fig. 4.18. From Eq. (4.71), the cross-modulation signal-to-interference ratio is:

$$
\begin{aligned}
CMR &= -2P_A + CMF \\
&= [-2(-30) + (-40)] \text{ dB} \\
&= +60 - 40 \text{ dB} = +20 \text{ dB}
\end{aligned}
$$

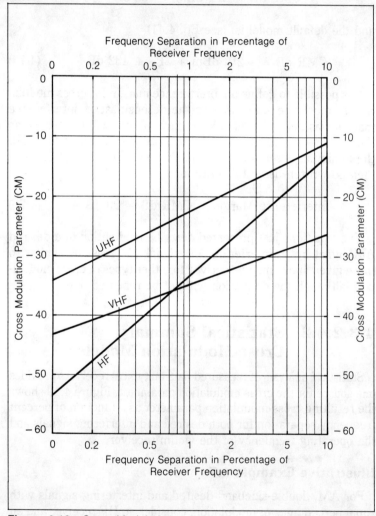

Figure 4.19—Cross Modulation

4.56

4.4 Out-of-Band Susceptibility Threshold Models

A receiver is subjected to a large number of undesired out-of-band signals. These signals can create interference by any one of several methods. Superheterodyne receivers are generally most susceptible to out-of-band signals that are capable of being mixed and translated to the IF passband frequencies which then produce a response. Either TRF or crystal-video receivers may respond to any out-of-band signal which is not adequately rejected by the receiver RF selectivity.

There are several ways that an out-of-band emission can be translated to one of the passband frequencies of a superheterodyne receiver. The most significant of these occurs in the first-mixer stage. Here, the desired signal is heterodyned with the local oscillator (LO) to translate the incoming signal to the intermediate frequency. In addition to desired signals, interfering emissions at many different frequencies are capable of being heterodyned with the LO or other signals and translated to the receiver IF. The amplitude of responses produced in this manner is directly proportional to the strength of the original signals. Because the level of the LO is typically on the order of 120 dB greater than the desired and interfering signals which are present at the input to the first mixer stage, heterodyne products which involve the LO are much larger in amplitude than those heterodyne products which do not involve the LO. Thus, superheterodyne receivers are most susceptible to out-of-band signals that heterodyne with the LO to produce a product in or near the IF passband.

In this volume, the term **spurious response** as applied to superheterodyne receivers refers specifically to those undesired responses that result from the mixing of the LO and an undesired emission. Those input interfering frequencies which are capable of appearing at the IF as a result of mixing with the LO are known as "spurious-response frequencies." The amount of power necessary to cause interference at any particular spurious-response frequency is a function of receiver susceptibility to the response.

4.4.1 Receiver Spurious Response Frequency

In general, superheterodyne receivers are susceptible to out-of-band signals that can generate a spurious response in the receiver. In order to predict the effect of mixer-generated spurious responses on receiver interference, it is necessary to use mathematical models that define frequencies at which spurious responses occur.

In order for a spurious response to be generated in a superheterodyne receiver, it is necessary that the interfering signal or one of its harmonics mix with the LO or one of its harmonics to produce an output in the receiver IF passband. (The signal and local oscillator harmonics that contribute to spurious responses are produced in the mixer as a result of its nonlinear operation.) Frequencies (f_{SR}) which are capable of producing spurious responses for a single conversion superheterodyne, are:

$$f_{SR} = \left| \frac{pf_{LO} \pm f_{IF}}{q} \right| \tag{4.77}$$

or,

$$f_{IF} = |pf_{LO} \pm qf_{SR}| \tag{4.78}$$

where, p = harmonic number of local oscillator
q = harmonic number of interfering signal
f_{LO} = LO frequency
f_{IF} = intermediate frequency

As shown in Eq. (4.77), there are two response frequencies for each value of p and q. The response pairs result from mixing which produces outputs at frequencies corresponding to both the sum and difference of harmonics of the local oscillator and the input signal.

The p, q relation given in Eq. (4.77) is the mathematical model used in interference analysis for determining spurious response frequencies of a receiver.

Investigators have concluded that Eq. (4.77) constitutes the majority of spurious responses for a superheterodyne receiver. Tests have shown that in multiconversion type receivers, spurious responses created by the second and higher order conversion processes occurring in more than one stage may be present but are not a serious source of interference susceptibility.[6]

Signal levels required to produce $q = 1$ responses (responses due to the fundamental of the interfering emission) are generally lower in amplitude than the signal levels required to produce high-order q responses. Those responses for which q = 2 are less significant than q = 1, and q = 3 responses are lower than q = 2 responses as illustrated in Fig. 4.20. A logical subdivision of receiver responses is therefore by q.

Integer values of p are analogous to harmonic number of the LO. For a fixed q, if the IF is small compared to the LO frequency (which is often the case), responses generated by Eq. (4.77) with both a plus and minus sign may be combined into one group.

For a TRF or crystal video receiver, the susceptibility to out-of-band signals is not as frequency dependent as it is for the superheterodyne receiver. The out-of-band susceptibility threshold is a relatively smooth function of frequency for TRF and crystal-video receivers instead of the discrete function of frequency which is characteristic of superheterodyne receivers.

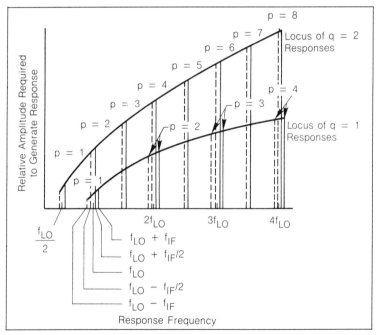

Figure 4.20—Spurious Response Generation

Illustrative Example 4.8

To illustrate the use of Eq. (4.77) in calculating receiver spurious response frequencies, consider a radar receiver used for aeronautical navigation with a fundamental frequency of 1,500 MHz, a 60 MHz IF and a local oscillator frequency of 1,560 MHz. The spurious-response frequencies may be calculated directly from Eq. (4.77) by substituting 1,560 MHz for f_{LO} and 60 MHz for f_{IF}, and letting p and q assume integer values over the frequency range of interest. The results are tabulated in Table 4.4.

Illustrative Example 4.9

A VHF receiver, tuned to 130 MHz in the aeronautical band, experiences interference from a nearby L-band radar transmitting at 1,250 MHz. The radar antenna modulation is heard in the receiver (the main and side lobes are audible when the radar antenna is scanning by, in other words, bore-sighting) at a P_{RF} rate of 800 pps—equal to that of the radar. Since the receiver has a 30 MHz IF(f_{IF}) and the LO (f_{LO}) is situated above the main response, is this an example of heterodyne spurious response (out-of-band susceptibility) in the receiver?

From the above, the receiver LO frequency is $f_{LO} = f_{OR} + f_{IF}$ = 130 MHz + 30 MHz = 160 MHz. Applying Eq. (4.77) for the eighth harmonic (p = 8) of the receiver's L0 and q = 1, yields:

$$f_{SR} = \frac{8 \times 160 \text{ MHz} \pm 30 \text{ MHz}}{1} = 1,250 \text{ and } 1,310 \text{ MHz}$$

Table 4.4—Spurious Response Frequencies for Radar Tuned to 1,500 MHz

P	Sign of IF	Spurious q = 1	Response q = 2	Frequencies q = 3
1	+	1,620	810	540
	−	Tuned Frequency	750	540
2	+	3,180	1,590	1,060
	−	3,060	1,530	1,020
3	+	4,740	2,370	1,580
	−	4,620	2,310	1,540
4	+	6,300	3,150	2,100
	−	6,180	3,090	2,060
5	+	7,860	3,930	2,620
	−	7,740	3,870	2,580

Thus, the 1,250 MHz radar is causing EMI to the receiver by heterodyning, spurious-response action. (Note that EMI can probably be eliminated by inserting a low-pass filter in the receiver antenna terminals. The filter's cutoff frequency should be between 200 and 500 MHz.)

4.4.2 General Spurious Response Amplitude Models

Basic characteristics of superheterodyne receiver susceptibility to spurious responses are illustrated in Fig. 4.21. It is noted that receiver spurious responses are similar in many respects to transmitter harmonic outputs. The following two principals serve as a basis for the spurious response models used in the amplitude analysis, EMI prediction process.[7]

Average Susceptibility Threshold: For each value of q in Eq. (4.77) or (4.78) the average spurious response susceptibility level increases with local oscillator harmonic number. The average level may be represented by one or more straight line segments when plotted as a function of logarithm of local oscillator harmonic number.

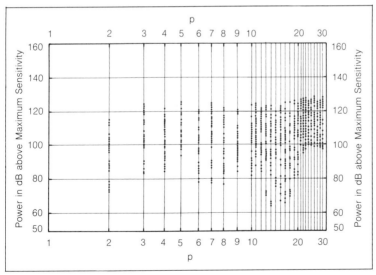

Figure 4.21—Measured Spurious Response Levels for a Typical Receiver

Standard Deviation: A number of random variables introduce a random deviation in the level required to produce interference at a particular response frequency. This random deviation is normally distributed and the standard deviation is independent of the response frequency.

The resultant model for the average spurious response susceptibility threshold for a specified q can now be expressed as:

$$P_R(f_{SR}) = P_R(f_{OR}) + I \log p + J \qquad (4.79)$$

where,

$P_R(f_{SR})$ = average spurious response susceptibility threshold in dBm for specific p

$P_R(f_{OR})$ = receiver co-channel susceptibility threshold in dBm

p = local oscillator harmonic number

I and J = constants to be determined for each receiver type

(I and J are the slope and intercept of the spurious response susceptibility function. I is given in dB/decade and J is given as dB above the fundamental sensitivity.)

Although a single straight line is adequate for representing q = 1 responses of many receivers, in some cases it may be necessary to use a broken line consisting of two or more segments. In this case, each line segment represents the receiver spurious response function over a particular frequency range. Different values of the constants I and J must be determined for each line segment.

The amplitude-analysis receiver model used for superheterodyne, TRF and crystal-video receivers tuned to any frequency f_{OR} is:

$$P_R(f) = P_R(f_{OR}) + I \log (f/f_{OR}) + J \qquad (4.80)$$

Equation (4.80) presents a general expression that is used to describe the average receiver susceptibility threshold to out-of-band interference over a wide range of frequencies. In order to apply the model to a specific problem, it is necessary to determine the parameters I and J for the particular receiver or receiver type being considered. Also it is necessary to determine the standard deviation $\sigma_R(f_{SR})$ associated with variations about the average susceptibility level. Thus, the entire range of probabilities may be determined.

These parameters [I, J and $\sigma_R(f_{SR})$] may be determined from statistical summaries of available data, receiver specifications or analysis of specific measured data. Each of these means of determining out-of-band receiver susceptibility models is discussed in the following sections.

4.4.3 Spurious Response Amplitude Models Based on MIL-STD-461

One source of information regarding receiver spurious-response levels is provided by applicable equipment specifications or standards. In certain EMC analysis problems, especially those involving system planning and design, it is desirable to identify EMI problems that will exist if the equipment conforms or fails to conform to certain specifications or standards. If this type of analysis is desired, the receiver model may be used to formulate default equations for spurious responses based on the (CS04) limits of MIL-STD-461 which specify limits for spurious responses as shown in Fig. 4.22. These limits will be used to solve for I and J in the various regions of interest. If this is done, the default models given in Table 4.5 will result.

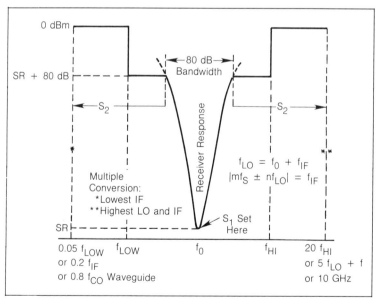

Figure 4.22—Rejection of Undesired Signals (CS04 & CS08)

Table 4.5—MIL-STD-461 Models for Spurious Responses

For interfering signals within the receiver 80 dB bandwidth:

$$(f_0 - BW/2 < - f_{sr} < f_0 + BW/2)$$

$$P_{SR} \text{ dBm} = P_R \text{ dBm} + \frac{160}{BW}(f - f_0)$$

For interfering signals outside the receiver 80 dB bandwidth but within the overall tuning range of the receiver, i.e., $f_L \leqslant f_{SR} \leqslant f_0 - BW/2$ or $f_0 + BW/2 \leqslant f_{SR} \leqslant f_H$:

$$P_{SR} \text{ dBm} = P_R \text{ dBm} + 80 \text{ dB}$$

For interfering signals outside the tuning range of the receiver (for $f_{SR} < f_L$ or $f_{SR} > f_H$):

$$P_{SR} \text{ dBm} = 0 \text{ dBm}$$

where, $\quad f_0$ = receiver-tuned frequency

$\quad\quad BW$ = receiver 80 dB bandwidth

$\quad\quad P_R$ = receiver sensitivity

$\quad\quad f_L$ = lowest tuned frequency of receiver

$\quad\quad f_H$ = highest tuned frequency of receiver

The equations presented in the table describe the response if q = 1. As stated previously, P_{SR} (in the region outside the 80 dB bandwidth) will be 15 dB lower if $q = 2$ and 20 dB lower if $Q = 3$ or 4. Inside the 80 dB bandwidth region, the default equations for higher values of q will be the same as the $q = 1$ equation.

Illustrative Example 4.10

A receiver having a sensitivity of -115 dBm must be analyzed. Based on MIL-STD-461, the receiver susceptibility threshold to signals that are outside of the 80 dB bandwidth but still within the overall tuning range of the receiver the susceptibility level would be -35 dBm (-115 dBm + 80 dB) over the frequency range of interest. Thus, predicted EMI emission levels, referred to the receiver input terminals [see Eq. (1.2)], less than -35 dBm would be eliminated by the amplitude analysis process.

4.4.4 Statistical Summary of Spurious Response

When specific measured receiver data are not available, one alternative for obtaining an out-of-band susceptibility model for use in the amplitude analysis process is to derive statistical summaries from data for groups of similar receivers. From these summaries, mathematical models are developed which are representative of a group or class of receivers. In the absence of measured data, pertinent group models should be used for the receiver under study. Statistical summary models have been evaluated from available spectrum signature data and the applicable constants are summarized in Table 4.6.[8] The first row entry presents values for I, J and $\sigma_R(f_{SR})$ derived from the data for all receivers combined. The second, third and fourth row entries provide values for I, J and $\sigma_R(f_{SR})$ which are found by grouping receiver data on the basis of the fundamental frequency range of operation. The appropriate set of values for I, J and $\sigma_R(f_{SR})$ may be used in Eqs. (4.79) or (4.80) to model receiver spurious response susceptibility levels for frequencies above the fundamental. The resulting average spurious response susceptibility level for receivers within each of the indicated frequency ranges are presented in Table 4.7.

Table 4.6—Constants for Receiver Spurious Response Models Obtained from Statistical Summary of Available Data*

Receiver Category Based on Fundamental Frequency	Summary Values for Constants in Spurious Response Amplitude Models		
	I dB/Decade	J dB above Fundamental	$\sigma_R\,(f_{SR})$ dB
All Receivers Combined	35	75	20
Below 30 MHz (MF & HF)	25	85	15
30 MHz to 300 MHz (VHF)	35	85	15
Above 300 MHz (UHF & SHF)	40	60	15

*These constants apply to q = 1 responses. For q = 2 responses and frequencies above the receiver fundamental add 15 dB to J, and for q = 3 responses add 20 dB to J.

Illustrative Example 4.11

To illustrate the application of receiver models derived from statistical summary of available data, consider a VHF communication receiver having a co-channel susceptibility (S = N noise level) equal to -115 dBm. The constants associated with the summary model are presented in Table 4.6. In Eq. (4.80) they are used to obtain the representation for receiver average susceptibility to $q = 1$ responses. Thus, since:

$$P_R(f) = P_R(f_{OR}) + I \log (f/f_{OR}) + J \text{ dBm}$$

and,

$$P_R(f_{OR}) = -115 \text{ dBm}, I = 35 \text{ and } J = 85 \text{ dB:}$$
$$P_R(f) = -115 + 35 \log (f/f_{OR}) + 85 \text{ dBm}$$
$$= -30 + 35 \log (f/f_{OR})$$

Table 4.7—Summary of Spurious Response Average Susceptibility

Local Oscillator Harmonic Number, (p)	Spurious Response Average Susceptibility Threshold (dB above Fundamental Sensitivity; $q = 1$)			
	All Receivers Combined $\sigma_R(f_{SR}) = 20$ dB	Receivers Categorized According to Tuned Frequency		
		Below 30 MHz $\sigma_R(f_{SR}) = 15$ dB	30 to 300 MHz $\sigma_R(f_{Sr}) = 15$ dB	Above 300 MHz $\sigma_R(f_{SR}) = 15$ dB
1 (image)	75	85	85	60
2	85	93	95	72
3	92	97	102	79
4	96	100	106	84
5	99	102	109	88
6	102	104	112	91
7	105	106	115	94
8	107	107	117	96
9	108	109	118	98
10	110	110	120	100

The resulting average receiver susceptibility function of this Eq. (4.80) is plotted in Fig. 4.23 for values of f/f_{OR} between one and ten. There is a 50 percent probability that the receiver will be susceptible to interfering signals equal to the level shown by the line. For example, a potential interfering signal source at a response frequency in the vicinity of four times the receiver-tuned frequency will produce 50 percent probability of interference if its level is -9 dBm (see 106 dB down in Table 4.7).

As explained in Chapter 3 for transmitter harmonic radiations, receiver susceptibility is represented in probabilistic terms. For the particular type of receiver being considered in this example, the standard deviation associated with out-of-band susceptibility is listed as 15 dB in Table 4.6. The associated probabilities of the receiver being susceptible to various interfering signal levels relative to the average value are presented in Fig. 4.24.

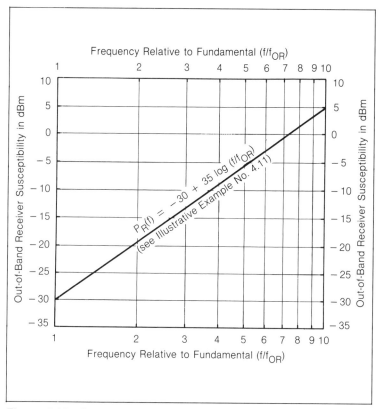

Figure 4.23—Sample Out-of-Band Susceptibility

There is only a 16 percent probability for $\sigma_R(f_{SR}) = 1$ that the receiver susceptibility threshold will exceed the average values by more than one standard deviation (15 dB) in Fig. 4.24. Conversely, there is an 84 percent probability (100 percent - 16 percent) that the receiver susceptibility threshold will exceed a level that is one standard deviation (15 dB) below the average level. Probabilities associated with other susceptibility threshold (relative to the average level) are obtained directly from Fig. 4.24.

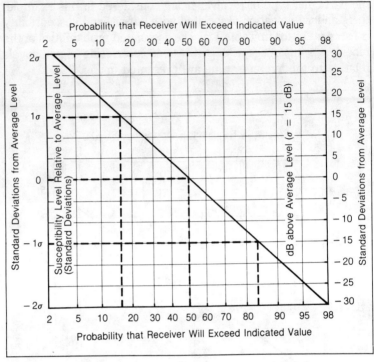

Figure 4.24—Probability Distribution for Receiver Susceptibility

4.4.5 Spurious Response Amplitude Models from Measured Data

If specific measured data are available on receiver susceptibility to out-of-band interference, these data provide one of the best sources for determining the constants in Eqs. (4.79) and (4.80) used in the receiver model. Techniques used to determine specific models from measured data are the same as those described in Chapter 3 for transmitters. Therefore, rather than repeating the technique here, the reader is referred to Chapter 3.

4.5 Analysis of Receiver Performance

One of the most important and difficult stages in an EMI prediction is translating the results into a form that is meaningful from the standpoint of operational performance. Because the evaluation of this performance requires consideration of many factors other than just those associated with the major elements of EMI prediction (transmitters, receivers, antennas and propagation), the specific considerations, models and techniques used in operational performance evaluation are presented separately in Chapter 7.

The basic approach used in performance prediction and the major factors that must be considered in using this approach to specify receiver performance are illustrated in Fig. 4.25. Receiver characteristics that influence performance are noise, dynamic range, desensitization, selectivity (RF, IF and output), adjacent-channel susceptibility, intermodulation, cross modulation and spurious-response susceptibility. For any particular interfering situation, receiver performance is influenced by the major receiver effects that occur in each stage of the receiver (RF, mixer, IF, detector and output).

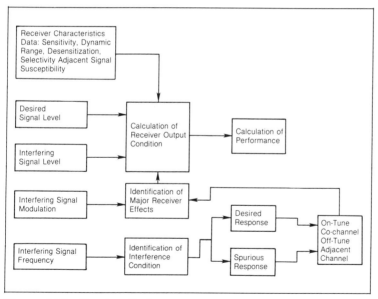

Figure 4.25—Receiver Performance Model

For any given interfering situation, it is possible to restrict consideration to a few predominant effects. Once the predominant effects are identified, the basic receiver characteristics obtained from measurements, theoretical analysis or a combination may be used to translate the desired and interfering input signals through the receiver to provide a description of the receiver output. The output factors that must be described in order to determine performance are the level, spectrum and time characteristics of (1) the desired signal, (2) the receiver noise, (3) the interfering signal and (4) products resulting from nonlinear mixing of the desired and interfering signal.

The next step is to define the performance resulting from the receiver output conditions. There are various performance measures that may be used and the particular type that is applicable to a given situation depends on the type of service being produced by the receiver. Examples of performance measures are articulation scores for voice communication receivers, error rate for digital data, scope conditions for radar receivers, etc. The reader is referred to Chapter 7 for a more detailed discussion of the various performance measures and for techniques for evaluating operational performance for a particular interference situation.

4.6 References

1. Babcock, L.F., "Equipment Operational Parameter Variability," *Proceedings of the Tenth Tri-Service Conference on EMC*, November 1964.
2. Volterra, V., *Theory of Functionals and of Integral and Integro-Differential Equations* (London: Blackie & Sons, 1930).
3. Wiener, N., "Response of a Non-Linear Device to Noise," M.I.T. Radiation Laboratory Report V-165, April 1942.
4. "Nonlinear System Modeling and Analysis with Applications to Communications Receivers," Signatron, RADC-TR-73-178, June 1978.
5. Spina, J.F., and Weiner, D.D., *Sinusoidal Analysis and Modeling of Weekly Nonlinear Circuits* (New York: Van Nostrand Reinhold Co., 1980).
6. Manuscript of Catalog, Vol. 5, "Interference Characteristics, Interference Suppression and Compatible Frequency Selection," Georgia Institute of Technology, Contract No. DA-36-039-SC-74855, October 1961.

7. Heisler, Jr., "Preparation of Statistical Input Functions for Interference Prediction," 7th Armour Research Foundation Conference, Chicago, 1961.
8. Duff, W.G., and Edwards, J.H., "Summary of Equipment EMC Characteristics," *1970 IEEE Regional EMC Symposium Record*, San Antonio.

4.7 Bibliography

1. Capraro, G.T., "Spurious Response Identification and Generation," Technical Memorandum No. EMC-TM-67-15, Rome Air Development Center, December 1967.
2. "Characteristics of USAF Electronic Equipment for Ground Use," RADC Technical Report 52-14, RADC, USAF Griffiss AFB, Electronic Development Div., New York, 1952.
3. Duff, W.G., et. al., "Transmitter and Receiver FOM Scoring," *1974 IEEE EMC Symposium Record*, (New York: IEEE, 1974).
4. Duff, W.G., "EMC Figure of Merit for Receivers," *1969 IEEE EMC Symposium Record* (New York: IEEE, 1969).
5. Duff, W.G., and Edwards, J.H., "Summary of Equipment EMC Characteristics," *1970 IEEE Regional EMC Symposium Record* (New York: IEEE, 1970).
6. Duff, W.G., et. al., "Prediction Routine Studies, Volume II, Intermodulation Analyses," RADC-TR-68-345, 1968.
7. Duff, W.G., et. al., "An Electromagnetic Compatibility Figure of Merit (EMC FOM) for Single-Channel, Voice Communications Equipment," *IEEE Transactions on EMC*, Vol. EMC-17, No. 1, February 1975.
8. Duff, W.G., et. al., "Nonlinear Effects Models for the Intrasystem Electromagnetic Compatibility/Intrasystem Analysis Program," *1979 IEEE EMC Symposium Record* (New York: IEEE, 1979).
9. Duff, W.G., "Broadband Nontunable Receiver for EMI Measurements," *1984 IEEE EMC Symposium Record* (New York: IEEE, 1984).
10. Duff, W.G., et. al., "EMC Design Criteria," *Southeastern Regional EMC Symposium Record* (New York: IEEE, 1969).
11. Duff, W.G., et. al., "Adjacent Signal Interference," *Communication Designer's Digest*, December 1968.

12. Duff, W.G., et. al., "Detecting and Locating Sources of Inter-modulation Interference," *1984 IEEE EMC Symposium Record* (New York: IEEE, 1984).
13. Duff, W.G., et. al., "Determination of Receiver Susceptibility Parameters," *1970 IEEE EMC Symposium Record* (New York: IEEE, 1970).
14. "Electromagnetic Interference Characteristics Requirements for Equipment," MIL-STD-461A, August 1968.
15. Heisler, K.G., Jr., "Preparation of Statistical Input Functions for Interference Prediction," *Proceedings of the Seventh Armour Research Foundation Conference*, 1961.
16. "Military Standard Radio Frequency Spectrum Characteristics, Measurement of," MIL-STD-449C.
17. "Nonlinear System Modeling and Analysis with Applications to Communications Receivers," RADC-TR-73-178, June 1978.
18. Spina, J.F., and Weiner, D.D., *Sinusoidal Analysis and Modeling of Weakly Nonlinear Circuits* (New York: Van Nostrand Reinhold Co., 1980).
19. Volterra, V., *Theory of Functionals and of Integral and Integro-Differential Equations* (London: Blackie and Sons Ltd., 1930).
20. Wass, C.A., "A Table of Intermodulation Products," *IEEE Journal*, Vol. 94, Part III, 1948, p. 31.
21. Wass, C.A., "A Table of Intermodulation Products," *IEEE Journal*, Vol. 95, Part 3, January 1949, pp. 31-9.
22. Wiener, N., "Response of a Non-Linear Device to Noise," MIT Radiation Laboratory Report V-16S, April 1942.

Chapter 5

Antenna Considerations for EMC Design

The preceding two chapters discussed EMC design considerations for transmitters and receivers, exclusive of their antennas. This chapter discusses antenna radiation characteristics and describes how they are used in EMC design. The considerations presented in this chapter are directed specifically toward CE equipments that radiate or receive electromagnetic energy. Basic techniques used to specify radiation in unintended directions and at nondesign frequencies for conventional antennas are presented. Primary emphasis in this chapter is on presenting antenna radiation characteristics and providing models and applicable analysis techniques that may be used for EMC design. Generalized antenna models that may be used for analysis when specific data are not available are presented in different sections.

Antennas are designed to radiate or receive signals over a specific solid angle and within a specified frequency range. Some antennas, such as those used in land mobile and broadcast applications, are designed to radiate or receive uniformly over all sectors surrounding the antenna. In other cases, such as fixed point-to-point communications, radar and certain telemetry systems, it is best to confine the functional radiated or received signals to certain limited sectors. In practice, however, it is not possible to accomplish perfect discrimination with antennas in either the spatial or frequency domain. Thus, antennas that are intended to restrict the radiation to specific regions also radiate into or receive signals from other unintentional regions. Additionally, undesired signals at nondesign frequencies are inadvertently radiated to or received by antennas, and the spatial characteristics of an antenna for spurious frequencies are significantly different from characteristics at the design frequency.

This first section describes antenna characteristics that must be considered in an EMC analysis. The last four sections discuss antenna considerations that apply at each stage of the prediction process and present applicable mathematical antenna models.

5.1 Antenna EMC Analysis Considerations

For EMC analysis, emission levels received at an antenna as a result of radiations from another must be determined. In order to provide this information, it is necessary to specify antenna radiation characteristics: (1) in both intended and unintended directions, (2) at both design and nondesign frequencies for different polarizations and (3) for situations in which either near-field or far-field conditions may prevail.

The antenna representation must be consistent with the overall objectives of the total EMI prediction and analysis and must be general enough so that it applies to the different types of antennas that may be encountered. It must be possible to extrapolate existing information and prepare generalized mathematical antenna models from antenna representations for use in cases where specific data are not available.

In a given analysis problem a wide variety of antenna types may exist, ranging from those that exhibit essentially omnidirectional radiation to those having a highly directional radiation characteristic. Although omnidirectional types of antennas must be considered in interference prediction and analysis, they do not present serious analysis problems because antenna gains are relatively low and are essentially independent of direction. The term **omnidirectional antenna** as used in this volume refers to a practical omni which generally is omni azimuth only and may have some gain relative to an ideal omni or isotropic antenna.

For directional antennas, problems involved in specifying antenna radiation characteristics are considerably more complex because of the variation that exists in the spatial domain. Furthermore, directional antennas are often used with both high-power transmitters and sensitive receivers in applications such as radar, satellite communications, troposcatter, etc. This combination of high-gain antennas with either high-power transmitters or sensitive receivers increases the propensity for EMI.

In order to rigorously determine the characteristics of the radiated fields from an antenna, an analysis based on electromagnetic theory and Maxwell's field equations must be performed.[1] From the analysis, some general vector relationships can be obtained which relate the electric and magnetic fields at a point in space to the current densities and coordinates of an arbitrary source or sources. Assuming only that the source distribution may be factored into components which vary sinusoidally with time (they depend on time through the factor $e^{j\omega t}$) and using the geometry defined in Fig. 5.1, these relationships become:

$$\bar{E} = \frac{1}{4\pi j\omega\epsilon} \int_{v'} (\bar{J} \bullet \mathbf{\nabla}_s \mathbf{\nabla}_s + k^2 \bar{J}$$

$$-j\omega\epsilon \ \bar{J}_m \times \mathbf{\nabla}_s) \frac{e^{-jkr}}{r} \ dv' \tag{5.1}$$

$$\bar{H} = \frac{1}{4\pi j\omega\mu} \int_{v'} (\bar{J}_m \bullet \mathbf{\nabla}_s \mathbf{\nabla}_s + k^2 \bar{J}_m$$

$$+j\omega\mu \ \bar{J} \times \mathbf{\nabla}_s) \frac{e^{-jkr}}{r} \ dv' \tag{5.2}$$

where, $\bar{E}$ = total electric-field intensity at a chosen field point (vector)

$\bar{H}$ = total magnetic-field intensity at a chosen field point (vector)

$\bar{J}$ = total distribution of electric-current density of the sources (vector)

$\bar{J}_m$ = total distribution of magnetic-current density of the sources (vector)

$\bar{\nabla}_s$ = vector operator taken with respect to source coordinate point

$$\hat{i} \ \frac{\partial}{\partial \xi} \ + \ \hat{j} \ \frac{\partial}{\partial n} \ + \ \hat{k} \ \frac{\partial}{\partial \gamma}$$

5.3

$$r = \text{radial distance from source point to field point}$$

ϵ = permitivity of propagation medium

μ = permeability of propagation medium

ω = $2\pi f$

f = frequency of operation

k = $\omega\sqrt{\mu\epsilon}$

$\hat{\imath}$ = unit vector in x-direction

$\hat{\jmath}$ = unit vector in y-direction

$\hat{k}$ = unit vector in z-direction

j = $\sqrt{-1}$

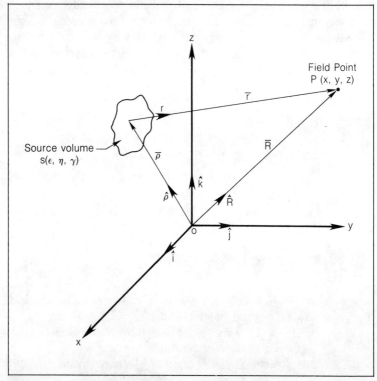

Figure 5.1—General Orientation of Arbitrary Source and Field Point

By performing the indicated vector and differential operations in Eqs. (5.1) and (5.2), the following two expressions can be obtained:

$$\bar{E} = \frac{1}{4\pi j\omega\epsilon} \int_{v'} \left[\bar{J}\left(\frac{-1}{r^3} - \frac{jk}{r^2} \right) \right.$$

$$+ (\bar{J}\bullet \hat{r})\hat{r} \left(\frac{3}{r^3} + \frac{3jk}{r^2} - \frac{k^2}{r} \right)$$ (5.3)

$$\left. + k^2\bar{J} - j\omega\epsilon\bar{J}_m \times \hat{r} \left(\frac{1}{r^2} + \frac{jk}{r} \right) \right] e^{-jkr} \, dv'$$

$$\bar{H} = \frac{1}{4\pi j\omega\mu} \int_{v'} \left[\bar{J}_m \left(\frac{-1}{r^3} - \frac{jk}{r^2} \right) \right.$$

$$+ (\bar{J}_m \bullet \hat{r}) \, \hat{r} \left(\frac{3}{r^3} + \frac{3jk}{r^2} - \frac{k^2}{r} \right)$$

$$\left. + k^2\bar{J}_m + j\omega\mu \, \bar{J} \times \hat{r} \left(\frac{1}{r^2} + \frac{jk}{r} \right) \right] e^{-jkr} \, dv'$$ (5.4)

Equations (5.3) and (5.4) show that both the E- and H-fields have components which vary as $1/r$, $1/r^2$ and $1/r^3$, where r is the distance from the elemental volume dv' of the antenna to the field point at which one wishes to determine field strength. The only quantities whose evaluations give any trouble are the electric and magnetic current density J and J_m which are functions of the coordinates of the antenna and vary in value from one elemental volume of the antenna to another. The primary problems of antenna analysis involve specifying the functions J and J_m and carrying out the necessary integration. Theoretical antenna analysis involves evaluating Eqs. (5.3) and (5.4) for particular cases of interest.

For example, the electric (E_θ, E_r) and magnetic (H_ϕ) fields existing about an oscillating doublet (tiny dipole in which its length (D<<λ), as illustrated in Fig. 5.2, are derived from applying Maxwell's equations:

$$E_\theta = \frac{Z_0 ID\pi \sin\theta}{\lambda^2} \left[\left(\frac{\lambda}{2\pi r} \right)^3 \cos\psi - \left(\frac{\lambda}{2\pi r} \right)^2 \sin\psi + \left(\frac{\lambda}{2\pi r} \right) \cos\psi \right] \quad (5.5)$$

$$E_r = \frac{2Z_0 ID\pi \cos\theta}{\lambda^2} \left[\left(\frac{\lambda}{2\pi r} \right)^3 \cos\psi + \left(\frac{\lambda}{2\pi r} \right)^2 \sin\psi \right]$$

$$(5.6)$$

$$H_\phi = \frac{ID\pi \sin\theta}{\lambda^2} \left[\left(\frac{\lambda}{2\pi r} \right)^2 \sin\psi + \left(\frac{\lambda}{2\pi r} \right) \cos\psi \right]$$

$$(5.7)$$

where,

Z_0 = free-space impedance (for $r \gg \lambda/2\pi = \sqrt{\mu/\epsilon} = 120\,\pi = 377\,\Omega$)

I = current in short wire (doublet)

D = length of short wire (doublet) in which $D \ll \lambda$

θ = zenith angle to radial distance r

λ = wavelength corresponding to frequency, $f = c/\lambda$

r = distance from short wire doublet to measuring or observation point

$\psi = 2\pi r/\lambda - \omega t$

ω = radial frequency = $2\,\pi f$

t = time = $1/f$

$C = 1\sqrt{\mu\epsilon} = 3 \times 10^8$ m/s

When $r \ll \lambda/2\pi$, only the first terms of Eqs. (5.5), (5.6) and (5.7) are significant and the electric and magnetic fields vary as $(1/r)^3$ and $(1/r)^2$, and the field is referred to as the "near-field." When $r \gg \lambda/2\pi$, only the last terms of Eqs. (5.5) and (5.7) are significant, the resulting electric and magnetic fields vary as $1/r$ and the field is referred to as the "radiation field" or "far-field."

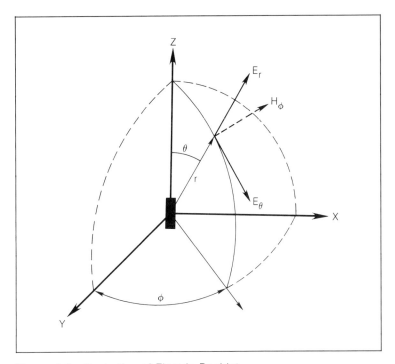

Figure 5.2—Illustration of Electric Doublet

In the preceding discussion, fundamental relationships were presented which describe the radiated fields at a point in space in their direct relation to the source current distribution. In many instances, such as for dipoles, whips, rhombics, long wire and linear array antennas, the exact current element distributions can be specified. However, in the case of aperture antennas such as horns and parabolic lenses or dishes, the description of exact current distribution of the radiating system becomes difficult.

For aperture-type antennas, the field intensity at any field point is related to the field intensity which the antenna produces on an imaginary surface surrounding the antenna. This imaginary surrounding surface is called the **aperture**. Often only a portion of the surrounding surface need be considered. If the surrounding surface is defined such that the surface current would exactly cancel the field of the enclosed radiating system at every point outside the surface, the volume integrals of Eqs. (5.1) and (5.2) may be reduced to surface integrals whose arguments are functions of the fields across the newly formed aperture. Assuming that:

1. The fields over the newly formed aperture are linearly polarized; therefore, it is not necessary to consider the E- and H-fields as vector functions but simply as scalar functions.
2. If the new surface is open, the contribution from the boundary line charge distribution is negligible.

The resulting surface integrals can be expressed in scalar form as:

$$U_p = -\frac{1}{4\pi} \int_A \left(\psi \frac{\partial u}{\partial n} - u \frac{\partial \psi}{\partial n} \right) dA \tag{5.8}$$

The geometry used is given in Fig. 5.3, and:

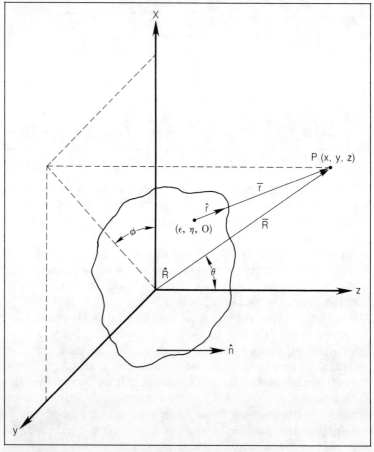

Figure 5.3—Plane Aperture Representation

U_p = the scalar field intensity at a point in space outside of the antenna

$$\psi = \frac{e^{-jkr}}{r}$$

u = distribution of field intensity over the surface which constitutes the aperture of the antenna (u is known as the aperture field distribution)

A = aperture surface area

n = coordinate which is normal to the surface of the aperture

The statement that Eq. (5.8) is a scalar relationship rather than a vector relationship means the field intensity at the field point of interest is given as a magnitude U_p rather than a vector $\overline{E}$. The direction that is associated with the scalar U_p is the direction of the linear polarization which was assumed over the aperture. Equation (5.8) may be further reduced by noting that for most antennas to which aperture analysis is applied, the wavelength is short enough to allow the approximation:

$$\frac{\partial u}{\partial n} \approx - jku \, \hat{n} \bullet \hat{s}$$

(5.9)

where s is defined as the unit vector in the direction of a ray passing through the aperture surface at any given point on the aperture, and n is a unit vector in the direction of an outward normal from the surface of the aperture.

Substituting Eq. (5.9) into Eq. (5.8) and carrying out the operation $d\psi/dn$ gives the familiar scalar diffraction integral:[2]

$$U_p = \frac{1}{4\pi} \int_A \left[u \, \frac{e^{-jkr}}{r} \left(jk + \frac{1}{r} \right) \hat{n} \bullet \hat{r} + jk \, \hat{n} \bullet \hat{s} \right] dA$$

(5.10)

The region in which no approximations are made to the general field relationship of Eq. (5.10) is defined as the aperture near-field and extends from the aperture out to the inner limit of the Fresnel region.

Using the approximation that $k \gg 1/r$ and $\hat{n} \bullet \hat{s} \approx 1$ (which is true if the phase error, or deviation from constant phase, over the aperture is small), the defining integral for the field becomes:

$$U_p = (1 + \cos \ominus)\ \frac{j}{2\lambda} \int_s u\ (\xi, \eta)\ \frac{e^{-jkr}}{r}\ d\xi\ d\eta \qquad (5.11)$$

This field expression applies within the Fresnel region.

The far-field, or **Fraunhofer region** as it is referred to when discussing the aperture antenna scalar field, is that region of space in which the following approximations are made to the scalar field expression represented by Eq. (5.10):

1. The factor 1/r within the brackets of Eq. (5.10) is negligible with respect to k
2. $\hat{n} \bullet \hat{r} \approx \hat{n} \bullet \hat{R} = \cos \ominus$
3. Variations of 1/r outside the bracket of Eq. (5.10) are neglected so that $1/r \approx 1/R$, (R) being defined from Fig. (5.3)
4. In the phase terms exp (−jkr), $r \approx R - \sin \ominus (\xi \cos \phi + \eta \sin \phi)$
5. $\hat{n} \bullet \hat{s} = 1$, i.e., deviations from constant phase over the aperture are small

Applying these approximations results in the following expression of the field within the Fraunhofer region:

$$U_p = (1 + \cos \ominus)\ \frac{je^{-jkR}}{2\lambda R} \int_s u(\xi, \eta)\ e^{jk \sin \ominus (\xi \cos \phi + \eta \sin \phi)} d\xi d\eta$$

$$(5.12)$$

The distance from the antenna at which the far-field approximations are no longer valid enough and at which the more complex near-field expressions must be used is called the **transition distance**. Basically, the transition from the near-field to the far-field is gradual. However, by specifying a criterion which limits the error in the far-field pattern to an acceptable level as one moves closer to the antenna, a specific transition distance relationship can be found. In the EMC community, far-field conditions for electrically large antennas, such as aperture antennas, are usually considered to prevail for distances R, such that:

$$R > \frac{L^2}{2\lambda}$$

where L is the largest dimension of the antenna. The reader is referred to Section 5.5 for a more detailed discussion of near-field and far-field considerations for EMC design.

5.1.1 Far-Field Radiation Representation

The far-field radiation characteristics of directional antennas are often represented by an antenna pattern as shown in Fig. 5.4. This pattern represents the radiation characteristics in one plane (horizontal shown) which may be contrasted with radiation which occurs in all directions. Thus, in order to completely describe an antenna with a pattern representation, it is necessary to use a three-dimensional pattern. From the antenna pattern shown in Fig. 5.4, there are two sectors (intentional- and unintentional-radiation regions) that must be considered.

5.1.1.1 Intentional-Radiation Region

The first sector consists of the intentional-radiation region, i.e., the region of space in which an antenna is designed to radiate. For the directional type of radiation illustrated, this region is relatively limited in solid angle. On the other hand, for a reference omnidirectional type of antenna, such as an isotrope, the intentional-radiation region would encompass all space (4π steradians) around the antenna.

Within the design frequency range of the antenna, the extent of the intentional-radiation region may be represented by azimuth and elevation beamwidths. The relative level of radiation may be represented by antenna gain over an isotropic reference. These parameters are usually obtained directly or calculated. For nondesign frequencies, the beamwidths and gains are more difficult to obtain or calculate.

5.1.1.2 Unintentional-Radiation Region

The second sector consists of the unintentional-radiation region, i.e., the region of space outside of the intentional-radiation region. Representation of antenna radiation in this region is also required for performing an EMC analysis. Although a specific antenna pattern provides a method for representing radiation characteristics of an antenna, it will be shown that such representation is not usually practical or adequate for EMC analysis. The primary problem results from the fact that patterns measured on different serial numbers of a given antenna nomenclature at different frequencies within the design bandwidth or at different geographical sites do not exhibit corresponding gains for the same off-axis angles. They may differ significantly in a particular direction.

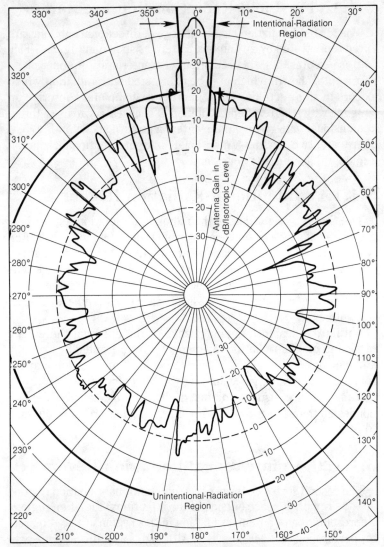

Figure 5.4—Typical Directional Antenna Pattern

5.1.2   Variations in Pattern Characteristics

Figure 5.5 shows the measured patterns for two antennas differing only in serial number. These patterns were measured at the same location using the same equipment and measurement techniques. The measured patterns do not exhibit a point-by-point correspondence and may, in fact, differ significantly at particular angular orientations. However, the fluctuations in the patterns are generally confined to the same range of values. If the main-beam and principal sidelobe region are excluded for different frequencies within the design band and for different sites, the fluctuations in the pattern occur at random. Therefore, at a given angular orientation, it is possible for a particular measured pattern to exhibit any level within a permissible range of values.

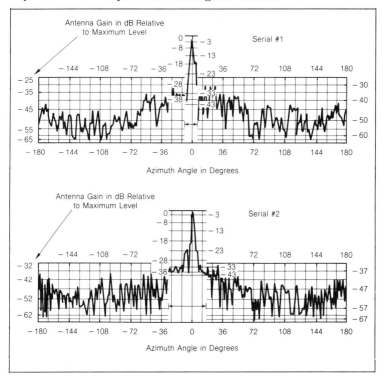

Figure 5.5—Antenna Patterns Corresponding to Two Different Serial Numbers

5.13

It is not practical to describe these random variations precisely. Futhermore, once the existence of these random variations is recognized, the large amount of detailed information which is represented by an antenna pattern is neither justified nor necessary for performing an EMC analysis.

One possibility for limiting the amount of useful antenna information that must be stored and handled in EMC analysis is to simply specify the maximum level of all sidelobe (off-axis) radiation. Although this approach has some merit, in many cases it leads to a gross overestimation of the potential interference. A more realistic approach is to represent the antenna by a pattern distribution function which specifies the probability that various radiation levels are exceeded in the unintentional-radiation region. When this pattern-distribution representation is used, radiation from an antenna may be expressed in terms of a mean radiation level, a standard deviation about this mean level and the type of statistical distribution involved. This representation has proved to be very useful for providing a statistical model of the random variables associated with antenna radiation characteristics.

Another advantage of using the pattern-distribution function representation for the unintentional-radiation region is that a single pattern distribution function may be used to represent a particular antenna type over a wide range of frequencies and polarizations in both the near- and far-field. The particular conditions for which similar pattern distribution functions are found are presented in Section 5.3. In that section some generalized pattern distribution functions are presented which may be used when specific data are not available.

5.1.3   Pattern Distribution Functions

The concept of representing the off-axis unintentional region by an antenna pattern distribution function is illustrated with reference to Fig. 5.6. Excluding the intentional-radiation region (which corresponds to a 5° sector centered about the point of maximum radiation), all of the remaining antenna pattern is considered. Because the intentional-radiation region represents only a 5° sector out of the total 360° pattern, the inclusion or exclusion of this region does not significantly affect the resulting cumulative distribution. The pattern distribution function for this antenna is given by the cumulative probability distribution of antenna gain. For example, the probability that radiation from the antenna exceeds a relative level that is −30 dB above the maximum gain can be obtained directly from Fig. 5.6. There, relative radiation level exceeds the −30 dB reference level over a cumulative total of 24° of the total 355° that remain after the intentional-radiation sector is excluded. Therefore, the probability that the relative radiation level is greater than −30 dB is 24/355 or 6.8 percent. The pattern distribution function may then be found by calculating the probability for each of a selected set of directive gains, typically in 5 or 10 dB increments.

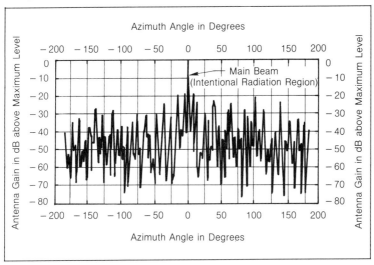

Figure 5.6—Typical Antenna Pattern

Although the pattern distribution function may be obtained graphically from the antenna pattern, it is generally easier to use a tabulation of the antenna pattern like that presented in Table 5.1. The table lists a sample of the relative radiation level at 2.5° increments (exclusive of the intentional-radiation region). A total of 141 samples covering 355° was taken for this particular pattern. When the pattern data are tabulated like this, the probability that a relative radiation level of −30 dB is exceeded is determined by the number of samples that are greater than −30 dB divided by the total number of samples. Thus, the probability of exceeding −30 dB is 5.7 percent when computed from the data in Table 5.1. This is to be compared with 6.8 percent obtained directly from Fig. 5.6. The difference arises from the quantified

5.15

nature of the data in the table and is not significant when averaged over the whole pattern distribution function.

Table 5.1—Tabulated Data for Antenna Pattern Distribution Function

Azimuth Angle + Degrees	Level in dB above Maximum	Azimuth Angle + Degrees	Level in dB above Maximum	Azimuth Angle − Degrees	Level in dB above Maximum	Azimuth Angle − Degrees	Level in dB above Maximum
5.0	− 25	92.5	− 53	5.0	− 23	92.5	− 77
7.5	− 19	95.0	− 48	7.5	− 48	95.0	− 53
10.0	− 45	97.5	− 36	10.0	− 42	97.5	− 45
12.5	− 48	100.0	− 50	12.5	− 50	100.0	− 45
15.0	− 63	102.5	− 50	15.0	− 19	102.5	− 48
17.5	− 63	105.0	− 42	17.5	− 48	105.0	− 42
20.0	− 60	107.5	− 53	20.0	− 65	107.5	− 60
22.5	− 48	110.0	− 48	22.5	− 63	110.0	− 39
25.0	− 33	112.5	− 31	25.0	− 33	112.5	− 31
27.5	− 60	115.0	− 55	27.5	− 53	115.0	− 60
30.0	− 36	117.5	− 60	30.0	− 63	117.5	− 53
32.5	− 53	120.0	− 53	32.5	− 65	120.0	− 55
35.0	− 48	122.5	− 39	35.0	− 39	122.5	− 48
37.5	− 27	125.0	− 73	37.5	− 27	125.0	− 73
40.0	− 39	127.5	− 60	40.0	− 48	127.5	− 36
42.5	− 53	130.0	− 45	42.5	− 60	130.0	− 50
45.0	− 45	132.5	− 60	45.0	− 36	132.5	− 53
47.5	− 55	135.0	− 48	47.5	− 42	135.0	− 42
50.0	− 69	137.5	− 27	50.0	− 69	137.5	− 27
52.5	− 50	140.0	− 42	52.5	− 60	140.0	− 48
55.0	− 60	142.5	− 80	55.0	− 60	142.5	− 55
57.5	− 36	145.0	− 50	57.5	− 45	145.0	− 42
60.0	− 50	147.5	− 55	60.0	− 48	147.5	− 60
62.5	− 50	150.0	− 36	62.5	− 50	150.0	− 77
65.0	− 39	152.5	− 50	65.0	− 39	152.5	− 48
67.5	− 48	155.0	− 53	67.5	− 53	155.0	− 53
70.0	− 53	157.5	− 73	70.0	− 73	157.5	− 55
72.5	− 42	160.0	− 60	72.5	− 50	160.0	− 48
75.0	− 31	162.5	− 42	75.0	− 31	162.5	− 36
77.5	− 48	165.0	− 48	77.5	− 55	165.0	− 50
80.0	− 73	167.5	− 77	80.0	− 48	167.5	− 39
82.5	− 33	170.0	− 39	82.5	− 36	170.0	− 42
85.0	− 42	172.5	− 60	85.0	− 60	172.5	− 69
87.5	− 69	175.0	− 69	87.5	− 69	175.0	− 53
90.0	− 39	177.5	− 55	90.0	− 42	177.5	− 63
		180.0	− 42				

The method for determining antenna pattern distribution functions from data tabulated in Table 5.1 is shown in Table 5.2. The first column of Table 5.2 lists 5 dB increments of radiation from the antenna in decreasing order. The second column gives the number of samples that occur at each level. The third column, which is simply the cumulative sum of the numbers given in the second column, presents the number of samples that equal or exceed each indicated level. The last column expresses the cumulative sum in terms of the corresponding percentage of the total number of samples. As such, it represents the antenna pattern distribution.

Table 5.2—Tabulated Cumulative Antenna Distribution Function from Table 5.1

Gain in dB above Maximum	Number of Samples	Cumulative Number of Samples	Cumulative Probability (Percent)
0 to − 5	0	0	0
− 6 to − 10	0	0	0
− 11 to − 15	0	0	0
− 16 to − 20	2	2	1.4
− 21 to − 25	2	4	2.8
− 26 to − 30	4	8	5.7
− 31 to − 35	7	15	10.6
− 36 to − 40	17	32	22.7
− 41 to − 45	19	51	36.2
− 46 to − 50	31	82	58.2
− 51 to − 55	22	104	73.6
− 56 to − 60	15	119	84.3
− 61 to − 65	7	126	89.3
− 66 to − 70	6	132	93.5
− 71 to − 75	5	137	97.0
− 76 to − 80	4	141	100.0

The data in Table 5.2 are then plotted on arithmetic probability paper (which is scaled so that a normal distribution is transformed into a straight line) in Fig. 5.7. Note that the pattern distribution function is closely approximated by a straight line. Thus, within the region of interest, the function may be represented by a normal distribution, and it is only necessary to specify the mean level and associated standard deviation. These may be determined directly from the data presented in Table 5.1. The mean antenna-gain level G(f, p) is given by:

$$G(f,p) = \frac{1}{M} \sum_{i=1}^{M} G_i \qquad (5.13)$$

where,

M = the total number of samples exclusive of the intentional-radiation region

G_i = the relative gain level of the ith sample (no samples are chosen from the intentional radiation region)

Similarly, the standard deviation $\sigma_A(f,p)$ is given by:

$$\sigma_A(f,p) = \left[\sum_{i=1}^{M} \frac{[G_i - G(f,p)]^2}{M - 1} \right]^{1/2} \quad (5.14)$$

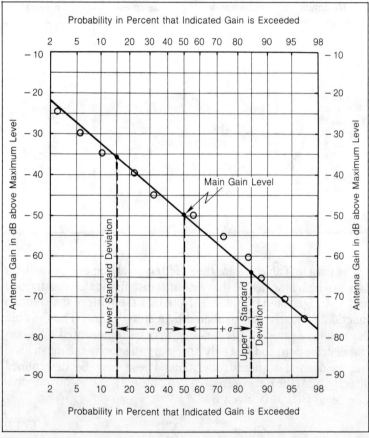

Figure 5.7—Typical Antenna Pattern Distribution Function

Application of Eqs. (5.13) and (5.14) to the data (exclusive of the intentional-radiation region) presented in Table 5.1 results in a mean level of -50 dB above the maximum level and a standard deviation of ± 13 dB. The resultant normal approximation to the pattern distribution function is illustrated by the solid line in Fig. 5.7.

The pattern distribution function thus provides a way of representing the random fluctuations in a particular antenna pattern in a realistic way. Although apparently identical antennas differing only in serial number exhibit different patterns, they may be represented by a single statistical distribution. These representations for antennas are widely used in EMC analysis.

5.1.4 Applications of Pattern-Distribution Functions

One of the major problems in performing an EMC analysis is to find information on specific equipments which are to be analyzed. One direct method of deriving required data-input functions is by statistically reducing empirical data. Thus, if measured antenna patterns are available, they should constitute the basis for deriving such functions.

When complete antenna pattern data are available, the mean value and standard deviation of the resulting pattern distribution function can be derived directly by the application of Eqs. (5.13) and (5.14). In figuring out pattern-distribution functions from measured patterns, it is necessary to group data so that significantly different conditions are analyzed separately. Specific conditions for which radiation characteristics are required may be categorized according to frequency (either within or outside of the design frequency band) and polarization (either parallel to or orthogonal to the design polarization) of the antenna. Specific antenna data required for EMI analysis are illustrated in Table 5.3.

When measured data are not available, other sources must be used for the information required to derive mathematical models of antennas. Information for design characteristics, i.e., the main-beam gain and beamwidth for the design frequency and polarization, may be obtained from antenna specifications or calculated from results of a theoretical analysis. However, realistic antenna characteristics for nondesign frequencies, polarizations and the unintentional-radiation region usually cannot be obtained from specifications or theoretical calculations. Thus, it is necessary to provide criteria for determining antenna input functions when measurements are not available.

Several generalizations that have been made as a result of both theoretical and empirical considerations are discussed in Sections 5.2 and 5.3. Generalized antenna functions which may be used in cases where specific antenna information is not available are presented in other sections of this chapter.

Table 5.3—Antenna Data Requirements

Region of Radiation	Operate Conditions		Gain		Beamwidth	
	Frequency	Polariz.	Mean dB/Iso	St. Dev. dB	Az. in Deg.	El. in Deg.
Intentional	Design	Design				
	Design	Orthog.				
	Nondesign	Any				
Unintentional	Design	Design				
	Design	Orthog.				
	Nondesign	Any				

5.1.5   Classes of Antennas

In addition to categorizing antenna data for representing significant conditions, it is also helpful to consider categorizing antennas for the purpose of obtaining generalized results through statistical analyses of pattern data. Although the pattern-distribution concept is applicable to all antennas, the implementation of the method depends somewhat on the characteristics of the antennas in question. Because an EMC analysis process must consider all applicable antennas in an environment, a method is desired for grouping similar antennas into classes.

There are several criteria that are used for classifying antennas; however, for EMC analysis purposes, one of the most important characteristics of an antenna is its relative gain above isotropic levels. Accordingly, three antenna classifications are suggested:

high-gain antennas (greater than 25 dB gain), medium-gain antennas (10 to 25 dB gain) and low-gain antennas (less than 10 dB gain). Each class may be further subdivided according to the analysis required for the antenna within its basic class. Table 5.4 presents the classification of some typical antennas.

Table 5.4—Antenna Classification by Gain*

Low Gain (G < 10 dB)	Medium Gain (10 dB ⩽ G ⩽ 25 dB)	High Gain (G > 25 dB)
1. Linear Cylindrical Biconical Dipoles Folded Dipoles Asymmetrical Dipoles Sleeve Dipoles Monopole Discone Quadrant Colinear Array 2. Traveling Wave Long Wire 3. Loop 4. Aperture Slot 5. Helix (Omnidirectional Mode)	1. Array Yagi Broadside Curtain End-Fire Curtain 2. Traveling Wave Rhombic Surface and Leaky Wave 3. Aperture Horn Corner Reflector 4. Equiangular Log Periodic Conical Log Spiral 5. Helix (Axial Mode)	1. Array Mattress Electronic Steerable 2. Aperture Horns Reflector Antennas Lens Antennas

* Gain in Units of dB above isotropic

5.1.6 Site Effects

Although pattern-distribution functions may be derived from either theoretical or experimental antenna patterns, there are large differences between the two methods. Differences result partly from the effects of reflecting and scattering objects located in the vicinity of a site.[3] The influences of a site on antenna radiation characteristics are shown by the lack of correspondence between antenna patterns and pattern-distribution functions derived from measurements on a given antenna located at several different sites.

The site-effect problem is illustrated graphically in Fig. 5.8 which compares antenna pattern-distribution functions derived from measurements on an antenna located at five different sites. Examination of the figure shows that in the unintentional-radiation region, there are differences in the mean values and standard deviations associated with the functions.

The sites on which these measurements were conducted represent a range of different conditions from open field to very crowded. Site No. 5 was an antenna pattern range located on top of a mountain at Newport, New York. This site was virtually free from reflecting objects. The pattern thus obtained is more representative of the actual antenna, per se. The other sites were located at Griffiss Air Force Base at Rome, New York, and were cluttered with objects that would scatter or reflect the antenna radiation.

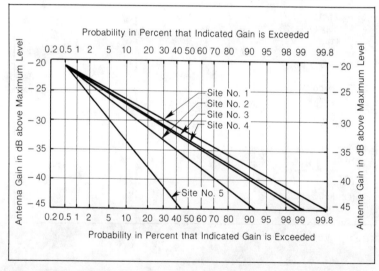

Figure 5.8—Pattern Distribution Functions Derived from Measurements at Different Sites

Comparisons of measured patterns and pattern distribution functions similar to the ones shown in Fig. 5.8 have been made for many antennas at many sites. Several observations may be made from these comparisons. First, the higher levels of antenna radiation (main beam and major sidelobes) are least affected by the site. Second, in sectors where antenna radiation levels are very low, energy which was reflected or scattered from site objects may be greater than energy which was radiated directly from the antenna. Thus, these lower radiation levels (particularly nulls) are most affected by a site.

Site effects have been evaluated quantitatively by comparing the pattern-distribution functions derived from patterns on a given antenna type measured at different sites. Functions derived from measurements on crowded sites generally exhibited slightly higher mean levels and slightly smaller standard deviations than corresponding pattern distribution functions derived from measurements at an open site. This is expected because crowded sites have more reflecting and scattering objects, and thus there will be more apparent sidelobes resulting from reflections off objects around the antenna.

The relative importance of the site effects on the apparent antenna characteristics depends on the directivity characteristics of the antenna, physical characteristics of the site and radio frequency. Site effects become more important as the antenna gain, the density of reflecting or scattering objects on the site and the frequency are increased.

From EMC analysis considerations, the most significant antenna lobes (the intentional-radiation region and the largest sidelobes) are the ones that are most likely to create a problem. These levels are least affected by the site. Although site effects do become significant in the region corresponding to nulls in the antenna pattern, these regions are less significant from an EMI standpoint.

Based on the above observations, site effects are not major factors in most EMC analysis. Most antenna pattern measurements are made on typical sites, and pattern-distribution functions derived from these measurements provide a good representation of the antenna characteristics on operational sites.

One major exception to the above is when objects in the immediate vicinity of a source or susceptible device tend to block or shield signals in specific spatial sectors. The effects of shielding by terrain or other large objects such as metal buildings must be included in the prediction models. These effects are evaluated along with propagation loss, as described in Chapter 6.

5.2   Intentional-Radiation Region

For EMC analysis, it is necessary to specify antenna radiation characteristics within the solid angle for which the antenna is designed to radiate or receive energy. It is necessary to define the gain and beamwidths of the antenna for both design and nondesign frequencies and polarizations. This section describes techniques used to derive EMI prediction models for radiation within this region, which is often referred to as the **main-beam region**.

For a given set of frequencies and polarizations, statistical techniques are used to represent the small variations in gain that occur between antennas of the same type, between different frequencies, for different sites, etc. Antenna gain is represented by a normal distribution, and the resulting antenna models for the intentional-radiation region are based on the following principles:

1. The intentional-radiation region is defined by the 10 dB azimuth and elevation **beamwidths**, α and β. It is recommended that 10 dB beamwidths be used for EMI prediction. If specific data on the 10 dB beamwidths are not available, they may be estimated by using two times the 3 dB beamwidths for high-gain antennas.

2. The **mean gain** levels G(f,p) are 3 dB below the maximum gain, i.e., the gain at the 3 dB beamwidth limits.

3. The **standard deviation** σ(f,p) accounts for gain variations that occur within the intentional-radiation region and between antennas and EMI prediction conditions. It is assumed that those gain variations are random and may be described by a normal distribution.

If specific data are available on antenna gain and beamwidths, they should be used as the basis for the antenna models. On the other hand, if specific data are not available (which is usually the case), the generalized antenna models presented in Table 5.5 may be used to represent antenna radiation characteristics in the intentional-radiation region. These generalized models were derived from available antenna data, and they define the relationship between design and nondesign conditions. The following sections discuss some of the major considerations that relate to the antenna intentional-radiation region.

Table 5.5—Generalized Antenna Models for Intentional-Radiation Region

Type Antenna	Operational Condition Frequency	Operational Condition Polarization	(α) Deg	(β) Deg	Gain (dB/iso)	(σ) dB	$C_{dB/}$ dcd	D dB	ΔG dB
High Gain $G(f°) > 25$ dB	Design	Design	$\alpha°$	$\beta°$	G_0	2	0	0	0
	Design	Orthogonal	$10\alpha°$	$10\beta°$	G_0-20	3	0	-0	-20
	Nondesign	Any	$4\alpha°$	$4\beta°$	G_0-13	3	0	-13	0
Medium Gain $10 \leqslant G(f_0) \leqslant 25$ dB	Design	Design	$\alpha°$	$\beta°$	G_0	2	0	0	0
	Design	Orthogonal	$10\alpha°$	$10\beta°$	G_0-20	3	0	0	-20
Resonant	Nondesign	Any	$3\alpha°$	$3\beta°$	G_0	3	0	-10	0
Non Resonant	Nondesign	Any	$\alpha°$	$\beta°$	G_0	3	0	0	0
Low-Gain $G(f°) < 10$ dB	Design	Design	$\alpha°$	$\beta°$	G_0	1	0	0	0
	Design	Orthogonal	$6\alpha°$	$6\beta°$	G_0-16	2	0	-0	-16
	Nondesign	Any	$360°$	$180°$	0	2	0	$-G_0$	0

$\alpha°$ = 10 dB Azimuth Beamwidth for Design Frequency and Polarization

$\beta°$ = 10 dB Elevation Beamwidth for Design Frequency and Polarization

G_0 = Mean-Gain for Design Frequency and Polarization (3 dB Below the Nominal Gain)

σ = Standard Deviation

$\alpha, \beta, G \& \sigma$ = Functions of Frequency and Polarization

$C \& D$ = Constants that Describe the Variation of Main-Beam Gain with Frequency (See Section 5.2.1.2)

$\Delta G(p)$ = Gain Change Resulting from Orthogonal Polarization (See Section 5.2.1.3)

5.2.1   Design Frequency and Polarization

For EMC analysis at the design frequency and polarization, the beamwidth corresponds to the nominal 10 dB azimuth and elevation beamwidths. The mean gain is 3 dB less than the nominal gain, and a 2 dB standard deviation is used to represent gain variations. If antenna nominal gain and beamwidth values are available from equipment specifications or other sources, these values should form the basis of the antenna models for EMC analysis. If nominal values are not available, they may be calculated from equations given in the following sections. Alternately, if sufficient information is not available to calculate the gain and beamwidths, estimates may be obtained from data presented in Table 5.6 which summarizes the radiation characteristics of a number of typical antenna types.

Table 5.6—Radiation Characteristics for Typical Antennas

Type Antennas	Pattern		Gain in dB/Isotrope
	Horizontal	Vertical	
Quarter-Wave Vertical Monopole	⊙	∞	3
Half-Wave Horizontal Dipole Vertical Loop	∞∞	⊙ ∞	3 3
Long Wire	✳	✳	6-10
Colinear Array	⊙	⊶	6-10
Broadside Array	⊶✳	⊶✳	6-10
End-Fire Array	✳◯	✳◯	6-10
Discone	✳◯	✳◯	6-10
Slot	✳◯	✳◯	6-10
Helix (Omnidirectional Mode)	⊙	⊶	6-10
Yagi	✳◯	✳◯	10-15
Broadside Curtain	✳◯	✳◯	10-15
End-Fire Curtain	✳◯	✳◯	10-15
Rhombic	✳◯	✳◯	15-25
Horn	✳◯	✳◯	15-25
Corner Reflector	✳◯	✳◯	15-20
Log Periodic	✳◯	✳◯	10-15
Helix Axial Mode	✳◯	✳◯	10-15
Aperture or Array	✳◯	✳◯	25-60

Table 5.6 shows that for directional antennas, the intentional-radiation region is very narrow, and hence the probability that an EMI problem will involve this region is relatively small. However, for those relatively few cases requiring EMC consideration within the region of intentional radiation, the potential for interference is greatly increased because of the increased emission levels. On the other hand, for low-gain, essentially omnidirectional types of antennas, the region of intentional radiation is large and will be the primary region that is considered for most EMC analysis.

Illustrative Example 5.1

Consider a 3 m parabolic dish designed to operate at 10 GHz with a nominal gain of 44 dB and 3 dB azimuth and elevation beamwidths of 1.1°. Determine the amplitude cull models for the gain and beamwidths of the main-beam region at the design frequency and polarization.

For EMC analysis, the gain of the main beam (intentional-radiation region) at the design frequency and polarization is represented by a normal distribution with a mean gain of 41 dB (3 dB below the nominal gain) and a standard deviation of 2 dB. The beamwidth of the region is defined by the 10 dB beamwidths which are approximately two times the 3 dB beamwidths, or 2.2°. In summary, for the amplitude culling prediction stage, the intentional-radiation region at the design frequency (f_o) and the design polarization (p_o) are described as:

$$\alpha(f_o, p_o) = 2.2°; \ \beta(f_o, p_o) = 2.2°$$

$$G(f_o, p_o) = 41 \text{ dB}; \ \alpha_A(f_o, p_o) = 2 \text{ dB}$$

5.2.1.1 Nominal Gain and Effective Area

The gain of an antenna provides a measure of its ability to concentrate radiated power in a given direction or to provide a capture area for reception. The gain is given by the ratio of the power radiated in its boresight direction to the power radiated in the same direction by an isotropic antenna. If the effective aperture or capture area of the antenna is known, the gain is:

$$G(\text{ratio}) = \frac{4\pi A_{\text{eff}}}{\lambda^2} \tag{5.15}$$

5.27

where, $G(\text{ratio})$ = gain (a numeric)
A_{eff} = effective area
λ = wavelength in same units as area

For high-gain, aperture-type antennas, the effective area may be somewhat less (1 to 3 dB) than the actual geometrical area of the antenna. Thus, the physical area of the aperture may be used in calculating gain.

The relationship between the antenna-effective area and the actual area for an aperture antenna is referred to as the efficiency of the antenna and depends on aperture illumination. A uniform aperture illumination produces maximum efficiency but also results in high sidelobe levels. Other aperture illuminations result in lower efficiencies, but may produce lower sidelobe levels. Because of the tradeoffs between efficiency and sidelobe levels, most antennas are designed with aperture distributions that provide a compromise between the two. The relationships that exist between aperture distribution, efficiency and sidelobe are listed in Table 5.7 for several different conditions.

Equation (5.15) may be expressed in a more convenient form by substituting frequency f for wavelength λ:

$$\lambda_m = \frac{0.3}{f_{GHz}} \tag{5.16}$$

Therefore,

$$G = \frac{4\pi A_{m2}\, f_{GHz}{}^2}{0.09} \tag{5.17}$$

where, A_m = antenna efficiency × actual area in m^2 (5.18)

or, $G_{dB} = 21 + 10 \log A_m{}^2 + 20 \log f_{GHz}$ (5.19)

Illustrative Example 5.2

To illustrate how Eq. (5.19) is used, consider an antenna with a circular aperture 1.8 m in diameter operating at a frequency of 10 GHz. Further, assume that the aperture illumination is circular.

To use Eq. (5.19) to calculate gain, it is first necessary to determine the effective area. Referring to Table 5.7, the antenna efficiency for a circular-aperture distribution is 0.75; thus, the effective area from Eq. (5.18) is:

$$A_{eff} = 0.75 \ \frac{\pi D^2}{4} = 0.75 \left(\frac{\pi(1.8)^2}{4} \right) = 1.9 \ m^2$$

The gain is then calculated from Eq. (5.17):

$$G_{dB} = 21 + 10 \log 1.9 + 20 \log 10 = 44 \ dB$$

Table 5.7—Antenna Efficiency and First Side-Lobe Level for Different Aperture Distributions

RECTANGULAR APERTURES			
Aperture Distribution	f(x)	Efficiency*	First Side Lobe Level (dB above main beam)
Rectangular		1.0	−13
Circular		0.833	−21
Cosine		0.810	−23
Cosine Squared		0.667	−32
Triangular		0.75	−26
CIRCULAR APERTURES			
Rectangular		1.0	−18
Circular		0.75	−25
Circular Squared		0.56	−31

5.2.1.2 Nominal Gain and Beamwidth

The antenna gain is related to the beamwidth; i.e., a high-gain antenna has a narrow beam whereas a low-gain antenna has a broad beam. If the half-power 3 dB beamwidths of a narrow-beam antenna are specified, the approximate gain may be calculated from the expression:[4]

$$G(\text{ratio}) \cong \frac{30{,}000}{\Theta_E \Theta_H} \qquad (5.20)$$

or,
$$G_{dB} = 45 - 10 \log(\Theta_E \Theta_H) \qquad (5.21)$$

where, Θ_E = E-plane, half power width in degrees
         Θ_H = H-plane, half-power width in degrees

Equation (5.21) provides relatively accurate results for antennas with Θ_E and Θ_H less than about 20° and gains greater than about 20 dB. Alternately, if the gain and the relationship between the beamwidths are known, Eq. (5.20) may be used to calculate the beamwidths.

Illustrative Example 5.3

To illustrate the use of Eq. (5.21), consider an antenna with 10° E- and H-plane, half-power beamwidths, i.e., $\Theta_E = \Theta_H = 10°$. From Eq. (5.21):

$$G_{dB} = 45 - 10 \log (10 \times 10) = 25 \text{ dB}$$

5.2.2   Frequency Dependence

Methods were presented in preceding sections for specifying characteristics of antennas at the intentional fundamental frequency. It is also necessary to provide methods for specifying characteristics for nondesign frequencies.

One factor that must be specified at transmitter and receiver spurious frequencies is antenna gain. For the dominant mode of polarization, the gain of a high-gain antenna will be lower at frequencies other than the design frequency, even though the gain given by Eq. (5.17) increases with frequency. This decrease in gain results from factors such as phase variation across the aperture and changes in the primary illumination or aperture distribution function. For the purpose of EMI prediction, the gain G(f) for nondesign frequencies (f) may be represented as illustrated in Fig. 5.9 by the function:[5]

$$G(f,p) = G(f_o,p_o) + C \log (f/f_o) + D \qquad (5.22)$$

where, $G(f_o,p_o)$ = mean gain at design frequency (f_o) and polarization (p_o)

C and D = constants that must be determined for a specific antenna or antenna type or class

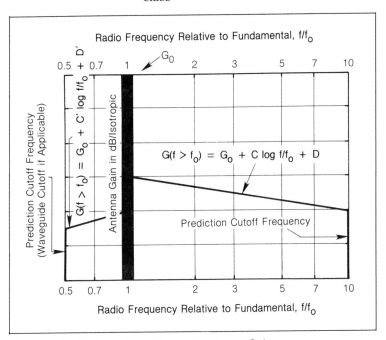

Figure 5.9—Mathematical Model of Antenna Gain

If specific characteristic data are available for the antenna gain at nondesign frequencies, the above function is determined by applying the **least-squares-fit** techniques described in Chapter 3. On the other hand, if specific data are not available, Table 5.5 may be used for various antenna types.

A second important factor that must be specified for the intentional-radiation region is the antenna beamwidth at spurious frequencies. For high-gain type antennas, the product of azimuth and elevation beamwidths and gain is a constant, such as shown in Eq. (5.20). Therefore, as the gain decreases, the azimuth and elevation beamwidths (α and β) increase. The azimuth or elevation beamwidths α (f,p) or β(f,p) for any frequency f and polarization p maybe approximated by the following:

$$\alpha(f,p) = \sqrt{\frac{G(f_o,p_o)}{G(f,p)}}\ \alpha(f_o,p_o) \qquad (5.23)$$

$$\beta(f,p) = \sqrt{\frac{G(f_o,p_o)}{G(f,p)}}\ \beta(f_o,p_o)$$

where,

$G(f_o,p_o)$ = antenna gain at design frequency and polarization

$G(f,p)$ = antenna gain at frequency (f) and polarization (p)

$\alpha(f_o,p_o)$ = azimuth beamwidth at design frequency and polarization

$\beta(f_o,p_o)$ = elevation beamwidth at design frequency and polarization

$\alpha(f,p)$ = azimuth beamwidth at frequency (f) and polarization (p)

$\beta(f,p)$ = elevation beamwidth at frequency (f) and polarization (p)

If the values presented in Table 5.5 are used to represent gain at nondesign frequencies, then corresponding values should be used for azimuth and elevation beamwidths.

Illustrative Example 5.4

Using Table 5.5, determine the amplitude analysis model for representing the antenna in Example 5.1 at nondesign frequencies. From Example 5.1, the following values were obtained for the parabolic antenna:

$\alpha(f_o,p_o) = 2.2°$; $\beta(f_o,p_o) = 2.2°$; $G(f_o,p_o) = 41$ dB; $\sigma(f_o,p_o) = 2$ dB

For high-gain antennas (G > 25 dB), the gain at nondesign frequencies in Table 5.5 is − 13 dB above the mean gain at the design frequency. The azimuth and elevation beamwidths are four times the beamwidths at the design frequency. Therefore, for frequencies other than the design frequency, the following values should be used to represent the antenna in the amplitude analysis stage of EMI prediction:

$$\alpha(f,p_0) = 8.8°, \ \beta(f,p_0) = 8.8°$$

$$G(f,p_0) = 28 \ dB, \ \sigma(f,p_0) = 3 \ dB$$

The gain at nondesign frequencies is obtained from Eq. (5.22) by letting $C = 0$, and $D = -13$ dB. Thus,

$$G(f,p_0) = G(f_0,p_0) + C \log (f/f_0) + D$$

$$= 41 \ dB + 0 \log(f/f_0) - 13 = 28 \ dB$$

5.2.3 Polarization Dependence

The remaining antenna characteristic that has to be specified is polarization. If the antenna is linearly polarized, there will be a difference between antenna gain for vertical and horizontal polarizations. This effect will be most pronounced at the fundamental frequency, and the gain will be maximum for the predominant mode of polarization.

For EMI prediction, the effects of polarization are represented by correction factors that reduce the gain by amounts related to the conditions of interest. Thus, for nondesign polarizations, the gain is:

$$G(f_0,p) = G(f_0,p_0) + \Delta G(p) \qquad (5.24)$$

where,

$G(f_0,p)$ = gain in dB at fundamental frequency (f_0) and polarization condition p

$\Delta G(p)$ = gain change in dB resulting from mismatched polarization effects

If specific polarization information is available, it should form the basis for the correction factor $\Delta G(p)$. For those EMI prediction situations for which specific information is not available, Table 5.5 may be used.

The beamwidths for nondesign polarization conditions may be calculated from the relationship given in Eq. (5.23). When this equation is used to calculate the beamwidths for nondesign polarization conditions, the expression $G(f,p)$ in the equation is replaced by $G(f_o,p)$.

Illustrative Example 5.5

Using Table 5.5, determine the model for representing the antenna in Example 5.1 at nondesign polarizations. From Example 5.1, the following values were obtained for the parabolic antenna:

$$\alpha(f_o,p_o) = 2.2°; \; \beta(f_o,p_o) = 2.2°; \; G(f_o,p_o) = 41 \text{ dB}; \; \sigma_A(f_o,p_o) = 2 \text{ dB}$$

In Table 5.5, at the design frequency and nondesign polarizations, high-gain antennas are represented by a polarization correction $\Delta G(p) = -20$ dB above the nominal gain. Beamwidths are 10 times those for the design conditions. Thus:

$$\alpha(f_o; \, p \neq p_o) = 22° \quad \beta(f_o; p \neq p_o) = 22°$$

$$G(f_o; \, p \neq p_o) = 21 \text{ dB, and } \sigma_A(f_o; \, p \neq p_o) = 3 \text{ dB}$$

For the design frequency and nondesign polarization, the antenna has a broader beam and lower gain than at the design polarization.

5.3   Unintentional-Radiation Region

For EMC analysis, it is necessary to specify antenna characteristics in the unintentional, off-axis radiation region. It was previously shown that the most logical, practical and adequate method for such a representation is the pattern-distribution function which describes probabilities that different gain levels will be exceeded. In order to specify the antenna, it is necessary to define the effect of frequency, polarization and site location on the resulting pattern distribution functions for the unintentional-radiation region.

If measured pattern data are available, Eqs. (5.13) and (5.14) should be used to derive pattern-distribution function models for specific antennas. As discussed in Section 5.1, normal distributions are used and these are specified by describing mean values and standard deviations for each set of significantly different conditions. Some special considerations that apply to deriving antenna pattern distribution functions from measured data are discussed in Section 5.3.3. If measured data are not available, the generalized antenna models presented in Table 5.8 are used for EMI prediction. The mean gain levels shown in Table 5.8 are given with respect to dB above an isotropic level. An example is presented below to illustrate how Table 5.8 may be used to model antenna radiation characteristics in the unintentional-radiation region. Important considerations concerning the pattern-distribution function models are discussed in the following sections.

Illustrative Example 5.6

Consider a high-gain parabolic dish with a 1.8 m diameter and a 10 GHz design frequency. It was previously determined that the main-beam gain for this antenna at the design frequency and polarization would be 45 dB/isotropic. Suppose that it is necessary to include this antenna in an EMI prediction involving the unintentional-radiation region and a nondesign frequency and polarization condition. For this situation, Table 5.8 shows that the mean gain is – 10 dB relative to an isotropic level.

Table 5.8—Generalized Antenna Models (Unintentional-Radiation Regions)

Antenna	Operating Conditions		Mean Gain	Standard
Type	Frequency	Polarization	dB/Isotrope	Dev. in dB
High-Gain G > 25 dB	Design Design Nondesign	Design Orthogonal Any	– 10 – 10 – 10	14 14 14
Median Gain 10 dB ≤ G ≤ 25 dB	Design Design Nondesign	Design Orthogonal Any	– 10 – 10 – 10	11 13 10
Low-Gain G < 10 dB	Design Design Nondesign	Design Orthogonal Any	0 – 13 – 3	6 8 6

5.3.1 Design Frequency and Polarization

Considering the entire radiation pattern with all antennas, the mean or average gain must be in unity with respect to an isotrope for lossless antennas. However, a significant portion of the total radiation power is concentrated in the intentional-radiation region. For example, typical directional antennas will develop 50 percent or more of the available power in the region of the main beam. In this case, 50 percent or less of the total power is available for radiation over the remainder of the pattern sectors. Thus, if the intentional-radiation region is excluded from analysis, the average gain of the pattern can be expected to be 50 percent (– 3 dB) with respect to an isotropic level. If 90 percent or more of the total power is directed in the region of intentional radiation (which may apply for well-designed high-gain antennas), the average gain of the remainder of the pattern is 10 percent (– 10 dB) or less with respect to an isotropic level.

The major lobe characteristics of different nomenclature antennas may exhibit large differences. However, analysis of antenna functions for a variety of different high-gain antennas has indicated that there are certain similarities in their pattern-distribution functions. This is illustrated in Fig. 5.10 which shows pattern-distribution functions (excluding the intentional-radiation region) for five different nomenclature antennas that have nominal gains ranging from 28 to 40 dB. The functions for nomenclature Numbers 1, 2, 3 and 5 were derived from data measured on the same site, whereas the function for nomenclature Number 4 was derived from data measured on a site that had similar properties.

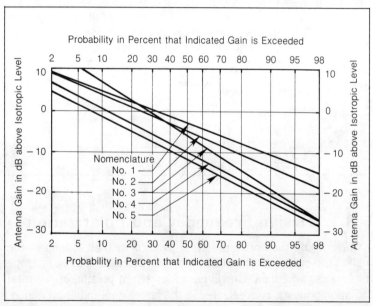

Figure 5.10—Pattern Distribution Function Variation with Nomenclature

It is important to note the similarities in the standard deviations associated with the pattern distribution functions for the five antennas. These similarities lend further support to the conclusion that the site has a significant effect on the standard deviation. Referring to Table 5.9, it is noted that there is no apparent correlation between the gains and the mean pattern distribution function levels for the sidelobe and backlobe regions.

**Table 5.9—Comparison of Mean Levels
for Gains and Pattern-Distribution Functions**

Nomenclature	Main-Beam Gain (dB/Isotropic)	P-D Function Level (dB/Isotropic Mean)
#1	34	− 3
#2	28	− 5
#3	40	− 6
#4	37	− 10
#5	30	− 12

5.3.2   Nondesign Frequency and Polarization

Investigations of pattern distribution functions for nondesign frequencies and polarizations have indicated that the mean levels of these functions are not significantly different from such functions derived for design conditions in realistic operational situations. Thus, the influence of antenna nomenclature, antenna serial number, frequency and polarization tend to be random and not pronounced. Because changes in these parameters bear no direct relationship to their influence on pattern-distribution functions, their effect must be considered in a statistical sense. These observations form the basis for the generalized antenna EMC analysis models which are presented in Table 5.8 for the unintentional-radiation region.

5.3.3   Antenna Models from Measured Patterns

Relationships given by Eqs. (5.13) and (5.14) should be applied only to data sets that are complete and contain samples taken at random from the entire population. However, antenna pattern data are often subject to limitations that result from practical measurement factors, such as dynamic range and receiver sensitivity. In these cases, part of the total statistical population may be beyond the range of the measurement instruments so that samples drawn from this region cannot be measured. Therefore, measured samples are obtained in a biased way from some particular fraction of the total population. If these data samples are reduced by the application of the previous equations without regard to the bias introduced, the statistical representation derived from the samples will not represent the total population. This fact is best illustrated by reviewing an example.

Consider an antenna pattern such as the one shown in Fig. 5.11. This pattern provides a measure of the antenna directive gain and is similar to that previously shown in Fig. 5.6. Analysis has shown that the directive gain (exclusive of the region of intentional radiation) can be represented by a random variable which is normally distributed. For the pattern shown, practical measurement considerations did not impose limitations on the data. Therefore, the characteristics of the statistical distribution associated with the pattern can be derived by applying the standard equations to samples of the relative gain taken at specified intervals on the patterns. Relative levels obtained by sampling an antenna pattern every 2.5° were presented in Table 5.1. Values of the mean gain G(f,p) and standard deviation $\sigma_A(f,p)$ as determined from Eqs. (5.13) and (5.14) were −50 dB above the main beam and 13 dB, respectively.

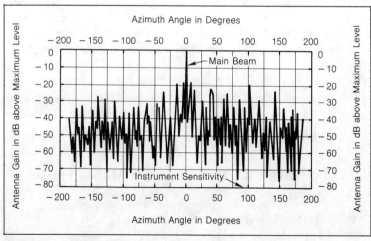

Figure 5.11—Typical Antenna Pattern with No Instrumentation Bias

Now suppose that the measurement system was less sensitive, so that those gain values of the pattern that were less than −41 dB above the main beam could not be measured. In this case, the measured pattern would appear as shown in Fig. 5.12. Here specific values are not available for the lower radiation levels. In fact, for this case more than 50 percent of the data has been truncated. Relative levels obtained by sampling the antenna pattern every 1.5° would be similar to those presented in Table 5.1 except that every sample with a value less than or equal to −41 dB ref. main beam would become −41 dB ref. main beam. If this antenna pattern were reduced without regard to the fact that the data were truncated, the results would be biased estimates of both the mean value and standard deviation. For the case shown, a mean value of −39 dB/main beam would be obtained instead of −50 dB/main beam and a standard deviation of 4 dB obtained instead of 13 dB.

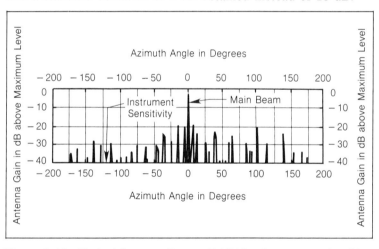

Figure 5.12—Typical Antenna Pattern Exhibiting Instrumentation Bias

Data truncation can produce large errors in the resulting antenna functions if proper consideration is not given to both data collection and data reduction. The question now is: how can one determine the mean value and standard deviation from truncated data?

There are several methods that can be used to estimate the characteristics from truncated data. The first method is based on the fact that, for the normal distribution, the median and the mean value are equal and the distribution is symmetrical about the mean value or median. Therefore, if data truncation is less than 50 percent, the median (middle value) can be used as an estimate of the mean, and the standard deviation can be computed by considering only that half of the data that is complete. For example, if this method is used to estimate the mean and standard deviation for the sample problem, (when 50 percent or more of the data are present) values of -49 dB ref. main beam and 11.4 dB would be found for the mean and standard deviation. These values compare favorably with those derived from calculations involving the complete data set.

The next two methods can best be described by plotting the simple cumulative distribution function on arithmetic probability paper. As mentioned earlier, the scale characteristics of this paper allow the cumulative probability to be represented by a straight line as shown in Fig. 5.13. It is now possible to project the line (even if less than half of the distribution is available) and thus obtain an estimate of the mean value and the standard deviation for the complete distribution.

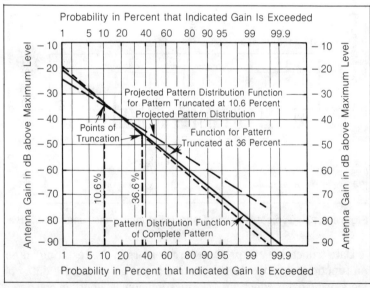

Figure 5.13—Representation of Truncated Antenna Gain Functions

If measured data are available for a sufficient number of points along the distribution, the projection of the cumulative-distribution function can be accomplished by the application of curve-fitting techniques. On the other hand, if there is an insufficient number of measured points to apply curve-fitting techniques, an estimated value can be used for the standard deviation (which is associated with the particular equipment characteristics being modeled). An extrapolation from the last measured data point can be used to find an estimate of the mean.

For example, consider truncating the distribution in Fig. 5.13 at the 36.6 percent probability value. In this case, it is possible to fit a line to the points that are below the 36.6 percent value, and project the line to determine an estimate of the mean as shown in the figure. The estimated values for the mean and standard deviation obtained in this way are −51 dB/main beam and 13.5 dB, respectively.

To illustrate the method used when the distribution is truncated so that there are insufficient data points to specify the line, suppose that only the data points that correspond to probabilities of 10.6 percent or less are available. Further, consider that the standard deviation associated with the particular equipment parameters is known to be approximately 10 dB. Recognizing that the standard deviation determines the slope of the distribution function, it is now possible to project the 10.6 percent point shown in Fig. 5.13 to obtain an estimated mean value of −47.8 dB/main beam.

The fourth method that is available for estimating the mean and standard deviation of a distribution from a truncated data set is represented in Hald's book.[6] This method, which provides a procedure for estimating the mean and standard deviation of a truncated distribution, makes use of formulas and tables presented in Hald's statistical tables and formulas.

Each of the methods outlined above offer certain advantages and disadvantages when considered in terms of the available data and the eventual application of results. For example, the first three methods discussed offer the advantage of simplicity. They may be readily applied to the type of data that is normally obtained from spectrum signature measurements. The fourth method of truncated-data reduction is somewhat more rigorous, but the calculation procedures are more complex. Considering some of the other aspects of EMI prediction, it is doubtful that the increased complexity is justified in many situations.

5.4 Determination of Applicable Antenna Region

In order to use the mathematical models described in the preceding sections for EMC analysis, it is necessary to determine the applicable antenna regions that must be considered for each combination of electromagnetic emission sources and susceptible receptor devices. The criteria and relationships used to determine the appropriate regions are presented in this section.

Consider the situation illustrated in Fig. 5.14 which shows a potentially interfering transmitter-receiver pair. The locations of the transmitter and receiver antennas are specified in rectangular coordinates and the angles are measured with respect to the ordinate or y-axis.

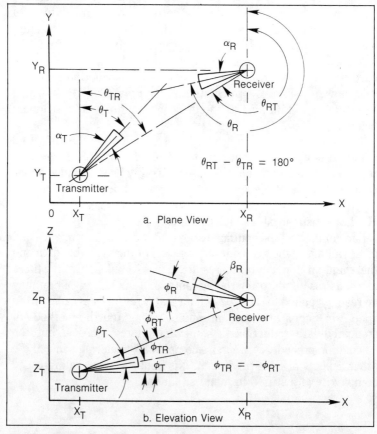

Figure 5.14—Transmitter-Receiver Deployment Used to Determine Applicable Antenna Pattern Region

Transmitting Antenna Region

The receiver is in the intentional-radiation region of the transmitter antenna and Section 5.2 applies when:

Azimuth: $|\Theta_T - \Theta_{TR}| \leqslant \alpha_T/2$ (5.25)
and
Elevation: $|\phi_T - \phi_{TR}| \leqslant \beta_T/2$ (5.26)

where,

Θ_T and ϕ_T = center of azimuth and elevation angle desired transmission (boresight)

Θ_{TR} and ϕ_{TR} = angular direction from interfering transmitter to receiver

α_T and β_T = azimuth and elevation beamwidths of transmitting antenna

When either Eq. (5.25) or Eq. (5.26) does not apply, then the receiver is located in the unintentional region of the transmitter and the relations of Section 5.3 apply.

Receiving Antenna Region

The transmitter is located in the intentional-receiving region of the receiver antenna, and Section 5.2 applies when:

Azimuth: $|\Theta_R - \Theta_{RT}| \leqslant \alpha_R/2$ (5.27)
and
Elevation: $|\phi_R - \phi_{RT}| \leqslant \beta_R/2$ (5.28)

or,

Azimuth: $|\Theta_R - \Theta_{TR} - 180| \leqslant \alpha/2$ (5.29)
and
Elevation: $|\phi_R + \phi_{TR}| \leqslant \beta_R/2$ (5.30)

where,

Θ_R and ϕ_R = angular direction of desired reception

Θ_{RT} and ϕ_{RT} = angular direction from receiver to interfering transmitter.

α_R and β_R = azimuth and elevation beamwidths of receiving antenna

When any of Eqs. (5.27) through (5.30) do not apply, then the transmitter is located in the unintentional region of the receiver, and the relations of Section 5.3 apply.

Determination of Angles

If the location of the transmitter and receiver are specified in rectangular coordinates, the angles Θ_{TR} and ϕ_{TR} are given by:

$$\text{Azimuth:} \quad \Theta_{TR} = \tan^{-1}\left[\frac{x_R - x_T}{y_R - y_T}\right] \qquad (5.31)$$

$$\text{Elevation: } \phi_{TR} = \tan^{-1}\left[\frac{z_R - z_T}{\sqrt{(x_R - x_T)^2 + (y_R - y_T)^2}}\right] \qquad (5.32)$$

If the locations of the transmitter and receiver are given in terms of the geodetic coordinate system, similar relationships are used to determine appropriate antenna regions that must be considered. For this case, Eqs. (5.25) through (5.30) may still be used to determine the appropriate antenna region provided that the effects of earth curvature are negligible, and the angles are now measured with respect to the longitudinal axis. This implies that the separation distances are small with respect to the earth's radius.

Illustrative Example 5.8

Consider a potentially interfering transmitter-receiver pair having the following conditions:

TX coordinates: $x_T = 0$, $y_T = 0$ and $z_T = 30$ m
Direction of desired radiation: $\Theta_T = 20°$ and $\phi_T = 2°$
Beamwidths: $\alpha_T = 5°$ and $\beta_T = 5°$
RX coordinates: $x_R = 16$ km, $y_R = 8$ km and $z_R = 60$ m
Direction of desired reception: $\Theta_R = 245°$ and $\phi_R = 5°$
Beamwidths: $\alpha_R = 10°$ and $\beta_R = 10°$

In order to determine the applicable antenna region, first calculate Θ_{TR} and ϕ_{TR} from Eqs. (5.31) and (5.32)

Thus,
$$\text{Azimuth:} \quad \Theta_{TR} = \tan^{-1}\left[\frac{x_R - x_T}{y_R - y_T}\right]$$

$$= \tan^{-1}\left[\frac{16 - 0}{8 - 0}\right]$$

$$= \tan^{-1}[\,2\,] = 63.4°$$

Elevation: $\quad \phi_{TR} = \tan^{-1}\left[\dfrac{z_R - z_T}{\sqrt{(x_R - x_T)^2 + (y_R - y_T)^2}}\right]$

$$= \tan^{-1}\left[\frac{60 - 30}{\sqrt{16,000^2 + 8,000^2}}\right]$$

$$= \tan^{-1}\left[\frac{30}{\sqrt{320 \times 10^6}}\right]$$

$$= \tan^{-1}[1.7 \times 10^{-3}]$$

$$= 0.1°$$

Equations (5.25) and (5.26) can now be used to determine whether the receiver is in the intentional-radiation region (main beam) of the transmitter:

Azimuth: $\quad |\Theta_T - \Theta_{TR}| \leqslant \alpha_T/2$

and $\quad |20° - 63.4°| = 43.4° \leqslant 5°/2 = 2.5°$: No

Elevation: $\quad |\phi_T - \phi_{TR}| \leqslant \beta_T/2$

$$|2° - 0.1°| = 1.9° \leqslant 5°/2 = 2.5°: \text{Yes}$$

Therefore, the receiver will not be in the intentional-radiation region of the transmitter because the azimuth condition is not satisfied. The considerations of Section 5.3 regarding the unintentional-radiation region apply.

Next, Eqs. (5.29) and (5.30) may be used to determine if the transmitter is in the main-beam region of the receiver:

Azimuth: $\quad |\Theta_R - \Theta_{TR} - 180| \leqslant \alpha_R/2$

$|\Theta_R - \Theta_{TR} - 180| = |245 - 63.4 - 180| = 1.6° \leqslant \alpha/2 = 5°:$ Yes

Elevation: $\quad |\phi_R + \phi_{TR}| \leqslant \beta_R/2$

$|\phi + \phi_{TR}| = |0° + 0.1°| = 0.1° \leqslant \beta_R/2 = 5°:$ Yes

Thus, the transmitter is in the main beam of the receiver.

5.5   Near-Field Models

For EMC analysis, it is often necessary to specify radiation characteristics of an antenna for near-field conditions. This is particularly necessary in the case of high-gain microwave antennas. Near-field conditions for these antennas may extend out to several kilometers. Because of the gains associated with these antennas they are potentially serious from an EMI viewpoint as well as possibly constituting a radiation hazard. In many cases, operational requirements of these systems are such that several potentially interfering systems may be co-located in a mutual near-field region. In the mainbeam of a high-gain antenna which is also radiating high power, the resulting power density may be a threat to human life or ordnance and fuel.

In the near-field region, the representation of characteristics presents a more complicated problem than in the far-field region. Under ideal conditions, near-field characteristics cannot be represented by a single pattern because radiation characteristics are functions of both angular position and distance with respect to the antenna. In the near-field region there are also complex relationships between the electric and magnetic fields, and there may be little correspondence between resulting field-intensity patterns.

For detailed analysis, it is necessary to examine each of the potentially interfering situations remaining after the amplitude and frequency analysis to determine whether a near-field situation exists. For those cases involving near-field situations, antenna gain models used in the amplitude and frequency analysis must be modified to account for near-field effects. The following sections present techniques for determining the near-field to far-field transition distances and calculating the gain reduction resulting from near-field effects.

5.5.1 Transition Distance

The distance for which the far-field approximations are no longer valid and for which near-field considerations must be applied is called the **transition distance**. Basically, the transition from near-field to far-field conditions is a gradual one. However, by specifying the error in the far-field pattern as one moves closer to the antenna, a specific transition distance relationship can be found. For electrically small antennas (antennas for which the maximum dimension, $D < \lambda/2$) the near-field-to-far-field transition will occur at a distance r from the antenna where the fields make the transition from a $1/r^3$ dependence to a $1/r$ dependence. For electrically short antennas this transition occurs at a distance $r = \lambda/2\pi$ away from the antenna.

For electrically large antennas, such as aperture types, the criterion that is often used to define the transition distance is to limit the phase error to 1/4 of a wavelength. This corresponds to a 1 dB error in gain obtainable at an arbitrarily large distance. Now consider the antenna configuration of Fig. 5.15. The distance to a field point along the normal axis of the antenna is different from the distance between the edge of the antenna and the field point. This difference is called the **space-phase error**.

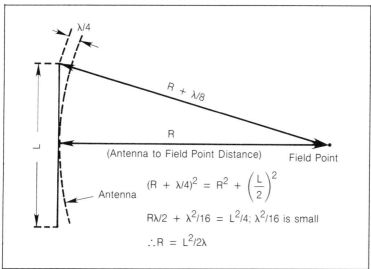

Figure 5.15—Illustration of Space Phase Error

Assuming that the antenna dimension is large compared to the wavelength $(L \gg \lambda)$ in order to limit this error to $\lambda/4$, the distance R to the field point P from the antenna must satisfy:

$$R > L^2/2\lambda \text{ for } L \gg \lambda \tag{5.33}$$

Equation (5.33) applies for high- and medium-gain antennas. When this requirement is not met (L is not $\gg \lambda$ for low-gain antennas), the equation is no longer valid, and it is necessary to adopt the criterion:

$$R > \frac{\lambda}{2\pi} \tag{5.34}$$

to ensure far-field conditions. Thus, to ensure that acceptable far-field conditions exist for EMI analysis, it is required that:

$$R > \frac{L^2}{2\lambda} \text{ and } R > \frac{\lambda}{2\pi}$$

Both conditions must be satisfied at all times. These transition-distance criteria are illustrated graphically in Fig. 5.16.

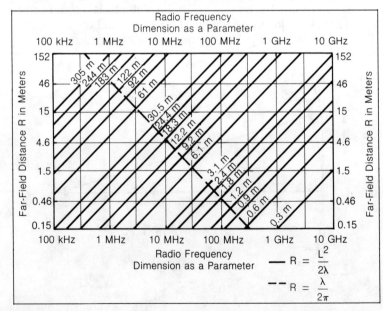

Figure 5.16—Far-Field vs. Frequency with Aperture Dimension as a Parameter

As one moves off main-beam axis, the near-field-to-far-field transition distance is reduced considerably. For high-gain antennas, the transition distance for this off-axis condition can be determined from Fig. 5.17 in the following way. First, locate the solid curve that corresponds to the aperture dimension L for the antenna of interest. Next, locate the intersection of this solid curve with the dashed curve that corresponds to the frequency of interest. The valid region of the solid curve lies above and to the left of the intersection with the frequency curve. For this region, the relationship between transition distance and angular displacement can be obtained directly from the solid curve. If the angular displacement is such that it lies in the invalid region of the solid curve, the near-field criteria given in Eq. (5.33) should be used to determine the near-field transition distance.

From Fig. 5.17 it is clear that the transition distances decrease significantly as one moves off axis. Thus, many EMI prediction problems that would require near-field analysis considerations for an on-axis condition can actually use far-field approximations for off-axis conditions. Futhermore, when moving into the near-field, one of the first effects is that antenna-gain nulls tend to become less pronounced. From the standpoint of EMI prediction, however, the nulls are least important because they represent the lowest levels of radiation from the antenna.

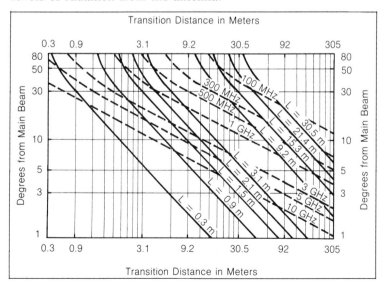

Figure 5.17—Transition Distance for Off-Axis Pointing of Antenna

Illustrative Example 5.9

Consider a parabolic antenna having an aperture dimension (diameter) of 9 m operating at a frequency of 1 GHz. Determine the near-field transition distance for an angular main-beam offset of 10°. From Fig. 5.17, the intersection between the solid curve representing the aperture dimension and the dashed curve representing frequency occurs at an angular offset of 7°. The corresponding transition distance is 82 m. Therefore, the solid curve representing the 9 m aperture dimension may be used directly to determine transition distance for angular offsets greater than 7°. Since the specific value of 10° in this example satisfies this requirement, the actual transition distance is determined to be 58 m by the intersection of L = 9 m and the 10° off-axis value.

5.5.2 Collimated Beam Approximation for Near-Field Gain

For the infrequent case where it is necessary to consider the on-axis, near-field situation, it may be assumed that all of the transmitted power is contained in a cylindrical volume around the antenna axis with a cross-sectional area equal to the antenna aperture. This is the collimated-beam effect. When this conservative approximation is used, the resulting antenna near-field gain at a distance R from the antenna is:

$$G = \frac{4\pi R^2}{area} \quad \text{for } G < G_{FF} \tag{5.35}$$

$$G_{dB} = 11 + 20 \log R - 10 \log A \tag{5.36}$$

where, $\qquad G_{FF}$ = far-field gain

Illustrative Example 5.10

Consider another parabolic antenna having a circular aperture 3 m in diameter, operating at 10 GHz and exhibiting a (far-field) gain of 45 dB. Determine whether a near-field condition exists on-axis at 30 m and, if so, calculate the near-field gain to be used for EMI analysis.

Equation (5.33) or Fig. 5.16 may be used to determine if a near-field condition exists. From Fig. 5.16 the transition near/far-field distance is about 305 m. For on-axis distances less than 305 m, near-field conditions must be considered together with the attendant reduction in gain.

Equation (5.35) is now used to calculate the antenna gain at a 30 m distance from the 45 dB nominal gain:

$$\frac{4\pi R^2}{area} = \frac{4\pi}{\pi/4} \left(\frac{R}{L}\right)^2 = 16 \left(\frac{R}{L}\right)^2$$

$$= 16 \left(\frac{30}{3}\right)^2 = 600 = 32 \text{ dB}$$

This corresponds to a 13 dB loss (45 dB − 32 dB) in gain at the specified near-field distance.

5.5.3 Near-Field Gain Correction

Within the near-field or Fresnel region, the antenna on-axis gain is always less than the far-field gain. For EMI analysis purposes, the near-field gain can be determined by subtracting the appropriate gain correction from the far-field gain. Figures 5.18 through 5.21 give resulting gain corrections for rectangular apertures with various aperture illumination functions.[7]

Illustrative Example 5.11

To illustrate how Figs. 5.18 through 5.21 are used to correct antenna gains for near-field conditions, consider a microwave communication system operating at approximately 10 GHz and using an antenna with dimensions of 3 m by 1.5 m. Assume that the antenna has a cosine aperture distribution and provides a nominal gain of 45 dB above isotropic. Calculate the effective near-field gain on-axis only 30 m from the antenna. The antenna dimension of 3 m is about 100 wavelengths, and 1.5 m is about 50 wavelengths. The 30 m distance from the antenna is 1,000 wavelengths. Using these dimensions and distances in wavelengths, the gain correction (see Fig. 5.19) for an aperture dimension of 100 wavelengths and a distance of 1,000 wavelengths is − 6 dB. Similarly, the gain correction for an aperture dimension of 50 wavelengths and a distance of 1,000 wavelengths is approximately − 1 dB. Hence the total gain correction that must be applied to the antenna for the situation considered is − 7 dB, and the resulting effective gain on-axis 30 m away is (45 dB - 7 dB) or 38 dB.

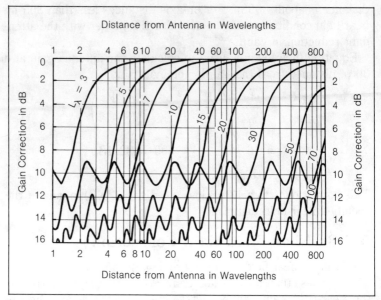

Figure 5.18—Fresnel Region Gain Correction for Uniform Illumination

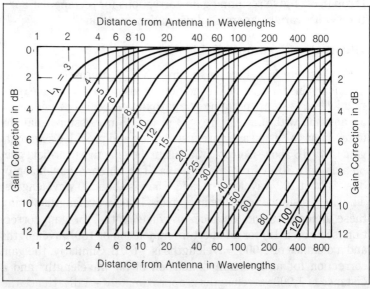

Figure 5.19—Fresnel Region Gain Correction for Cosine Illumination

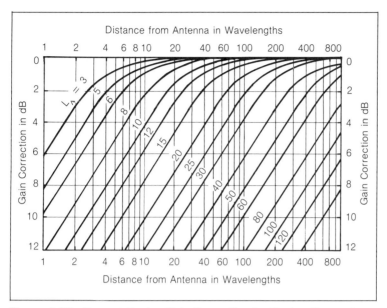

Figure 5.20—Fresnel Region Gain Correction for Cosine Squared

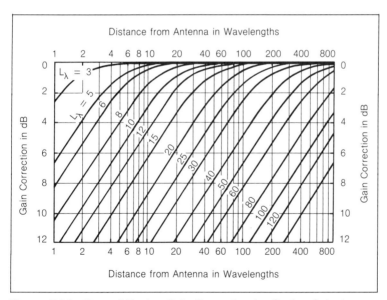

Figure 5.21—Fresnel Region Gain Correction for Cosine Cubed

5.6 Time-Dependent Considerations

If the antennas of the emission sources and susceptible devices in an EMI prediction problem are fixed in orientation, their relative orientations are defined. Thus, either the intentional or unintentional-radiation regions can be established for each applicable combination as discussed in Section 5.4. On the other hand, if one or both antennas are free to scan or change orientation, such as shown in Fig. 5.22, then it is necessary to account for these.

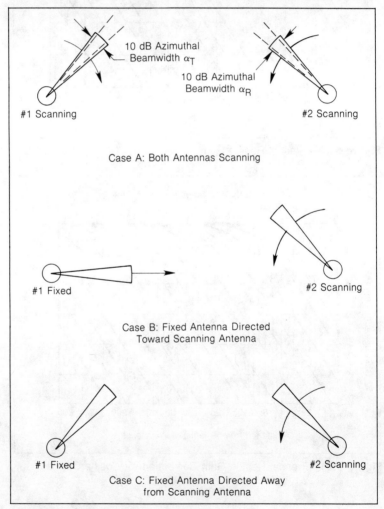

Figure 5.22—Relative Antenna Orientations

If it is assumed that two antennas are scanning in the same plane in a random manner, the relative orientations for the two antennas can be described in terms of the percentage of time (or probability) that various conditions apply. For the situations illustrated in Fig. 5.22, the probabilities P of a single or mutual illumination are:

Case A: Both Antennas Scanning

$$P(\text{TXMB to RXMB}) = \alpha_T\, \alpha_R/360^2 \tag{5.37}$$

$$P(\text{TXMB to RXUR}) = \alpha_T(360 - \alpha_R)/360^2 \tag{5.38}$$

$$\approx \alpha_T/360° \text{ for } 360° > 10\alpha_R \tag{5.39}$$

$$P(\text{TXUR to RXMB}) = (360 - \alpha_T)\, \alpha_R/360^2 \tag{5.40}$$

$$\approx \alpha_R/360° \text{ for } 360° > 10\alpha_T \tag{5.41}$$

$$P(\text{TXUR to RXUR}) = (360 - \alpha_T)(360 - \alpha_R)/360^2 \tag{5.42}$$

$$\frac{360 - (\alpha_T + \alpha_R)}{360} \text{ for } 360° > 10\,\alpha_T \text{ and } 10\alpha_R \tag{5.43}$$

Case B: Fixed Antenna Directed Toward Scanning Antenna

$$P(\text{MB to MB}) = \alpha \text{ scanning}/360° \tag{5.44}$$

$$P(\text{MB to UR}) = (360° - \alpha \text{ scanning})/360° \tag{5.45}$$

$$P(\text{UR to UR}) = \text{NA} = 0 \tag{5.46}$$

Case C: Fixed Antenna Directed Away From Scanning Antenna

$$P(\text{MB to MB}) = \text{NA} = 0 \tag{5.47}$$

$$P(\text{MB to UR}) = \alpha \text{ scanning}/360° \tag{5.48}$$

$$P(\text{UR to UR}) = (360 - \alpha \text{ scanning})/360° \tag{5.49}$$

where,   P = probability condition given
           MB = main-beam or intentional-region condition
               for transmitter (TX) or receiver (RX)
           UR = unintentional region (other than main-beam)
               condition for transmitter (TX) or receiver
               (RX)

The probabilities of main-beam conditions are plotted in Fig. 5.23 as a function of beamwidth. The probability that a main-beam-to-main-beam condition exists is small for narrow-beam antennas. For example, if the transmitting and receiving antennas both have a beamwidth of 10°, the probability of a main-beam-to-main-beam condition (assuming random overtaking of the antennas) is only 0.08 percent, or less than one part in a thousand.

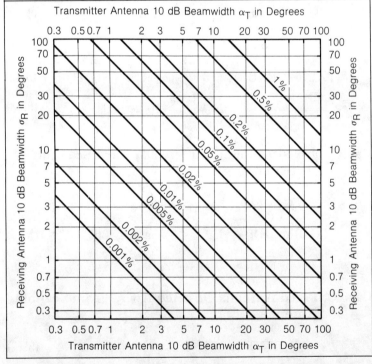

Figure 5.23—Probability of Main-Beam-to-Main-Beam Illumination for Two Scanning Antennas

5.7 References

1. Cf. Stratton, J.H., *Electromagnetic Theory* (New York: McGraw Hill Company, Inc., 1941).
2. Silver, S., *Microwave Antenna Theory and Design*, M.I.T. Radiation Laboratory Series, Vol. 12 (New York: McGraw Hill Company, Inc., 1959).
3. Duff, W.G., and Heisler, Jr., K.G., "The Effect of Sites Upon the Radiation Characteristics of Antennas," *Proceedings of the Tenth Tri-Service Conference on Electromagnetic Compatibility*, Chicago, 1964.
4. *Reference Data for Radio Engineers* (International Telephone and Telegraph Corp., fifth ed., pp. 25-42).
5. Heisler, Jr.; K.G., Hewitt, H.J., et. al., RADC TR-66-1.
6. Hald, A., *Statistical Theory with Engineering Applications* (New York: John Wiley & Sons, 1952).
7. Heisler, Jr.; Hewitt, K.G., et. al.

5.8 Bibliography

1. Baldwin, T.E., Jr., and Adams, A.T., "Near Field Prediction for Antenna Arrays," *1971 IEEE International EMC Symposium Record*, p. 137 (New York: IEEE, 1971).
2. Cain, F.L., et. al., "Prediction Method to Statistically Determine Potential Antenna Interference," *1970 IEEE International EMC Symposium Record*, p. 407 (New York: IEEE, 1970).
3. Cain, F.L., and Byers, Jr., K.G., "Relations of Site Effects to Statistical Gain Characteristics of Radar Antennas," *1968 IEEE EMC Symposium Record*, p. 339 (New York: IEEE, 1969).
4. Cheng, D.K., "Defocus Characteristics of Microwave Reflectors and Lenses," Syracuse University Research Institute, Final Report, RADC-TR-57-56, AF 30(602)-1360, November 1956.
5. Cherot, T.E., Jr., "Calculation of Near Field Antenna Patterns of Aperture Antennas," *1967 IEEE EMC Symposium Record*, p. 145 (New York: IEEE, 1967).
6. Duff, W.G., and Edwards, J.H., "Summary of Equipment EMC Characteristics," *1970 IEEE Regional EMC Symposium Record* (New York: IEEE, 1970).
7. Duff, W.G., and Heisler, K.G., Jr., "The Effects of Sites Upon the Radiation Characteristics of Antennas," *Proceedings of the Tenth Tri-Service Conference on EMC*, November 1964.

8. Gerlock, R.A., "Study of Interference Aspects of Fresnel Region Phenomena," American Systems, Inc., Final Reports, Vols. 1 and 2, RADC-TDR-62-496, AF 30(602)-2507, August 1, 1962.

9. Jacobs, E., "Maximum Power Transfer between Large Aperture Antennas in the Fresnel Region," The Institute of Cooperative Research, University of Pennsylvania, RADC-TR-60-173, AF 30(602)-1785.

10. Jacobs, E., "Fresnel Region Patterns and Gain Corrections of Large Rectangular Apertures," University of Pennsylvania, TADC-TN-60-250, AF 30(602)-1795, December 15, 1959.

11. Jasik, H., ed., *Antenna Engineering Handbook* (New York: McGraw-Hill Book Co., Inc., 1961).

12. Kraus, J.D., *Antennas* (New York: McGraw-Hill Book Co., Inc., 1950).

13. Lindeman, B., "Interference Aspects of Fresnel Region Phenomena," Rome Air Development Center, RADC-TN-60-214, Project 4540, December 1960.

14. Lindeman, B., "A New Look at Fresnel Region Phenomena," Electromagnetic Vulnerability Laboratory, Rome Air Development Center, RAU-TM-62-6, Project 4540, October 1962.

15. Melpar, Inc., "Calculations of Free-Space Radiation Characteristics of Horn Antennas at Spurious Frequencies," Final Report, Vol. II, RADC-TR-61-191B, AF 30(602)-2295, May 1961.

16. Moseley, ST., "On-Axis Defocus Characteristics of the Paraboloidal Reflector," Syracuse Univ. Research Institute, Final Report, AF 30(602)-925, August 1, 1954.

17. Palos, R.J., "Near-Field Antenna-to-Antenna Coupling Calculation Procedures," *1971 IEEE International EMC Symposium Record*, p. 132 (New York: IEEE, 1971).

18. Polk, C., "The Fresnel Region of Large Aperture Antennas," Systems Interference Evaluation, University of Pennsylvania, Final Report, Vol. II, AF 30(602)-583, June 1956.

19. Siegal, M.D., "Near Field Antenna Coupling on Aerospace Vehicles," *1970 IEEE EMC Symposium Record*, p. 211 (New York: IEEE, 1970).

20. Silver, S., "Microwave Antenna Theory and Design," *MIT Radiation Laboratory Series No. 12* (New York: McGraw-Hill Book Col, Inc., 1956).

Chapter 6

Propagation Considerations for EMC Design

Previous chapters discussed EMC analysis models for transmitters, receivers and antennas. This chapter continues the approach by presenting propagation models. It describes different ways in which an interfering signal may be propagated to a victim receiver. It provides criteria that may be used to identify the most significant modes of propagation and presents mathematical models which describe the propagation loss resulting from these modes. The chapter also indicates how these models may be used to calculate the propagation loss in EMC design and analysis.

Most communication-electronic (CE) systems depend on electromagnetic propagation for the transfer of signals between the transmitter and receiver. In addition to being propagated to the intended point of reception, signals are also radiated into and received from unintended directions and locations. Thus, strong signals that are intended for reception at a distant point may produce an undesired electromagnetic field at a nearby receiver and result in EMI. In evaluating EMC, it is necessary to examine various propagation modes that may exist between emission sources and susceptible devices to determine the amount of isolation (or attenuation) provided by the physical separation of equipments.

In performing an EMC analysis, realize that interference often results from undesired modes of propagation, and thus each significant mode must be considered. The analysis must include any mode of propagation which yields a strong enough signal to cause interference, even with low probability. There is a definite contrast between the system-design criteria of one mode with high reliability and the EMI criteria of any mode with low reliability. It is necessary to provide a high degree of protection against interfering emissions so that a basic system design has the high degree of reliability demanded of present CE circuits. The following section identifies the parameters that are important in analyzing propagation loss and briefly describes various propagation modes that must be considered.

6.1 Propagation Modes

Many parameters affect the mode of propagation and the propagation loss between two given points. Some of the more important factors which must be considered include frequency, distance, polarization, antenna heights, terrain, ground constants, time, season, weather and radiated power. Specific factors that must be considered in a given circumstance and the degree to which they influence the resulting propagation loss depend on the frequency, distance and antenna heights. The following paragraphs discuss some of the major propagation modes that are important in EMC analysis.

A great deal of confusion exists concerning the various modes of radio propagation; therefore, it is essential that careful definitions for the various possible propagation modes be established. For EMC analysis applications in general, the major modes of propagation can be categorized as **ground-wave**, **ionospheric**, **scatter** and **complex co-site**.

Figure 6.1 illustrates the primary propagation modes, and Fig. 6.2 provides general frequency and distance limits for these modes. The major characteristics for each of the primary propagation modes are summarized in Table 6.1, parts a through g. The following sections describe some of the major considerations that apply to each of the primary propagation modes.

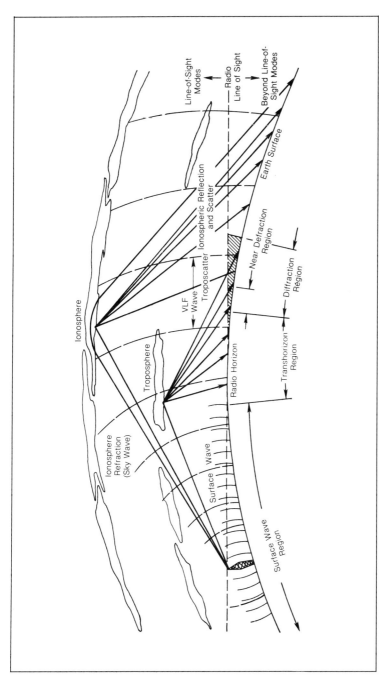

Figure 6.1—Illustration of Primary Propagating Modes

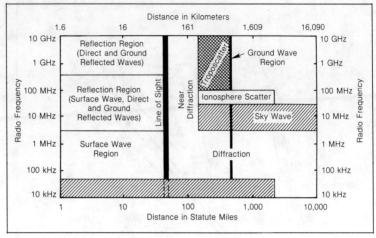

Figure 6.2—Generalized Frequency and Distance Limits of Primary Propagation Modes.

Table 6.1—Summary of Characteristics for Primary Propagation Modes

6.1a Surface-Wave Characteristics		
Characteristic Type	**Characteristic**	**Remarks**
Frequency Range	0.03 - 3 MHz	At 0.03 - 3 MHz primary mode, used to 100 MHz for mobile communication.
Distance Range	Radio Horizon or Less	The distance range depends mainly on frequency, radiated power, terrain, and antenna heights.
Fading	Insignificant	
Diurnal Variation	Insignificant	
Reliability	95 Percent	Atmospheric noise is especially significant at low latitudes.
Polarization	Vertical	Vertical polarization predominates over horizontal polarization.

6.1b Reflection Region Propagation Characteristics

Characteristic Type	Characteristic	Remarks
Frequency Range	3 - 12,000 MHz	No definite limits
Distance Range	1.6 - 80 km (1 - 50 ml)	Typical ground-to-ground propagation limits
Predominant Polarization	Horizontal or vertical	Horizontal presents deeper nulls
Fading	Rapid	Multipath Changes in atmospheric layering
Diurnal Variation	Day: Standard atmosphere Night: Possible temperature inversion resulting in fading and ducting	
Seasonal Variation	Deeper fades in summer than in winter	20 dB fades in winter, 6 dB fades in summer
Reliability	≅ 100 percent	

6.1c Summary of Propagation Characteristics in the Near Diffraction Region

Characteristic Type	Characteristic	Remarks
Frequency Range	0.080 - 1,000 MHz	
Distance Range	≤ 1,920 km (≤ 1,200 mi)	Greatest over sea water, least over poor soil
Predominant Polarization	Vertical	
Fading	Very slow	Signal fadeouts for periods of one minute to several hours
Diurnal Variation	Small	Just beyond radio horizon
Seasonal Variations	Small	Greater variation in winter than in summer

6.1d Skywave Propagation Characteristics		
Characteristic Type	**Characteristic**	**Remarks**
Frequency Range	6 kHz - 30 kHz 30 kHz - 30 MHz	6 kHz - 30 kHz VLF waveguide propagation, 30 kHz - 30 MHz ionospheric reflection
Distance Range	No limit	
Fading	1. Rapid multipath fading 2 Polarization fading ≈ 3 db 3. Skip fading when frequency is close to MUF 4. Absorption	
Diurnal Variation	MUF varies greatly being lower at night, highest at noon. Absorption highest during day, noise highest during night	
Seasonal Variations	MUF, absorption, and noise levels shift over the earth's surface with the seasons	
Polarization	Horizontal predominant over vertical	

6.1e Summary of Characteristics for Tropospheric Scatter Propagation

Characteristic Type	Characteristic	Remarks
Frequency Range	100 - 10,000 MHz	Very broad frequency range, limits not well defined
Distance Range	Well beyond the radio horizon	Depends upon the particular propagation path
Predominant Polarization	None	
Fading (short term)	Multipath rapid fading; usually does not exceed Rayleigh distribution	20 dB fades expected about 1 percent of time; 30 dB fades expected about 0.1 percent of time
Fading (long term)	Depends upon average refraction in atmosphere; LOS normal distribution of hourly medians with standard deviation, 8 dB	
Diurnal Variation	Small diurnal variation	Signal levels higher between midnight and noon, diurnal variation more pronounced in summer than winter
Seasonal Variation	Significant seasonal variation	Highest signal levels recorded during summer and fall. Lowest levels during winter and spring
Reliability	Approximately 100 percent	

6.1f Ionospheric Scatter Propagation Characteristics		
Characteristic Type	Characteristic	Remarks
Frequency Range	10 - 50 MHz	
Distance Range	320 - 2,240 km (200 - 1,400 mi)	Most useful 960 - 1,920 km (600 - 1,200 mi)
Predominant Polarization	Horizontal	Results from antenna considerations
Fading	Rapid due to multipath	Excluding meteor bursts, Rayleigh distributed
	Slow due to variation in height of reflecting layers	Distribution of hourly median loss relative to long term medians approximately normal with standard deviation of 6 - 8 dB
Diurnal Variation	10 - 12 dB	Strongest at noon, weakest at 8 p.m.
Seasonal Variation	Hourly median varies with 6 - 8 dB standard deviation about yearly median. Signal strongest in June - July; weakest in September	
Reliability	≈ 95 percent	

6.1g Summary of Characteristics for Meteor Propagation		
Characteristic Type	Characteristic	Remarks
Frequency Range	5 - 75 MHz	
Distance Ranges	320 - 1,920 km (200 - 1,200 mi)	Lower limit can go to zero depending upon radiated power
Fading	Continuous weak rapidly fluctuating signal	
Diurnal Variation	Maximum signal levels at 6 A.M., minimum signal levels at 6 P.M.	Very approximate, signal level depends on meteor characteristics and not on regular ionospheric layers
Seasonal Variation	Maximum incidence of meteors occurs in summer, minimum in spring	
Predominant Polarization	Horizontal	Scattering of an ionized volume

6.1.1 Free-Space Propagation

Free-space propagation forms the basis for the propagation loss calculations that apply to many EMC analysis situations. This mode is often used for EMC analysis situations for which line-of-sight conditions prevail. For situations where there is no reflection, diffraction or scattering, the free-space propagation model will provide reasonably accurate representations of the propagation loss. This type of condition would be expected to exist for situations where: (1) high-gain antennas are used, e.g., radar antennas where there are no reflections from the ground or other conducting surfaces and only the direct ray exists and (2) the transmitter or receiver systems are air- or spaceborne and the reflected waves, if any, are minimal.

6.1.2 Ground-Wave Propagation

The previous section discussed a propagation mode called free space, i.e., the area where there are no objects or surfaces in the propagating path (other than the two antennas). This section discusses the more realistic situation where there are surfaces between the transmitter and receiver.

The ground wave is a radio wave which is propagated over the earth and is ordinarily affected by the presence of the ground and the troposphere but is not affected by the ionosphere. The ground wave includes all components of a radio wave over the earth except ionospheric and tropospheric waves and is the sum of their components. For instance, in the surface-wave region the ground wave is the sum of the direct, the ground-reflected and the surface wave. The following components are included under the general heading of ground wave and are illustrated in Figs. 6.1 and 6.2.

6.1.2.1 Surface Wave

The surface wave is that part of the ground wave which travels over the surface of the earth. Within this section the surface wave is considered only out to the radio horizon (line of sight). Beyond the radio horizon, diffraction is considered to be the predominate ground-wave component.

6.1.2.2 Reflection Region

The reflection region is that region in which the interaction between a direct and earth-reflected ray must be considered. This region lies within and above the radio horizon. Reflection-region techniques apply only when the antennas have significant elevations with respect to a wavelength.

6.1.2.3 Diffraction

Well beyond the radio horizon, diffraction over rough or irregular terrain is considered to be the principal source of ground-wave energy. However, in the region well beyond the radio horizon the other two principal modes, ionospheric propagation and scatter propagation must be considered. The diffraction region applies to frequencies greater than 30 kHz.

6.1.2.4. Transhorizon

The transhorizon region lies between the reflection region and the diffraction region. Because this region is also beyond the radio horizon, reflection theory is not applicable. Additionally, neither surface-wave theory nor diffraction theory describe the signal levels adequately.

6.1.3 Ionospheric Propagation

The ionospheric propagation mode as defined here includes all means of propagation in which the ionosphere plays a role, except ionospheric scatter. Two basic ionospheric modes are identifiable. The first mode, sky-wave, is that portion of a radio wave which travels upward in space and is returned to the earth by refraction in the ionosphere. The lower boundaries of the ionosphere play an important part in the propagation of energy at VLF. VLF depends on the existence of the ionosphere and the surface of the earth for support. The ionospheric modes involve relatively high losses and thus are less likely to contribute to EMI. For this reason, ionospheric modes are not emphasized in this volume.

6.1.4 Scatter Propagation

Propagation of electromagnetic energy by scattering in either the ionosphere or the troposphere represents the fourth basic form of propagation to be considered. Propagation by these modes is characterized by extremely high losses. However, these modes have become significant with the advent of high-power, high-gain and highly directive antenna systems. Three propagation modes arc included under the heading of scatter propagation: (1) ionospheric scatter, (2) tropospheric scatter and (3) meteor burst scatter.

Ionospheric scatter involves the scattering of energy which takes place in an ionospheric volume of space. Ionospheric scatter is significant in the frequency range from about 30 MHz to 100 MHz and over distances from about 800 to 2,400 km (500 to 1,500 mi).

Tropospheric scatter involves the scattering of energy within the troposphere. It is significant over the frequency range from 100 MHz to 10 GHz and over distances from 160 to 800 km (100 to 500 mi).

Meteor scatter represents a rather exotic mode of propagation which has attracted attention in recent years. This mode is supported by scattering from the ionized trails left by meteors as they pass through the outer atmosphere. Meteor scatter will support intermittent propagation over the frequency range from about 50 MHz to 150 MHz and over distance ranging from about 800 to 2,400 km (500 to 1,500 mi).

In general, scatter propagation modes involve large losses, and thus they are not usually primary modes from the standpoint of EMI. For this reason, these modes are not emphasized in this handbook.

6.1.5 Complex Co-site Propagation

In many EMI situations involving co-site transmitting and receiving systems, the antenna-to-antenna coupling is influenced by reflecting and scattering objects in the vicinity of the antennas. This type of situation is likely to exist between antennas mounted on a ship, an aircraft, a tower, adjacent buildings in an urban environment, etc. For this type of co-site situation, it may be necessary to consider the effects of reflection, scattering, obstacle blockage and diffraction that influence the antenna coupling.

6.2 Propagation Mode Selection

For a particular situation, the applicable propagation mode depends on frequency, distance, antenna heights and polarization. Frequency is usually the first parameter used to determine the applicable mode. Five categories of frequency ranges may be identified, and the applicable mode or modes may be defined for each. These categories are described below, and Table 6.2 summarizes the applicable mode within each category.

Table 6.2—Frequency Check in Propagation Mode Selection Process

Category	Frequency Range MHz	Primary Propagation Modes	Others
I	$f < 0.03$	Very Low Frequency	
II	$0.03 \leqslant f < 3$	Surface Wave Transhorizon Region Diffraction Region	Sky Wave Reflection
III	$3 \leqslant f < 30$	High-Frequency Sky Wave	Surface Wave Reflection Region Transhorizon Region Diffraction Region
IV	$30 \leqslant f < 100$	Reflection Region Transhorizon Region Diffraction Region	Surface Wave Knife-Edge Diffraction Ionospheric Scatter Meteor Burst
V	$100 \leqslant f$	Reflection Region Transhorizon Region Diffraction Region	Knife-Edge Diffraction Tropospheric Scatter

Category I includes frequencies less than 30 kHz. All propagation in this frequency range can be adequately described by VLF waveguide mode theory.

Category II includes frequencies from 30 kHz to 3 MHz. In this frequency range, the primary mode of propagation is the ground wave.

The surface-wave region, transhorizon region and diffraction region fields which make up the ground-wave field at these frequencies are separated as a function of distance so that only one of the three modes applies at any one time. The criteria for using the surface-wave, transhorizon or the diffraction modes are as follows. Compute the factor D, which is the maximum distance for which the antennas are within radio line of sight.

$$D = 4.1\left(\sqrt{h_T} + \sqrt{h_R} \right) \qquad (6.1)$$

where,

h_T = height of transmitting antenna in meters

h_R = height of receiving antenna in meters

d = distance in kilometers

For h_T and h_R in feet and d in miles, the equation is:

$$D = \sqrt{2\,h_T} + \sqrt{2\,h_R}$$

If the propagation distance d over which one is interested in calculating loss is less than D, the surface-wave mode will dominate for vertically polarized situations where the antenna heights are much less than a wavelength. If the distance d is greater than or equal to D, then compute the factor K.

$$K = \frac{2.14 \times 10^2\ k^{2/3}}{f_{mHz}^{1/3}} \text{ (kilometers)} \tag{6.2}$$

$$K = \frac{1.33 \times 10^2\ k^{2/3}}{f_{MHz}^{1/3}} \text{ (miles)}$$

where,   k = effective earth radius factor,
                  usually considered to be 4/3

If the distance d is such that:

$$D \leqslant d \leqslant D + K \tag{6.3}$$

the transhorizon region applies.

If the distance d is such that:

$$d > D + K \tag{6.4}$$

the diffraction region applies.

Although the ground wave (surface wave, transhorizon or diffraction modes) generally dominate in this frequency range, sky-wave or reflection modes of propagation may also apply.

Category III includes frequencies from 3 MHz to 30 MHz. At distances beyond 800 km (500 mi), ionospheric propagation dominates exclusively in the 3 to 30 MHz range. For distances less than 80 km (50 mi), the vertically polarized surface wave supports most of the propagation load. At points between 80 and 800 km (50 and 500 mi), the ground-wave mode or sky-wave mode may either be dominant or of equal importance. In these cases, the losses for both the sky-wave mode and the surface-wave, transhorizon region or diffraction region mode must be calculated. The results of the loss calculations are then compared to determine whether to use surface-wave, transhorizon region or diffraction region techniques.

Category IV includes frequencies from 30 to 100 MHz. Within Category IV, the primary mode of propagation is ground wave. The significant ground-wave phenomena can fall within either the surface-wave region, the reflection region, the transhorizon region or the diffraction region. A preliminary decision concerning the specific region can be made in the following way:

If the separation distance d is greater than D + K, where D + K is computed by Eqs. (6.1) and (6.2) from Category II, then the diffraction region methods are used. The above test is only approximate. There is a more detailed check which will either verify that the diffraction region applies or will refer the user to the transhorizon region.

If the separation distance is between D and D + K, the transhorizon region is to be used. If the distance d is less than D, it is necessary to decide whether to compute the reflection field, surface wave or both.

The surest way to make the decision between surface wave and reflection region is to compute the basic transmission loss for both modes, compare the results and take the lower loss. Other possible modes are transhorizon region, diffraction region or the knife edge diffraction region. For distances well beyond the radio horizon and certainly beyond 320 km (200 mi), the effects of ionospheric scattering and meteor burst scattering must be considered.

Category V includes frequencies greater than 100 MHz. The same criteria apply to Category V as Category IV, with two exceptions. First, ionospheric and meteor burst scattering no longer have to be considered. Second, for distances well beyond the radio horizon, the losses due to tropospheric scattering must be checked.

6.3 Characteristics of Free-Space Propagation

In discussing concepts regarding the various propagation modes, it is helpful to begin with a discussion of free-space propagation between lossless isotropic antennas. Once the principles governing propagation under these conditions are understood, it is easier to follow the concept of propagation between either omnidirectional or directional antennas in the presence of earth and atmospheric discontinuities such as the ionosphere and the troposphere.

If a transmitted signal is radiated from an isotropic antenna in free space, the signal spreads uniformly in all directions as illustrated in Fig. 6.3.

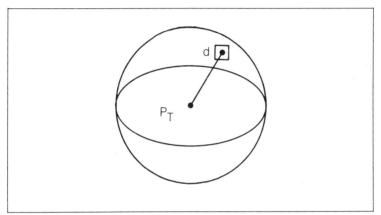

Figure 6.3—Illustration of Free-Space Propagation

Thus, at a distance d from the source, the power density is:

$$P_D = \frac{P_T}{4\pi d^2} \qquad (6.5)$$

where, P_D = power density (i.e., power per unit area)

P_T = transmitted power

d = distance from antenna to observation point

The power available at the terminals of a lossless isotropic receiving antenna having an effective area, A_R, and a gain G = 1, is:

$$P_R = P_D A_R = P_D \frac{G\lambda^2}{4\pi} = \frac{P_T \lambda^2}{(4\pi d)^2} \qquad (6.6)$$

where, λ = wavelength in the same units as d

The above relationship can be expressed in terms of frequency in MHz, f_{MHz} and distance d in kilometers (or statute miles) by substituting for λ:

$$\lambda(km) = \frac{0.3 \text{ km/s}}{f_{MHz}} \tag{6.7}$$

or $\qquad \lambda(miles) = \dfrac{984}{f_{MHz} \times 5{,}280}$

Then,

$$P_T/P_R = \frac{(4\pi)^2}{(0.3)^2} f_{MHz}^2 \, d_{km}^2 \tag{6.8}$$

$$= 1.75 \times 10^3 \, f_{MHz}^2 \, d_{km}^2$$

or, $\qquad P_T/P_R = \dfrac{(4\pi)^2 \, (5{,}280)^2}{(984)^2} \, f_{MHz}^2 \, d_{mi}^2$

$$= 4.56 \times 10^3 \, f_{MHz}^2 \, d_{mi}^2$$

Therefore, the free-space attenuation in dB between lossless isotropic antennas for far-field conditions is:[1]

$$L(f, d) = 10 \log P_T/P_R \tag{6.9}$$

$$= 32 + 20 \log f_{MHz} + 20 \log d_{km}$$

or $\qquad = 37 + 20 \log f_{MHz} + 20 \log d_{mi}$

Equation (6.9) is plotted in Fig. 6.4 for a frequency from 0.01 MHz to 100 GHz and a distance from 0.16 to 1,600 km (0.1 to 1,000 mi).

The propagation attenuation given by Eq. (6.9) is called free-space basic transmission loss. In this handbook, the term basic transmission loss refers to the propagation attenuation between isotropic antennas. Another interesting term in EMI prediction is transmission coupling which includes the effects of antenna directivity.

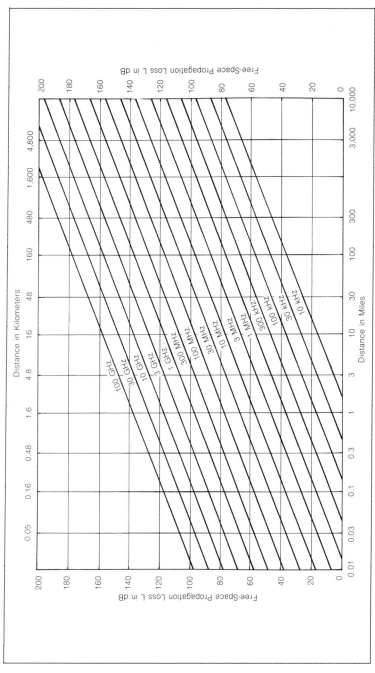

Figure 6.4—Free-Space Propagation Loss

For far-field (see Chapter 5) free-space conditions, the transmission coupling C_{TR} (in dB) is a function of frequency (f), time (t), distance (d) and direction (p) and is given by:

$$C_{TR}(f, t, d, p) = G_{TR}(f, t, d, p) - L(f, t, d, p) + G_{RT}(f, t, d, p)$$

(6.10)

where,

$L(f, t, d, p)$ = free-space basic transmission loss in dB

$G_{TR}(f, t, d, p)$ = transmitting antenna gain in direction of receiving antenna in dB

$G_{RT}(f, t, d, p)$ = receiving antenna gain in direction of transmitter in dB

Free-space propagation conditions are generally used as the basis for amplitude and frequency analysis phases of EMI prediction and also provide a basis for many propagation considerations that are applied during the detailed prediction. Therefore, it is essential to have a firm understanding of the techniques used in these calculations.

Illustrative Example 6.1: Free-Space Coupling Loss Between Isotropic Antennas

A strong, potentially interfering signal (30 MHz) source is known to exist 6.4 km (4 mi) from a planned telecommunication network. It is necessary to determine the free-space coupling (C_{TR}) and fundamental interference margin (FIM) at the planned receiver to assign the network frequency so that it will affect an EMI-free operation. Assume that both transmitter and receiving antenna gains are 0 dB, the interfering transmitter power P_T is 0.1 W (+20 dBm) and the victim receiver sensitivity P_R is –110 dBm.

Substituting Eq. (6.9) into Eq. (6.10) yields for C_{TR}:

$$C_{TR} = G_{TR} - (32 + \log f_{MHz} + 20 \log d_{km}) + G_{RT}$$

$$= -[32 + 20 \log (30) + 20 \log(6.4)]$$

$$= -(32 + 30 + 16) = -78 \text{ dB}$$

Thus, the FIM from Eq. (6.9), is:

$$FIM = P_T + C_{TR} - P_R$$

$$= 20 \text{ dBm} - 78 \text{ dB} + 110 \text{ dBm} = 52 \text{ dB}$$

This means that the fundamental of the potentially interfering transmitter produces a signal at the receiver which is 52 dB above the receiver sensitivity. To ensure EMC for weak desired signal conditions it will be necessary to assign the transmitter and receiver frequencies so that approximately 50 dB of rejection is provided to the potentially interfering signal.

Illustrative Example 6.2: Free-Space Coupling Loss Between Gain Antennas

Determine the free-space transmission coupling and the resulting EMI situation between a UHF transmitter operating at 400 MHz and a receiver operating in the same frequency range. Consider that the transmitter and receiver are separated by 0.16 km (0.1 mi) and the antenna gains for both transmitter and receiver are 6 dB. From Eqs. (6.9) and (6.10), the transmission coupling is:

$$C_{TR} = G_{TR} - (32 + 20 \log f_{MHz} + 20 \log d_{km}) + G_{RT}$$

$$= 6 - [32 + 20 \log(400) + 20 \log(0.16)] + 6$$

$$= 6 - (32 + 52 - 16) + 6 = -56 \text{ dB}$$

Referring to the basic prediction equation, Eq. (2.2), the power available at the receiver is:

$$P_A = P_T + C_{TR}$$

For a transmitter power of 100 W (50 dBm), the potentially interfering power available P_A at the receiver fundamental frequency would be:

$$P_A = P_T + C_{TR}$$

$$= 50 \text{ dBm} - 56 \text{ dB} = -6 \text{ dBm}$$

If the receiver sensitivity PR is −100 dBm, the FIM obtained by applying Eq. (2.5) is:

$$FIM = P_A - P_R$$

$$= -6 \text{ dBm} - (-100 \text{ dBm}) = 94 \text{ dB}$$

Thus, the potentially interfering signal level available at the receiver is 94 dB above the receiver sensitivity.

6.4 Ground-Wave Propagation Models

When a radio wave is propagated over the earth, there are several different phenomena that occur. The selection of an applicable model depends on the particular phenomena that are most significant for the specific conditions being considered. Important factors which influence the selection of an appropriate model are the frequency range of interest and whether line-of-sight or beyond line-of-sight conditions prevail.

For line-of-sight (LOS) propagation conditions, the ground wave consists of three components: a surface wave, a direct wave and a ground-reflected wave. The resulting field at a particular location is the vector sum of the three components. Mathematically, the electric-field intensity E is given by:[2]

$$E = \frac{E_o}{d} \left[(1 - \bar{R}) \, f(P, B) \cos^2 \psi_2 e^{j2\pi[(r_2/\lambda) + \phi]} + \cos^3 \psi_1 e^{j2\pi r_1/\lambda} + \bar{R} \cos^3 \psi_2 e^{j2\pi r_2/\lambda} \right] \tag{6.11}$$

The first term in Eq. (6.11) is the surface-wave component, the second is the direct wave and the third term is the ground-reflected wave. The three components are illustrated in Fig. 6.5, and the parameters d, r_1, r_2, ψ_1 and ψ_2 are defined in Fig. 6.6. The parameters d, r_1, r_2 and λ are expressed in the same units. The units of E and E_o are also identical. The surface-wave attenuation function f(P, B) is discussed later. The parameter E_o is the free-space field strength at a unit distance from the transmitting antenna; R is the complex plane-earth reflection coefficient.

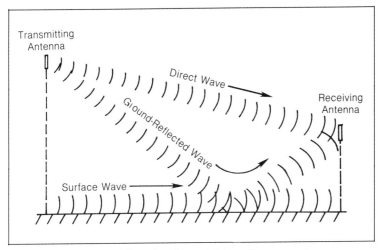

Figure 6.5—Diagram Showing Ground Wave Components

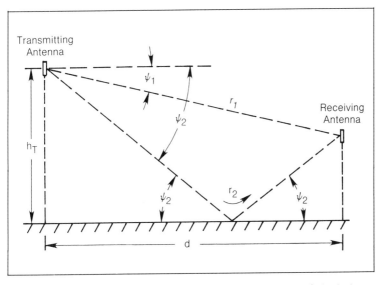

Figure 6.6—Configuration for Plane Earth Ground Wave Calculation

The first term of Eq. (6.11) represents the surface wave which applies to EMI prediction situations involving line-of-sight propagation in the frequency range between 30 kHz and 30 MHz. For most applications, the vertically polarized surface wave is the only significant mode. For surface-wave propagation, antenna heights must be small compared to a wavelength. Under these conditions, effects of irregular terrain generally need not be considered. Techniques for calculating surface-wave basic transmission loss are presented in Section 6.4.1.

The reflection region (where the direct wave and ground-reflected waves are predominant) applies to line-of-sight situations in the frequency range above 30 MHz. Propagation in this region is significantly influenced by terrain effects. These effects cannot usually be subjected to precise treatment in an EMI prediction. For this reason it is often best to use empirically derived, statistical models for the basic transmission loss in this region. One such model is presented later in Eq. (6.31). To gain an understanding of the major considerations that apply to the reflection-region mode of propagation, theoretical analysis models are presented for a plane earth and a smooth spherical earth.

For beyond line-of-sight propagation conditions, applicable regions for ground-wave propagation are the transhorizon region and the diffraction region as presented in Section 6.1.2. The transhorizon region applies to situations in the vicinity of the boundary between "line-of-sight" and beyond line-of-sight, whereas the diffraction region applies to situations that are well beyond the radio horizon. Diffraction region models for EMI prediction are presented in Section 6.4.3, and techniques for calculating propagation loss in the transhorizon region are presented in Section 6.4.4.

6.4.1 Surface Wave

The surface-wave mode of propagation applies to line-of-sight situations involving vertically polarized antennas within the frequency range between approximately 30 kHz and 30 MHz. From Eq. (6.11) the magnitude of the plane earth surface wave is given by:[3]

$$|E| = \left| \frac{E_o}{d} \ (1 - \bar{R}) \ f \ (P, B) \ \cos^2 \psi_2 \right| \qquad (6.12)$$

The plane-earth, surface-wave assumption is valid for distances less than $80 \ f_{MHz}^{-1/3}$ km (or $50 \ f_{MHz}^{-1/3}$ statute mi). The maximum applicable range for the plane-earth surface wave is plotted in Fig. 6.7 as a function of frequency.

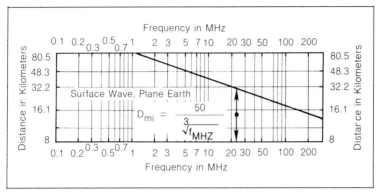

Figure 6.7—Model Validity Limits—Surface Wave Plane Earth vs. Surface Wave Spherical Earth

6.4.1.1 Basic Transmission Loss for Surface-Wave Propagation with Zero-Height Antenna

For frequencies involved in surface-wave propagation, antenna heights are small relative to a wavelength. The surface-wave propagation loss is minimal for zero-height antennas and increases when the antennas are elevated. For this reason, the zero-height antenna assumption provides a good approximation for most EMI prediction. For the special condition in which the transmitting and receiving antennas are at the surface of the earth and their antenna heights are zero, the magnitude of $\cos \psi_2 = 1$ and $(1 - \bar{R}) = 2$ in Eq. (6.12). Therefore, substituting these simplifying conditions into Eq. (6.12) results in the following equation [note that in the case of zero-height antennas the function f(P, B) is replaced by f(p, b)].

$$|E| = \frac{2E_o}{d} f(p, b) \tag{6.13}$$

or alternatively, the equation for basic transmission loss is:

$$L_b = 26.47 + 20 \log f_{MHz} + 20 \log d_{km} - 20 \log f(p, b) \tag{6.14}$$

or,

$$L_b = 30.55 + 20 \log f_{MHz} + 20 \log d_{mi} - 20 \log f(p, b)$$

6.23

where, for vertical polarization:

$$p = \frac{\pi r_2}{\lambda} \frac{\cos^2 b''}{X \cos b'} \tag{6.15}$$

$$b = 2b'' - b'$$

and, for horizontal polarization:

$$p = \frac{\pi r_2}{\lambda} \frac{X}{\cos b'} \tag{6.16}$$

$$b = 180° - b'$$

with,

$$r_2 = \frac{1{,}000d}{\cos \psi_2} \tag{6.17}$$

$$X = \frac{18{,}000\,\sigma}{f_{MHz}} \tag{6.18}$$

$$b' = \tan^{-1} \frac{\epsilon_r - 1}{X} \tag{6.19}$$

$$b'' = \tan^{-1} \frac{\epsilon_r}{X} \tag{6.20}$$

where,

ϵ_r = relative permittivity of earth

σ = earth conductivity in mho meters per meter^2

In Eq. (6.17), r_2 is in meters and d is in kilometers.

The surface-wave attenuation function, f(p, b), is given graphically in Fig. 6.8 as f(p, b) versus p for several values of b.* For values of p > 100 the attenuation function for all values of b is:

---

*Figure 6.8 should be used if manual techniques are used to evaluate the propagation loss. If a computer is used, the convergent series may be used to evaluate f(p, b). For a more detailed discussion, the reader is referred to K.A. Norton, "The Propagation of Radio Waves over the Surface of the Earth and in the Upper Atmosphere," Proceedings IRE, Volume 24, pp. 1,367-87, Oct. 1936.

$$f(p, b) = \frac{1}{2p} \qquad (6.21)$$

6.4.1.2 Basic Transmission Loss for Surface Wave with Elevated Antennas

As mentioned above, surface-wave basic transmission loss increases from the value found for zero-height antennas as antenna are elevated. The effect of antenna height on propagation loss is more pronounced at higher frequencies. In the case where one or both of the antennas are elevated and plane earth conditions apply, Eq. (6.12) gives the magnitude of the surface wave, i.e.:

$$|E| = \left| \frac{E_o}{d} (1 - \bar{R}) f(P, B) \cos^2 \psi_2 \right| \qquad (6.22)$$

or alternatively,

$$L = 32 + 20 \log(f_{MHz}) + 20 \log d_{km} - 20 \log[f(P, B)] \qquad (6.23)$$

$$- 40 \log(\cos \psi_2) - 20 \log(1 - \bar{R})$$

where,

$$\psi_2 = \tan^{-1}\left(\frac{h_T + h_R}{1,000 d_{km}}\right) \qquad (6.24)$$

$\bar{R}$ = plane-earth reflection coefficient

h_T = height of transmitting antenna in meters

h_R = height of receiving antenna in meters

d_{km} = distance in kilometers

$$Pe^{jB} = \left[1 + \frac{q_1 + q_2}{2p} e^{j(\pi/4 - b/2)} \right]^2 e^{jb} \qquad (6.25)$$

For vertical polarization:

$$q_1 = 0.021 \ f_{MHz} \ h_T \left[\frac{\cos^2 b''}{X \cos b'} \right]^{1/2} \tag{6.26}$$

$$q_2 = 0.021 \ f_{MHz} \ h_R \left[\frac{\cos^2 b''}{X \cos b'} \right]^{1/2} \tag{6.27}$$

For horizontal polarization:

$$q_1 = 0.021 \ f_{MHz} \ h_T \left[\frac{X}{\cos b'} \right]^{1/2} \tag{6.28}$$

$$q_2 = 0.021 \ f_{MHz} \ h_R \left[\frac{X}{\cos b'} \right]^{1/2} \tag{6.29}$$

If $(q_1 + q_2) < 0.01$, the zero-height antenna calculations may be used. For elevated antennas, the surface-wave attenuation function is derived from Fig. 6.8 by replacing p, b as determined for zero-height antennas with P, B. Again, as in the case with zero-height antennas, if $P > 100$ then:

$$f(P, B) = \frac{1}{2p} \tag{6.30}$$

6.4.1.3 Curves for Surface-Wave Basic Transmission Loss

Figures 6.9 and 6.10 illustrate basic transmission loss for the surface wave. The two figures correspond to average land and salt water, respectively. Each figure is plotted for zero-height antennas and vertical polarization. These curves may be used to provide estimates of surface-wave basic transmission loss for use in EMI prediction. The curves are valid only for plane-earth, surface-wave region distances. For greater distances, transhorizon and diffraction methods must be applied. Many curves of the type shown are presented in other references. For example, see *Propagation Data for Interference Analysis*, prepared for Rome Air Development Center by Atlantic Research Corporation, Contract No. AF 30(602)-1934, RADC-TDR-61-613, Volume 1, January 1962.

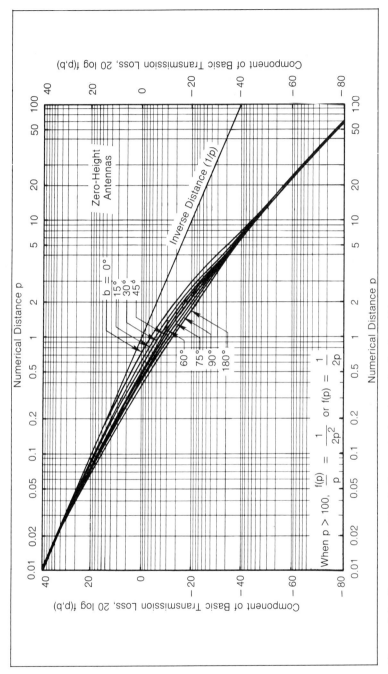

Figure 6.8—Component of Basic Transmission Loss for Surface Wave, Plane Earth

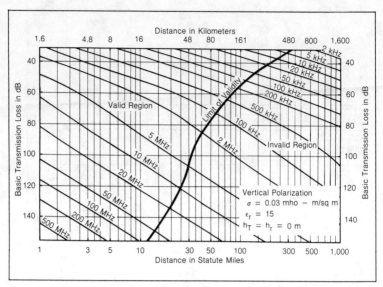

Figure 6.9—Surface-Wave Region, Average Land

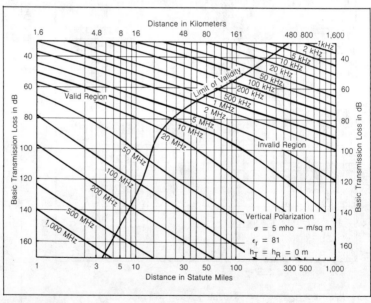

Figure 6.10—Surface-Wave Region, Salt Water

The only significant polarization in the surface-wave mode is vertical. Figure 6.11 illustrates surface-wave basic transmission loss for vertical and horizontal polarization with a frequency of 2 MHz, zero-height antennas and average land. As shown in Fig. 6.11, the horizontally polarized surface wave has a basic transmission loss approximately 100 dB greater than the vertically polarized surface wave.

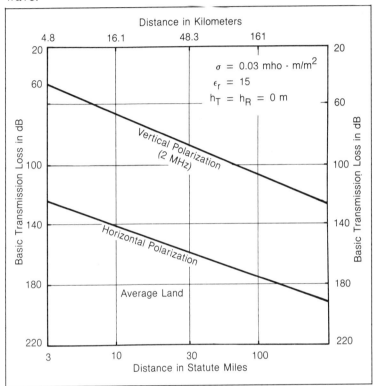

Figure 6.11—Surface Wave, Vertical and Horizontal Polarization

Normally, antenna heights must be small compared to a wavelength for surface-wave propagation to apply. As the antennas are elevated, surface-wave basic transmission loss increases. The effect of antenna height on surface-wave loss is most pronounced at short distances and decreases as a function of distance. Close to the antenna, grazing angles are greater which produces smaller values for the magnitude of the reflection coefficient. However, as distance from the transmitting antenna is increased, the grazing angle tends to zero and the reflection coefficient magnitude tends to one. At long ranges, therefore, small changes in antenna height have much less effect on the basic transmission loss.

Depending on frequency and distance, basic transmission loss can vary considerably with ground constants. Table 6.3 lists basic transmission losses in dB for different ground constants corresponding to a vertically polarized surface wave, zero-height antennas, frequencies of 5 and 20 MHz and a propagation distance of 5 km. As indicated in the table the losses tend to increase with decreasing moisture content, and the spread of loss is greater at high frequencies.

Table 6.3—Basic Transmission Loss for Surface Wave, Zero-Height Antennas, Vertical Polarization at 3 Miles

Ground Type	σ mho-m/m^2	ϵ_r	Basic Transmission Loss in dB 5 MHz	20 MHz
Sea Water	5.0	81	54	67
Marsh Land	0.111	30	57	90
Average Land	0.03	15	64	102
Desert Land	0.011	3	72	112

Illustrative Example 6.3: Application of Surface-Wave Basic Transmission Loss

Determine basic transmission loss between: (1) a 5 MHz signal transmitted from the National Bureau of Standards' WWV transmitter which transmits 9 kW (+69 dBm) from a vertical dipole and (2) a land-mobile receiver which is tuned to 5.3 MHz, has a sensitivity of −115 dBm and uses a vertical whip, operating approximately 16 km away.

Because of the frequency and distances involved and the fact that both transmitting and receiving antennas are vertically polarized, the surface wave is a primary mode of propagation and must be considered in EMI prediction. Referring to Fig. 6.9, basic transmission loss over average land would be 86 dB for the frequency and distance involved.

Because the actual antennas are not zero height, the basic transmission loss may be slightly greater (1 to 3 dB) than the value obtained. However, for the frequency, distances and antenna heights involved, the zero-height assumption provides a good approximation of basic transmission loss.

6.30

To illustrate how the above would be used in EMI prediction, assume that both transmitting and receiving antennas have 0 dB gain (G_{TR} = 0). Then the power available at the receiver as given in Eq. (2.2), is:

$$P_A = P_T + C_{TR}$$

$$= 69 \text{ dBm} \quad 86 \text{ dB} = -17 \text{ dBm}$$

Thus, the power available (-17 dBm) is 98 dB above receiver sensitivity (-115 dBm) and to avoid EMI problems when the receiver is operating with a weak desired signal, approximately 100 dB of EMI rejection must be provided at the frequency separation involved (0.3 MHz).

6.4.2 Reflection Region

Reflection region propagation applies to line-of-sight situations and is usually limited to frequencies above 30 MHz. Within the reflection region, RF energy may be propagated by a combination of surface, direct and ground-reflected waves. However, as frequency is increased, surface-wave losses increase relative to the direct and ground-reflected wave losses until the surface wave is no longer a significant mode of propagation. This may occur between 3 MHz and 300 MHz, depending on the significant propagation parameters. For practical purposes, the surface wave is limited to heights of about one wavelength over ground and five to 10 wavelengths over sea water.[4]

6.4.2.1 General Empirical Model

Within the reflection region, propagation loss is significantly influenced by the terrain in the vicinity of the propagation path. Because it is not usually practical or feasible to consider detailed terrain characteristics for all propagation paths that must be considered in an EMI prediction, it is often best to resort to empirical models that have been derived from a statistical analysis of measured data. One such empirical model that applies to propagation within the reflection region was developed by Egli. This model was derived from conditions involving ground-based antennas with separation distance less than 64 km (40 mi) and frequencies in the range of 40 to 400 MHz. The resulting mathematical model is:[5]

$$L_b = 88 + 20 \log f_{MHz} - 20 \log h_T h_R + 40 \log d \qquad (6.31)$$

where,

h_T = transmitting antenna height above ground in meters

h_R = receiving antenna height above ground in meters

d = distance in kilometers

The same equation can be expressed as:

$$L_b = 117 + 20 \log f_{MHz} - 20 \log h_T h_R + 40 \log d$$

where,
h_T = transmitting antenna height above ground in feet

h_R = receiving antenna height above ground in feet

d = distance in miles

This model provides an estimate of the average propagation loss for reflection-region conditions involving ground-based antennas and may be used for frequencies up to approximately 1,000 MHz.

Illustrative Example 6.4: Application of General Empirical Model

Determine basic transmission loss between an interfering VHF transmitter and a land-mobile receiver. The transmitter is operating at 100 MHz with an antenna height of 30 m (100 ft) and the land-mobile receiver antenna height is 3 m (10 ft), operating approximately 64 km (40 mi) away at the same frequency but attempting to receive signals from a different base station. From Eq. (6.31), the basic transmission loss is given as:

$$L_b = 88 + 20 \log f_{MHz} - 20 \log h_T h_R + 40 \log d$$

$$= 88 + 20 \log(100) - 20 \log(30 \times 3) + 40 \log(64)$$

$$= 88 + 40 - 39 + 72 = 161 \text{ dB}$$

for h_T and h_R in meters and d in kilometers. For these variables in feet and miles, the calculation becomes:

$$L_b = 117 + 20 \log f_{MHz} - 20 \log h_T h_R + 40 \log d$$

$$= 117 + 20 \log(100) - 20 \log (100 \times 10) + 40 \log(40)$$

$$= 117 + 40 - 60 + 64 = 161 \text{ dB}$$

To illustrate how this might be used in EMI prediction, assume that the base-station transmitter power is 100 W (+50 dBm), the receiver sensitivity is −110 dBm and the transmitter and receiver antenna gains are both equal to 0 dB. From Eq. (2.2) the power available at the receiver is:

$$P_A = P_T + C_{TR}$$

$$= 50 \text{ dBm} + G_T - L_b + G_R$$

$$= 50 \text{ dBm} - 161 \text{ dB} = -111 \text{ dBm}$$

In this case, the power available at the receiver is 1 dB below the receiver sensitivity, and under the assumed conditions the base station will not likely interfere with the receiver.

6.4.2.2 Specific Reflection Region Models

The following paragraphs present specific models that describe reflection-region propagation characteristics for plane earth and smooth, spherical earth conditions. These techniques may be used to estimate loss for applicable situations.

The calculation of basic transmission loss in the reflection region may be considered to be plane earth for ($d_{km} < 80 \ f_{MHz}^{-1/3}$ or spherical earth for ($d_{km} \geqslant 80 \ f_{MHz}^{-1/3}$), where d is the propagation path length.

6.4.2.2.1 Basic Transmission Loss for Reflection Region over Plane Earth

For elevated antennas and $d_{km} < 80 \ f_{MHz}^{-1/3}$, a decision is introduced to determine when the surface-wave component of the ground wave (see Fig. 6.5) can be neglected. The parameter is:

$$\Delta = \frac{4\pi h_T h_R}{\lambda d} \qquad (6.32)$$

For rough terrain, a least square curve is fitted to the terrain profile. In this case, antenna heights are measured above the least square curve. If $\Delta > 0.5$, the surface wave is practically insignificant and the basic transmission loss is computed for the space wave alone.

Figure 6.12 illustrates the reflection field as a function of distance from the transmitting antenna. For close ranges (before the last field strength maximum) the reflection field strength varies about the free-space field strength. For a direct and ground-reflected situation, the reflection field strength will be 6 dB above the free-space level for the maximum conditions.

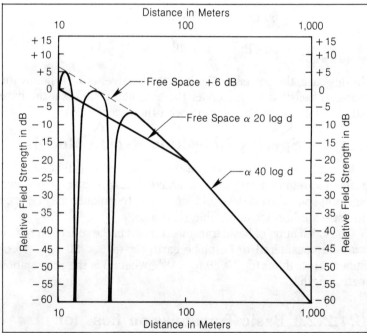

Figure 6.12—Reflection Field

For distances beyond the last maximum, the reflection field will fall off at 40 log d. The propagation loss at long range is given by the plane earth model as shown below.

$$L_{dB} = 115 + 40 \log d - 20 \log h_T h_R \qquad (6.33)$$

for h_T and h_R in meters and d in kilometers. For these variables in feet and miles, the equation is:

$$L_{dB} = 144 + 40 \log d - 20 \log h_T h_R$$

Note that the loss is independent of frequency, increases as 40 log d and decreases as 20 log h_T h_R.

For $\Delta < 0.5$, it is necessary to compute the basic transmission loss for both the surface-wave mode [see Eqs. (6.14) and (6.23)] and the reflection-region mode [see Eq. (6.31)]. If the two losses differ by more than 8 dB, the lower loss should be used. If the losses are within 8 dB of each other, the minimum loss can be found by using Fig. 6.13. The resulting loss L_b is:

$$L_b = L_{b\ max} - f(\Delta L) \qquad (6.34)$$

where $L_{b\ max}$ is the maximum of the surface-wave loss or the reflection-mode loss. The modifying factor, $f(\Delta L)$, is given in the figure as a function of the difference ΔL between the two losses.

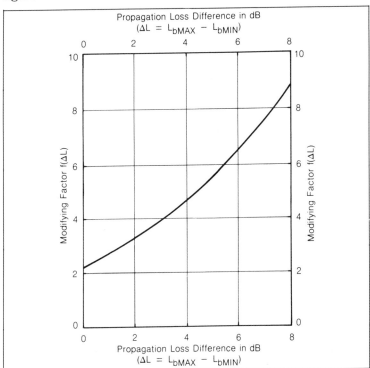

Figure 6.13—Reflection Region Modifying Factor

6.4.2.2.2 Basic Transmission Loss for Reflection Region over Spherical Earth

For propagation distances of d in kilometers, $d \geqslant 80 \, f_{MHz}^{-1/3}$ and transmitting and receiving antennas within line-of-sight and $\Delta \geqslant 0.5$, a smooth spherical earth model may be used in calculating basic transmission loss L_b. Basic transmission loss in the reflection region at a point d kilometers from the transmitting antenna over smooth spherical earth is:

$$L_b = 32 + 20 \log f_{MHz} + 20 \log d - 20 \log g(\Theta) \quad (6.35)$$

where $g(\Theta)$ is calculated by means of the following six steps.[6]

Step 1: The distance d_1 from the transmitting antenna to the point of reflection is shown in Fig. 6.14. To find d_1, three parameters must be determined. First, calculate:

$$c = \left| \frac{h_T - h_R}{h_T + h_R} \right| \quad (6.36)$$

Then, calculate:

$$m = \frac{(d_1/1.6)^2}{9.8k \, (h_T + h_R)} \quad (6.37)$$

where,

k = the effective earth's radius factor (usually considered to be 4/3)

d_1 = units of kilometers

h_T and h_R = units of meters

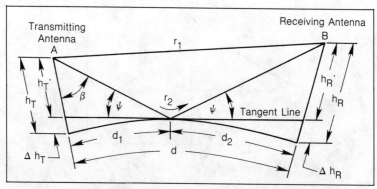

Figure 6.14—Geometry of Reflection Region, Spherical Earth

With parameters c and m, determine from Fig 6.15 the parameter b, interpolating between the curves if necessary. The distance d_1 is then:

$$d_1 = d(1 + b) \quad (6.38)$$

where,

d = total propagation path length in kilometers

The factor d_2, as shown in Fig. 6.14, is:

$$d_2 = d - d_1 \quad (6.39)$$

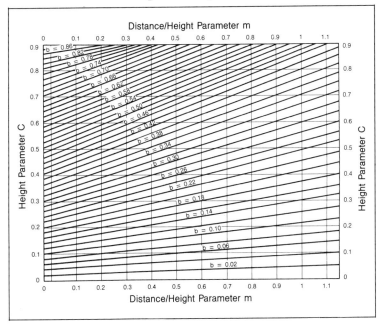

Figure 6.15—Nomogram for Determining b for Eq. (6.38)

Step 2: Check to be sure reflection-region methods apply. If the following inequality exists, then calculation is deferred to the trans-horizon region as described in Section 6.4.4.

$$\frac{h_T - 0.2 \, d_1^{\,2}}{1,000 \, d_1} < 0.01777 \, f_{MHz}^{-1/3} \quad (6.40)$$

Step 3: Calculate the divergence factor D for a smooth spherical earth:

$$D = \left[1 + \frac{d_1^2 d_2}{3k \, d \, h_T'} \right]^{-1/2} \tag{6.41}$$

where,

$$h_T' = h_T - d_1^2/12.6k \tag{6.42}$$

$$h_R' = h_R - d_2^2/12.6k \tag{6.43}$$

Step 4: Compute the path length difference $\ominus$ in degrees. The path length difference between the direct and ground-reflected wave is:

$$\ominus = \frac{2.39 \times 10^{-3} \, h_T' h_R' \, f_{MHz}}{d} \tag{6.44}$$

Step 5: Determine the magnitude and phase of the reflection coefficient as follows:

Horizontal Polarization:

$$R_h e^{j\phi}h = \frac{\sin \psi - \sqrt{\bar{n}^2 - \cos^2 \psi}}{\sin \psi + \sqrt{\bar{n}^2 - \cos^2 \psi}} \tag{6.45}$$

Vertical Polarization:

$$R_v e^{j\phi}v = \frac{\bar{n}^2 \sin \psi - \sqrt{\bar{n}^2 - \cos^2 \psi}}{\bar{n}^2 \sin \psi + \sqrt{\bar{n}^2 - \cos^2 \psi}} \tag{6.46}$$

where,

$\bar{n}$ = index of refraction of the medium
ψ = grazing angle
R_h, R_v = magnitude of reflection coefficient
ϕ_h, ϕ_v = spatial phase difference between reflected and incident waves
e = natural logarithm base (2.718)

The grazing angle ψ for a smooth spherical earth is:

$$\psi = \tan^{-1} \left[\frac{3.281 \, h_T - \dfrac{0.78 \, d_1^2}{3k}}{3,300 \, d_1} \right] \qquad (6.47)$$

where,

h_T = antenna height above surface in meters
d_1 = distance from antenna to reflection point in kilometers
k = earth radius factor (4/3 for standard atmosphere)

The value of d_1 is derived by solving the following cubic equation:

$$d_1^3 - (1.5d) \, d_1^2 + [0.5d^2 - 6.15 \, (h_T + h_R)] \, d_1 + 6.15 \, h_T d = 0 \qquad (6.48)$$

The index of refraction $\bar{n}$ is obtained from:

$$\bar{n}^2 = \epsilon_{r2} - \frac{j \, 1.8 \times 10^4 \sigma_2}{f_{MHz}} \qquad (6.49)$$

where,

ϵ_{r2} = relative permittivity of medium 2
σ_2 = conductivity of medium 2 in mho meters per meter^2

Step 6: Calculate the earth gain factor $g(\ominus)$ from the following:

$$g(\ominus) = [1 + (DR)^2 + 2DR \cos(\ominus - \phi)]^{1/2} \qquad (6.50)$$

As an example of losses in the reflection region, Figs. 6.16 and 6.17 give ground-wave basic transmission loss as a function of distance for a smooth spherical earth over average land and salt water. Loss calculations may be accomplished by either using the first few terms of an infinite series representation of the parameter or function or by approximating the function which has been graphed over intervals.

Illustrative Example 6.5: Application of Spherical Earth Curves

Determine basic transmission loss for a 100 MHz signal propagated a distance of 16 km (10 mi) over land from a vertically polarized transmitting antenna with a height of 10 m (30 ft) to a receiving antenna that is also vertically polarized and 10 m high. For this case, basic transmission loss is determined directly from Fig. 6.16 to be 130 dB.

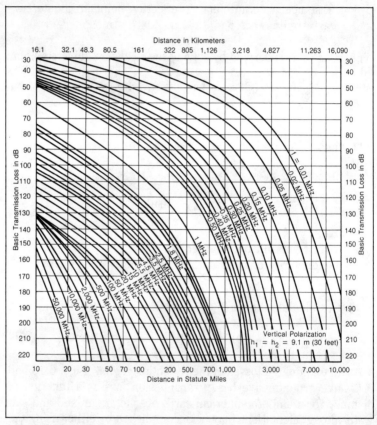

Figure 6.16—Reflection Region, Smooth Spherical Earth, Land

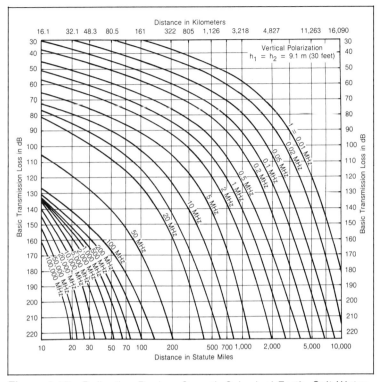

Figure 6.17—Reflection Region, Smooth Spherical Earth, Salt Water

6.4.2.3 Diffraction Region

At distances just beyond the radio horizon, the diffracted surface wave (and in the case of elevated antennas, the diffracted ground wave) is the predominant source of propagation as shown in Fig. 6.2. As distance is increased still further beyond the radio horizon, the level of the tropospheric scatter signal approaches the level of the diffracted surface wave. This discussion is limited to that region where the effect of the tropospheric scatter signal need not be considered. For convenience, this region is called the near-diffraction region.

6.4.3 Smooth Earth

For smooth-earth conditions, the diffraction region model is based on the zero-height surface wave discussed in Section 6.4.1. The calculation requires determining the zero-height surface-wave field strength and then modifying this value by appropriate antenna-height gain functions.[8]

This diffraction region applies to situations for which the distance d satisfies the criterion:

$$d > 1.6 \left\{ [5k \ h_T]^{1/2} + [5k \ h_R]^{1/2} + 1.5/\beta_o \eta_o \right\} \qquad (6.51)$$

where,

$$k = \text{effective earth radius factor (usually 4/3)}$$
$$h_T, h_R = \text{antenna heights in meters}$$
$$\beta_o = \text{as determined from Fig. 6.18}$$
$$\eta_o = 0.007 \ f_{MHz}^{1/3} \ k^{-2/3}$$

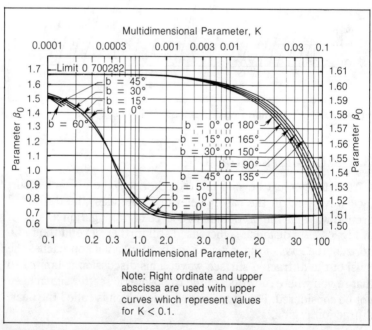

Figure 6.18—Parameter β_0

6.42

For h_T and h_R, less than $610\ f_{MHz}^{-2/3}$, basic transmission loss is:

$$L_b = 37 + 20 \log f_{MHz} - 20 \log E \qquad (6.52)$$

where, $\qquad -20 \log f(q_1) - 20 \log f(q_2)$

$$
\begin{aligned}
E &= 2\eta_0 \gamma M \\
\gamma &= 0.0762\ K^2 \text{ for } K < 0.1 \\
\gamma &= \text{as determined from Fig. 6.19 for } K > 0.1 \\
M &= 56.66\ e^{-1.84\eta'/(n')1/2} \\
\eta' &= \eta_0 \beta_0 d
\end{aligned}
$$

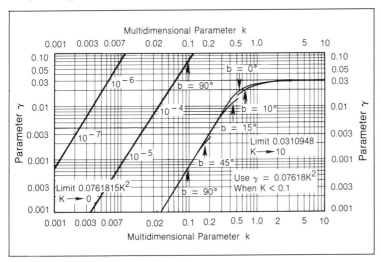

Figure 6.19—Parameter γ for Eq. (6.47)

The values of $f(q_1)$, $f(q_2)$ are determined from Figs. 6.20 and 6.21 with:[7]

$$
\begin{aligned}
q &= h\ f_{MHz}/47.8\ A^{1/2} \\
b &= 2b'' - b'
\end{aligned}
$$

where,

$$
\begin{aligned}
b'' &= \tan^{-1}[\epsilon_r/X] \\
b' &= \tan^{-1}[(\epsilon_r - 1)/X]
\end{aligned}
$$

Curves are plotted for frequencies from 10 kHz to 100 GHz, with both antennas 10 m (30 ft) above the surface and vertical polarization. For frequencies less than 10 MHz the space-wave component is negligible, while for frequencies above 100 MHz the field is primarily due to the space wave.

The entire calculation is aided by several of the required parameters and functions shown graphically because the functions are complicated mathematical expressions. If the procedure outlined here is to be done on a computer, then the graphic information must be approximated in some form for efficient use. The approximations are as follows.

ϵ_r = relative permittivity
X = 18,000 σ/f_{MHz}
σ = soil conductivity in mho – m/m^2

$$K = \frac{0.01954\ A^{1/2}}{f_{MHZ}^{1/3}\ k^{1/3}} \qquad (6.53)$$

where,

A = (cos b') /X for horizontal polarization
A = (X cos b') /cos^2 b'' for vertical polarization

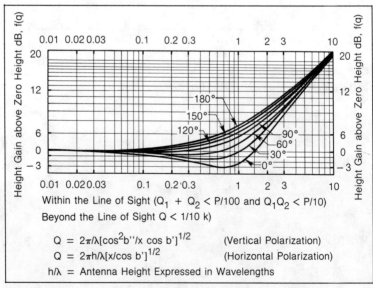

Within the Line of Sight ($Q_1 + Q_2 < P/100$ and $Q_1 Q_2 < P/10$)

Beyond the Line of Sight $Q < 1/10\ k$)

$Q = 2\pi/\lambda[\cos^2 b''/x \cos b']^{1/2}$ (Vertical Polarization)

$Q = 2\pi h/\lambda[x/\cos b']^{1/2}$ (Horizontal Polarization)

h/λ = Antenna Height Expressed in Wavelengths

Figure 6.20—Height Gain Correction, Plane Earth

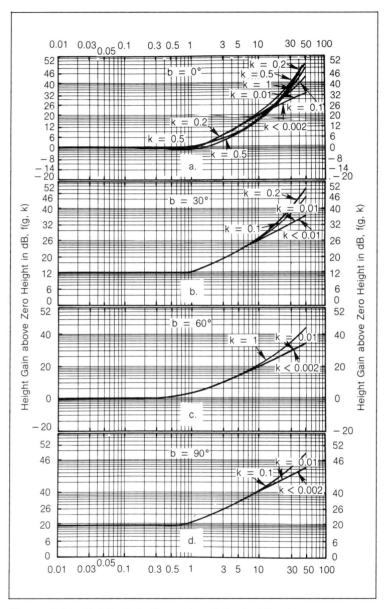

Figure 6.21—Height Gain Correction, Spherical Earth

If h_T and h_R are greater than $610\,f_{MHz}^{-2/3}$, the basic transmission loss is:

$$L_b = 37 + 20 \log (f_{MHz}) - 20 \log(E) - 40 \log (\delta)$$

$$- 20 \log[f(H_T) - 20 \log[f(H_R)]$$

where,

E is the same as in Eq. (6.52)

$\delta = 0.3288/K$ for $K < 0.1$

δ = as given by Fig. 6.22 for $K > 0.1$

$H_T = 12 \times 10^{-5}\,h_T\beta_o^2\,f_{MHz}^{2/3}\,k^{-1/3}$

$H_R = 12 \times 10^{-5}\,h_R\beta_o^2\,f_{MHz}\,k^{-1/3}$

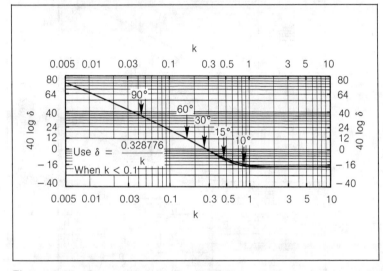

Figure 6.22—Parameter δ for Eq. (6.53)

The values of $f(H_T)$ and $f(H_R)$ are determined by Fig. 6.23. (Note that Fig. 6.23a is for small values of H and Fig. 6.23b is for large values of H.)

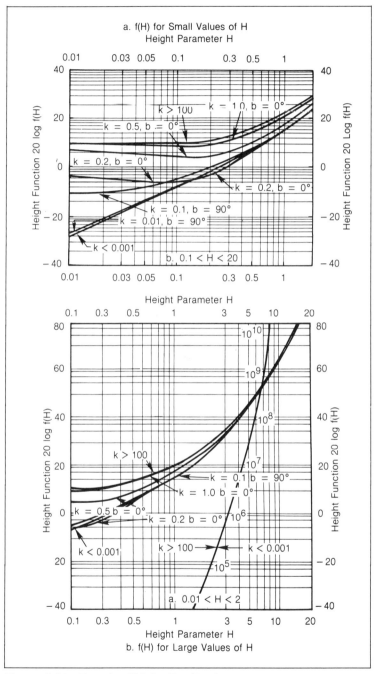

Figure 6.23—Function f(H) for Eq. (6.53)

Figures 6.24 and 6.25 present curves of the diffraction region basic transmission loss for two representative sets of ground constants, i.e., average land and salt water. The curves are plotted for zero-height antennas, vertical polarization with frequency as a parameter.

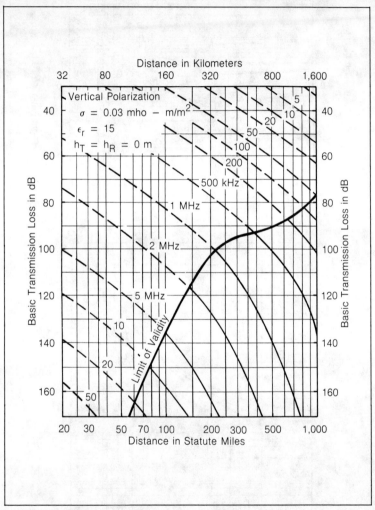

Figure 6.24—Diffraction Region, Land

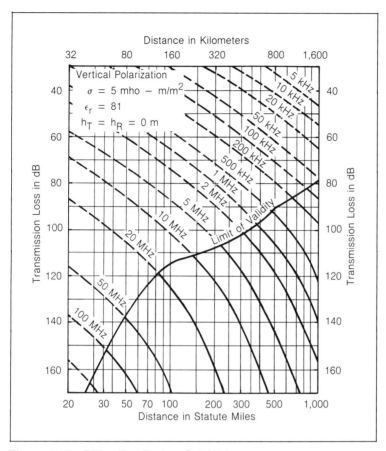

Figure 6.25—Diffraction Region, Salt Water

Figures 6.26 through 6.29 are antenna-height gain curves which are used with the zero-height antenna diffraction region curves. The ordinates of the figures are interpreted as the reduction in path loss achieved with elevated antennas over ground-based antennas. It should be noted, however, that the values of height-gain are not positive for all values of distance, frequency and antenna height. The curves in Figs. 6.26 and 6.28 are for use with antenna of heights:

$$h > 269 \, f_{MHz}^{-2/3} \text{ in meters} \qquad (6.54)$$

Figures 6.27 and 6.29 correspond to antenna heights of:

$$h < 610 \, f_{MHz}^{-2/3} \text{ in meters} \qquad (6.55)$$

For antenna heights that fall between the stated conditions, either set of curves may be used.

The curves given in Figs. 6.24 through 6.29 may be used directly to determine diffraction-region basic transmission loss. The procedure is:

1. Use Fig. 6.24 or 6.25 to determine the basic transmission loss for the zero-height situation.
2. Use Figs. 6.26 through 6.29 to determine the height gain of the transmitting and receiving antennas.
3. Calculate the basic transmission loss for the elevated antenna by subtracting the two height gains from the zero-height basic transmission loss.

Another convenient representation of basic transmission loss data over smooth earth diffraction paths is illustrated in Fig. 6.30. Here, for a frequency of 100 MHz, basic transmission loss for paths ranging from 16 to 160 km (10 to 100 statute mi) is given as a function of antenna height in meters.

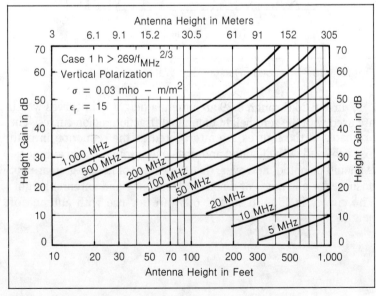

Figure 6.26—Height Gain Correction, Case 1, over Land

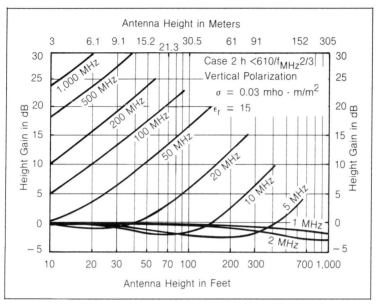

Figure 6.27—Height Gain Correction, Case 2, over Land

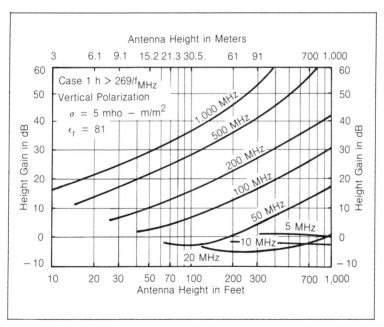

Figure 6.28—Height Gain Correction, Case 1, over Sea Water

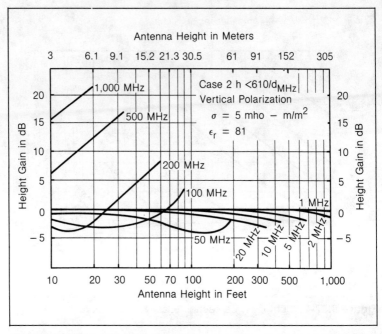

Figure 6.29—Height Gain Correction

Many curves of the types shown in Figs. 6.24 through 6.30 have been plotted for various sets of propagation parameters. These curves, in many cases, greatly relieve the work in determining the basic transmission loss over smooth earth diffraction paths.

Illustrative Example 6.6: Application of Diffraction Region Curves

Determine the basic transmission loss in a 27 MHz potentially interfering signal transmitted from a vertically polarized antenna with a height of 91 m (300 ft) and received by a vertically polarized land-mobile antenna with a height of 3 m (10 ft) located 96 km (60 mi) from the transmitter. Assume that the intervening path is over land.

The first step is to use Fig. 6.24 or 6.25 to determine the basic transmission loss over a 96 km path for zero-height antennas. Because the transmission is over land, Fig. 6.24 is used and the basic transmission loss for zero-height antennas is found to be 170 dB.

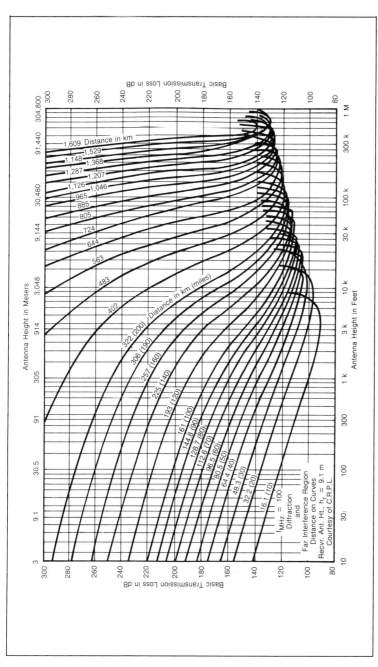

Figure 6.30—Transmission Loss for Diffraction Region

The next step is to use Figs. 6.26 through 6.29 to determine the height gain for the transmitting and receiving antennas. Because the transmission is over land, Figs. 6.26 and 6.27 are used. It is necessary to examine the relationship between the antenna heights and frequency to determine which of the two figures apply. For the transmitting height of 91 m:

$$h_T > \frac{269}{f_{MHz}^{2/3}} = \frac{269}{27^{2/3}} = 30 \text{ m}$$

Therefore, Fig. 6.26 is used to determine the antenna-height gain. From the figure, this gain is approximately 16 dB. For the receiving antenna height of 3 m:

$$h_R < \frac{610}{f_{MHz}^{2/3}} = \frac{610}{27^{2/3}} = 68 \text{ m}$$

Therefore, Fig. 6.27 is used to determine the antenna height gain, or approximately -1 dB.

The last step is to subtract the transmitting and receiving antenna-height gains from the zero-height basic transmission loss to determine the diffraction-region loss for the elevated antenna. Thus, for the situation:

$$\text{Corrected loss} = 170 \text{ dB} - 16 \text{ db} - (-1 \text{ dB}) = 155 \text{ dB}$$

6.4.4 Transhorizon Region

Methods were presented in Sections 6.4.1 and 6.4.3 for determining basic transmission loss over paths within line-of-sight and significantly beyond (diffraction region) the radio horizon. The basic transmission loss curves which can be calculated for LOS paths are valid for distances from the transmitting antenna such that (1) the earth can be a considered to be a plane in the case of surface wave over a smooth earth, or (2) $\tan \psi > 0.01954 \, (f_{MHz}^{-1/3}) \, (k^{-1/2})$ for LOS ground reflection paths [see Eq. (6.47)].

The smooth earth diffraction method is valid only for those distances, such that:

$$d > 1.6 \left[(5k \, h_T)^{1/2} + (5k \, h_R)^{1/2} + \frac{1.5}{\beta_o \eta_o} \right] \qquad (6.56)$$

Values of basic transmission loss in the intervening transhorizon region may be found by constructing smooth transition curves between the LOS and smooth earth diffraction curves. This concept is presented in Fig. 6.31 where the basic transmission loss curves for the surface-wave region and also for the diffraction region are plotted together. The intervening space between these two regions is "smoothed in" to show the transhorizon region. Data for this curve comes from Figs. 6.9 and 6.24. Similar curves can be constructed, such as Fig. 6.32 for elevated antennas where the loss data for the reflection region is smoothed into the loss data for the near-diffraction region.

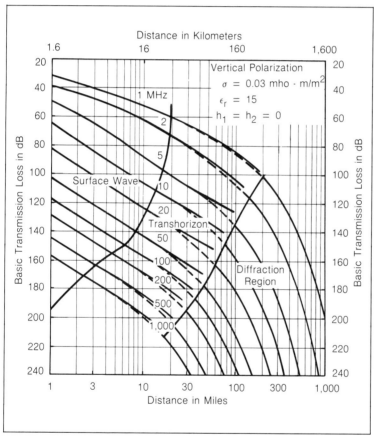

Figure 6.31—Surface Wave, Transhorizon Region and Diffraction Region, Land

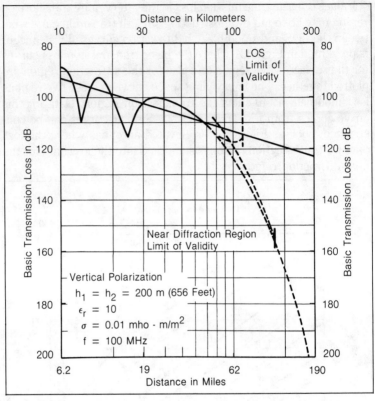

Figure 6.32—Interpolation between LOS Reflection and Near Diffraction Regions

6.5 Ionospheric Propagation Models

Ionospheric propagation refers to all of those modes dependent upon one or more ionized layers of the atmosphere with the exception of ionospheric scattering. The ionosphere is a complex, variable and sometimes unpredictable result of the periodic and anomalous characteristics of the sun. The absorption of polychromatic, ultraviolet radiation from the sun produces ionized layers in the upper atmosphere with the most strongly absorbed radiation forming the highest layers. The height of the maximum ionization level for a particular layer varies with the zenith angle of the sun while the lower limit is a function of the rate of absorption of the radiant energy. The layers from the lowest to the highest are the D, E, sporadic-E, F_1 and F_2 layers. The layers responsible for the bulk of HF communication are the E and F_2 layers.

Propagation which involves reflection from the ionosphere layers is called sky-wave propagation and falls into two cases, VLF and LF-HF frequency ranges. In the VLF range, the lower boundary of the D-layer and the surface of the earth form a waveguide and all propagation in this frequency range can be accounted for by waveguide theory. EMI is seldom associated with VLF propagation because of the low frequencies involved. For this reason, only a brief summary of the resulting propagation losses is presented in Figs. 6.33 and 6.34, however, references to more detailed models are provided.

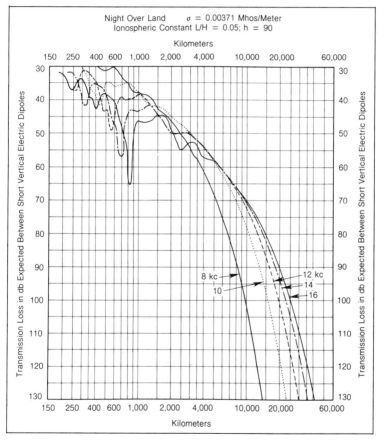

Figure 6.33—Transmission Loss Expected Between Short Vertical Electric Dipole Antennas

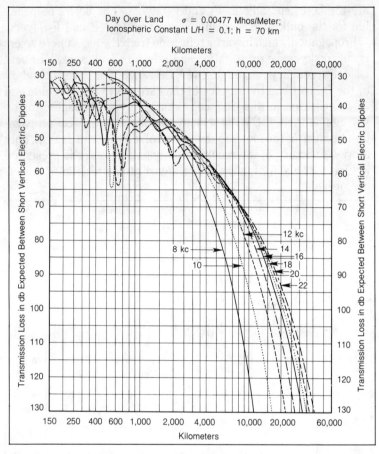

Figure 6.34—Transmission Loss Expected Between Short Vertical Electric Dipole Antennas

In the LF-HF band, two basic approaches are available for calculating the propagation loss on a sky-wave path. Either the median transmission loss can be computed directly by a relatively simple equation or by a more cumbersome process using many graphs, charts and overlays. Because sky-wave propagation is not likely to result in large interfering signals, specific techniques for calculating the propagation loss are not presented in this section. The median transmission loss equation and techniques for the field-strength calculation are provided in the references.

6.6 Scatter Propagation Models

Just beyond the radio horizon, the dominant mode of propagation is diffraction. However, the diffraction losses increase rapidly with increasing distance until a new mechanism, tropospheric scattering becomes significant. As distance increases still further, (beyond the limits of troposcatter) ionospheric scattering becomes significant. RF signals scattered off the lower regions of the ionospheric E-layer for frequencies between 3 and 75 MHz attenuate very slowly with increasing distance. Figure 6.35 is a plot of median basic transmission loss curves versus distance for the ground wave, troposcatter and ionospheric scatter modes. This curve points out the relation between the three modes.

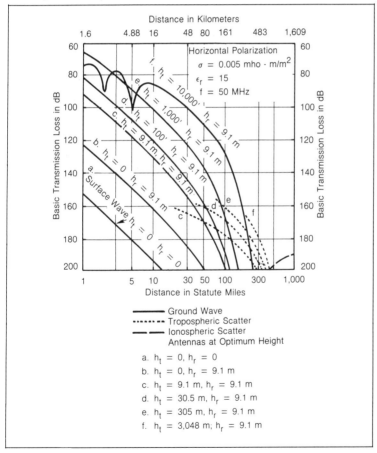

Figure 6.35—Troposcatter Ground Wave and Ionospheric Scatter Propagation

6.7 Complex Co-site Propagation

Electromagnetic field models may be used to supplement conventional propagation models and to extend the analysis capabilities for radiation and scattering from objects, such as a ship, aircraft antenna tower, buildings, etc. These electromagnetic fields may be used to determine the field strength at an antenna by simulating the antenna and its immediate environment more accurately.

The modeling techniques discussed here are method of moments (MOM), geometrical theory of diffraction (GTD) and a combination of both. The MOM is associated with an antenna configuration as well as other parameters of interest, e.g., impedance and current distribution.

6.7.1 Method of Moments

The MOM, unlike conventional propagation models, takes into account the total complex structure as appropriate. Complex structures may be represented by thin wires, wire grids or surface patches as appropriate to the specific problem. Examples of the representation of an aircraft are shown in Figs. 6.36 and 6.37. The stick model representation would be used at low frequencies where the wavelength is large relative to the radius of the fuselage or the cord of the wings or stabilizers. Thus, for low frequencies, the aircraft surfaces may be represented as thin wires. At higher frequencies, the detailed geometry of the aircraft becomes important and it is necessary to model the aircraft in terms of wire grids or surface patches. The numerical electromagnetic code (NEC) described in Chapter 10 is an example of a MOM code. It could be used for complex co-site problems for the conditions for which it is applicable. These conditions are discussed in the following paragraphs.

The MOM is a unifying concept of reducing a linear, inhomogeneous integrodifferential equation of the form:

$$L\,(I,\,L) \;=\; \sum_i \hat{V}_i \; \delta \,(1 \,-\, L_i) \tag{6.57}$$

where,

$$L\,(I,\,L) \;=\; -\underset{\sim}{E} \bullet \hat{L}$$

to set a simultaneous, linear, algebraic equation. In matrix form, this equation becomes:

$$[Z] \vec{I} = \vec{V} \qquad (6.58)$$

where [Z] is a known square matrix and V and I are known and unknown column vectors respectively. Once suitable [Z] and V are known, Eq. (6.58) can be solved for I. The elements of I are the coefficients in an expansion of the current that satisfies the original equation. Only V contains information on the sources of the original equation; thus, [Z] needs to be computed only to solve a problem for a fixed geometry and frequency where the source distribution varies.

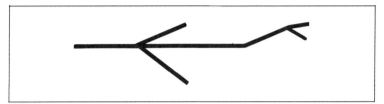

Figure 6.36—Stick Model Representation of an Aircraft

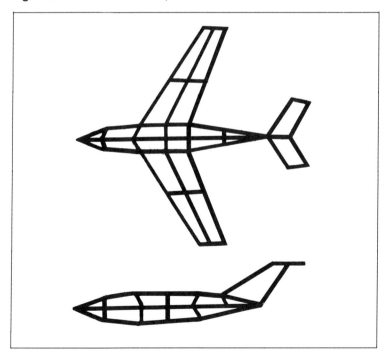

Figure 6.37—Wire Grid Model Representations of an Aircraft

Equation (6.58) is part of a form that often appears in network theory as relating voltages and currents of an N-port network; thus [Z] is often referred to as the "generalized impedance" matrix and I and V the "generalized current" and "generalized voltage" column matrices respectively.

The MOM technique is justified for frequencies where the dimensions of the reflecting and scattering objects are not too large relative to wavelength. The effects of an imperfect, flat, homogeneous ground on wire antennas or scatterers have been included in thin-wire MOM approximately via the plane-wave reflection coefficient method. When greater accuracy is desired, as is necessarily the case if some wires are within a small fraction of a wavelength to the ground, then Sommerfeld's formulation is appropriate and is available in thin-wire MOM.

With many (but not all) moment methods, lumped impedance loads can be handled by thin-wire type analyses. The loads may be placed almost anywhere along the wires and may represent the input or output impedances of entire linear circuits. Distributed loads, such as with wires of finite conductivity, can also be handled by thin-wire techniques. For example, this technique could be used to represent the properties of composite material that may be used in reflecting and scattering structures.

The ease with which moment method thin-wire models can be applied to arbitrary wire geometries justifies their use in solving radiation and scattering from solid conducting surfaces by approximating the latter with wire grids.

With wire grids, the user is given the task of choosing reasonable wire radii and grid size so that the wire grid model is "equivalent" to the surface structure. This often difficult decision, of course, lacks surface formulations; however, as previously mentioned, wire grid modeling has been used more extensively than, for example, surface patch modeling because the former is more easily applied to general surfaces, especially if open surfaces are involved.

Conducting surfaces occur in many coupling paths between emitters and receptors. These conducting surfaces may be represented as surface patches and solved by applying either the magnetic or electric field integral equation. Examples include aircraft fuselages and wings and satellite solar panels. The magnetic field integral equation (MFIE) applies only to lossless, closed-conducting scatterers.

Scatterers with edges such as an aircraft fuselage with a non-conducting nose are not amenable to the MFIE. Radiation problems, however, can usually be solved indirectly by solving the reciprocal scattering problem. On the other hand, the electric field integral equation (EFIE) applies to a wider range of problems.
Rectangular patches are not suited for many curved surfaces. A convenient patch shape of general applicability is the triangle. Triangular patches are better than general quadrilaterals for the following reasons:

1. A minimum number of possible points is required to specify patch boundaries.
2. Triangular patches are always planar whereas quadrilaterals may not be and planar patches help numerical computation.
3. Triangular patches conform more readily to rapidly changing surface boundaries or curvatures as well as help sampling the unknown current more densely in critical regions.

Figure 6.38 illustrates a triangular patch implementation which has been developed and used effectively. The triangular patch representation would be justified for higher frequency applications of MOM where the geometry of the conducting surfaces is important.

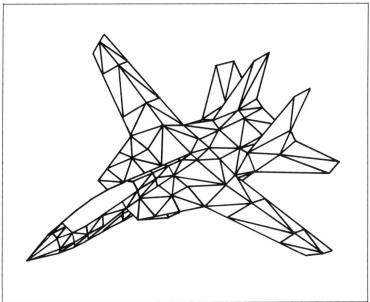

Figure 6.38—Triangular Patch Model of an Aircraft

Many problems in EMC involve structures that are either exactly or approximately rotationally symmetric. Such structures, called bodies of revolution (BOR), are efficient to model because of their modal decoupling properties, where a Fourier-size wave component (with respect to the rotational or ϕ coordinate) of excitation (incident field, voltage, etc.) results in the same Fourier component of response (induced current, scattered field). In a MOM formulation, choosing expansion functions having sinusoidal ϕ variation immediately leads to the reduction of one hugh matrix to a number of relatively small matrices. Large matrices often result from problems with arbitrarily shaped bodies devoid of symmetries. The BOR formulation has been applied to many EMC-related problems.

6.7.2 Geometric Theory of Diffraction

The Geometric Theory of Diffraction (GTD) is a procedure for including the effects of waves diffracted from edges or around curved surfaces in an electromagnetic scattering or radiation problem. With the Geometrical Optics (GO) field obtained from the GO model, GTD usually produces a more accurate total field for the problem under consideration than with GO alone. The theory of GTD has been successfully applied to a variety of high-frequency radiation and scattering problems. The use of GTD is justified by the excellent agreement between GTD analyses and scale model experiments regarding radiation patterns of aircraft antennas.

The Aircraft interAntenna Propagation with Graphics (AAPG) computer program that is described in more detail in Chapter 10 is based on the GTD. The program uses interactive computer graphics to assist the engineer in the prediction and display of antenna-to-antenna-coupled EMI on an aircraft or missile. Such EMI is a function of two components. The first is governed by the electronic characteristics. The second component, which is the one on which AAPG concentrates, is given by the losses incurred along the coupling path between the transmitting and receiving antennas. AAPG is primarily an antenna-to-antenna coupling model.

The general diffraction case for GTD is handled similarly to geometric optics. Again, because of the high frequency, the diffraction process is a local one involving rays. The appropriate rays and points of diffraction are chosen according to a modified form of Fermat's principle which states that a diffracted ray traveling from point P to point Q transverses the minimum path length, subject to the constraint that one path point lies on the diffracting edge. In the case of a smooth surface and homogeneous medium, the point on the diffracting edge is replaced by a geodesic path segment (shortest path constrained to lie on the surface). The canonical problem for edge diffraction is a two-dimensional plane wave scattering from an infinite wedge. The canonical problem for smooth convex surface diffraction is a two-dimensional plane wave scattering from an infinite cylinder. These problems form the basis for finding diffraction coefficients from which result the magnitudes and phases of diffracted rays relative to the amplitudes and phases of rays incident on the scatterer.

The original GTD formulas for edge-diffracted rays are wrong near reflection and shadow boundaries. Subsequent theories improved these formulas by either adjusting them to provide continuity of total field across the optical boundaries or adjusting both the GO formulas and the GTD formulas to assure this continuity. The elements in the basic theory of the GTD model involve diffraction from the edge of a conducting "wedge" with perhaps nonflat surfaces; the wedge need not be straight. If the ray $\underline{E}^i(\underline{P}_o)$ incident on the edge at point $\underline{P}_o$ is assumed polarized parallel to the plane formed by the edge and the incident ray path (electric polarization), then the diffracted ray at $\underline{r}$, which is added to the GO rays in arriving at a better approximation to the total field by accounting for edges, is given by:

$$\underline{E}^d(\underline{r}) = D^e \underline{E}^i(\underline{P}_o) \left[\frac{\rho^d}{s^d(\rho^d + s^d)} \right]^{1/2} e^{-jks^d} \quad (6.59)$$

where,

s^d = the distance between $\underline{P}_o$ and $\underline{r}$

ρ^d = the principal radius of curvature of the diffracted ray in the plane formed by the diffracted ray and the edge

D^e = the electric polarization edge diffraction coefficient

The edge diffraction coefficient D^e is a simple function of s_d, ρ_d, the angular directions of the incident ray with respect to the point of diffraction $\underline{P}_o$ on the edge, the radii of curvature of the incident and reflected rays at $\underline{P}_o$, the curvature of the edge at $\underline{P}_o$, the angle of the wedge containing the edge at which diffraction is occurring and the Fresnel integral. Additionally, ρ^d depends on the curvature of the edge at $\underline{P}_o$.

6.65

The Fresnel integral does not have an exact closed-form solution; however, it is well-tabulated; accurate approximating polynomial expansions exist for the full range of its argument. Furthermore, a quite simple asymptotic approximation of the Fresnel integral is available and often employed; however, it is not accurate in the vicinity of the shadow and reflection boundaries. In fact, this approximation is infinite along these boundaries.

An expression exists for diffracted rays arising from incident rays polarized normal to the plane formed by the incident ray path and the edge (magnetic polarization). An arbitrary ray can be decomposed into electrically and magnetically polarized rays.

The GTD coefficients associated with edges and surfaces of complicated shapes may be costly to determine. A lot of computer time may be required if many diffracted rays have to be computed and if the curvatures of the edges and surfaces can only be described numerically. As with GO, arbitrarily curved edges and surfaces may require many trial computations until the ray that minimizes the path length is found.

The GTD model for analyzing diffraction around smooth convex curved surfaces such as aircraft fuselages is developed similarly to the edge diffraction development. As previously mentioned, the canonical problem is plane wave diffraction around a circular cylinder. The scattering process, as with any convex surface, involves a region of deep illumination, a region of deep shadow and a transition region. The deeply illuminated regions involve the incident and reflected ray fields obtainable from GO. The fields which exist in the deep shadow region are referred to as creeping rays. These rays are launched from points of incidence on the cylinder and propagate around the cylinder on geodesic paths, shedding rays tangentially as they travel. The geodesic path is the shortest path on the surface between the points at which the incident ray impinges on the surface and the diffracted ray leaves the surface.

Analysis here proceeds in a way similar to that with edge diffraction. The principal difficulty with applying surface diffraction to general surfaces is in determining the geodesic path over which the creeping waves travel. If the surface shape is not simple, such as cylindrical, conical, etc., and can only be described numerically, then time-consuming trial and error is required.

The application of GTD is justified for frequencies where the reflecting and scattering objects are large relative to the wavelength, and the fields coupled between antennas are affected by diffraction or scattering by surfaces associated with these objects.

6.7.3 Combined MOM and GTD

An accurate antenna analysis cannot ignore nearby electrically large conducting bodies; however, a MOM representation of the entire structure is likely to result in a forbiddingly large generalized impedance matrix [Z] at, for example, microwave frequencies; thus, a technique that combines a MOM treatment of the antenna with a ray theory (GO/GTD model) treatment of the neighboring scatters is justified. Although the following discussion is in terms of wire-type antennas, the technique can be straightforwardly recast, via moment methods, in terms of nonwire antennas or arbitrary structures.

In the application of MOM/GTD to wire type antennas, only the wire current I is expanded in typical moment method fashion; however, the resulting matrix equation, Eq. (6.58), which is usually solved for the current expansion coefficients I_n is modified to reflect scattering from nearby surfaces and edges. This is done by modifying the operator L in Eq. (6.57), such that L now represents not only the tangential component along the antenna surface of free-space field radiated by I, but also the reflected or diffracted fields from the scattering surfaces as well. With I expanded by moment method fashion, the reflected or diffracted fields are determined by application of GO/GTD. In general, each I_n will "excite" a different set of reflected or diffracted rays. These rays, in addition to the free-space field radiated by each I, result in the total field radiated by each I_n. According to Eq. (6.57) and appropriate expansion and testing functions, the resulting matrix equation replacing Eq. (6.58) that must be solved is:

$$\left([Z] + [Z^G] \right) \bar{I} = \bar{V} \qquad (6.60)$$

where the elements of $[Z^G]$ are the diffracted or reflected ray contributions between expansion and testing function segments for I. In Eq. (6.60), [Z], I and V are the same as in Eq. (6.58).

Note that the order of the matrix equation, Eq. (6.60), is not greater than the number of antenna current expansion functions, even though scattering from electrically large nearby structures (finite ground planes, curved aircraft fuselages, aircraft wings, etc.) is largely accounted for. Thus, with MOM/GTD, an electrically large problem can be accurately solved with a reasonably sized matrix equation. This significant reduction in the size of the matrix equation justifies the use of the combined MOM/GTD for problems requiring accurate analysis of electrically small antennas in the presence of electrically large reflectors, diffractors or scatterers.

6.8 Probability Distributions for Transmission Loss

Propagation models described in previous sections provide values of basic transmission loss for various typical situations. When these models are used for EMC analysis, realize that there are a number of factors that influence loss over a specific path. It is not practical to specify the effects of all these parameters on propagation loss in a detailed, deterministic way. Instead, many parameters are regarded as random variables and their effects are treated statistically by specifying the resulting loss in terms of a probability distribution function.

For EMC analysis, propagation loss expressed in dB between two points is often assumed to be a normally distributed random variable. In general, propagation loss is a function of both time-dependent and time-independent parameters. Examples of time-dependent parameters are temperature, relative humidity and wind velocity which directly influence atmospheric refractive index. Other time-dependent parameters are the amount of foliage along the propagation path (winter to summer differences) and the moisture content of the ground. Examples of time-independent parameters are roughness of the propagation path length and uncertainty of antenna heights.

Table 6.4 provides estimates of the standard deviation for time-dependent (σD) and time-independent (σI) propagation loss variations. Also included in Table 6.4 are estimates of the total standard deviation (σ_T):

$$\sigma_T = \sqrt{\sigma_D^2 + \sigma_I^2} \tag{6.61}$$

Table 6.4—Standard Deviations for Propagating Loss

Propagation Mode	Condition	Standard Deviation		
		Time Dependent σ_D in dB	Time Dependent σ_I in dB	Total σ_T (dB)
Surface Wave	Any	1	2	2
Reflection Region	Smooth Earth	5	5	7
	Rough Earth VHF	5	8	9
	Rough Earth UHF	5	12	13
Diffraction Region	Smooth Earth VHF	4	2	4
	Smooth Earth UHF	8	2	8
	Rough Earth VHF	4	8	9
	Rough Earth UHF	8	12	14
Knife Edge	VHF	3	8	8
	UHF	6	12	14
Transhorizon	VHF	4	8	9
	UHF	8	12	14
Troposcatter	Any	8	8	12

In performing an EMC analysis, the total standard deviation is used. Estimates of standard deviation are given in the table for both VHF and UHF, corresponding to certain cases. VHF estimates should be used for all frequencies in and below the VHF band (30 MHz to 300 MHz), and UHF estimates should be used for all frequencies in or above the UHF band (300 MHz to 3 GHz).

6.9 References

1. *Reference Data for Radio Engineers* (International Telephone and Telegraph Corp., fifth ed.).
2. Norton, K.A., "The Calculation of Ground Wave Field Intensity over a Finitely Conducting Sperical Earth," *Proceedings of the Institute of Radio Engineers*, Vol. 29, December 1941, pp. 623-39.
3. Ibid.
4. Bullington, K., "Radio Propagation at Frequencies above 30 Megacycles," *Proceedings of the Institute of Radio Engineers*, Vol. 35, October 1947, pp. 1,122-36.
5. Egli, J.J., "Radio Propagation above 40 MHz over Irregular Terrain," *Proceedings of the Institute of Radio Engineers*, October 1957.
6. Reed, H.R. and Russel, C.M, *Ultra High Frequency Propagation* (New York: John Wiley and Sons, Inc.).
7. Norton, K.A., "Transmission Loss in Radio Propagation II," NBS Technical Note No. 12, June 1959.
8. Norton, K.A., "The Calculation of Ground Wave Field Intensity over a Finitely Conducting Spherical Earth," *Proceedings of the Institute of Radio Engineers*, Vol. 29, December 1941, pp. 623-39.

6.10 Bibliography

1. Barsis, A.P., and Miles, M.J., "Cumulative Distributions of VHF Field Strength over Irregular Terrain Using Low Antenna Heights," NBS Report 8891, October 1965.
2. Bullington, K., "Radio Propagation at Frequencies above 30 Megacycles, *Proceedings of the IRE*, Vol. 35, October 1947, pp. 112-13.
3. Bullington, K., "Radio Propagation Fundamentals," *Bell System Technical Journal*, Vol. 36, May 1957, pp. 593-626.
4. Damelin, J., et. al., "Development of VHF and UHF Propagation Curves for TV and FM Broadcasting," FCC Report Nol R-6602, September 7, 1966.
5. Egli, J.J., "Radio Propagation above 40 Megacycles over Irregular Terrain," *Proceedings of the IRE*, October, 1957.
6. Electromagnetic Compatibility Analysis Center, "CRPL Propagation Path Loss-Statistical," April 2, 1963.

7. Fine, H., *UHF Propagation within Line of Sight*, FCC TRR Report No. 2, 4 and 12, June 1, 1951.
8. HRB-Siner, Inc., "Propagation Models for Interference Prediction," Signal Corps Contract DA-36-039-AMC-03757(E), Final Report, May 1, 1964 to April 30, 1965.
9. Jansky and Bailey, a Div. of Atlantic Research Corp., "Tropical Propagation Research," Final Report, Signal Corps Contract No. DA36-039-SC-90889, 1970.
10. Jansky and Bailey, a Div. of Atlantic Research Corp., "Propagation for Interference Analysis," RADC-TDR-61-313, Vol. I, Contract No. AF30(602)-1934, 1962.
11. Johnson, M.E.; Miles, J.J.; et. al., "Tabulation of VHF Propagation Data Obtained over Irregular Terrain at 20, 50 and 100 MHz," Institute for Telecommunication Sciences and Aeronomy, ESSA Technical Report IER-38-ITSA-38, Part II, Colorado Mountain Data, May 1967.
12. Kritikos, H., et. al., "Investigation of Rough Earth Propagation Models," Univ. of Pennsylvania, RADC-TR-67-531, Contract AF 30(602)-3290, 1967.
13. LaGrone, A.H.; Martin, P.E.; and Chapman, C.W., "Frequency Characteristics of Radio Propagation over a Grove of Trees in Full Leaf," Electrical Engineering Research Laboratory Report No. 6-44, pp. 13-20 (Austin, Texas: Univ. of Texas, January 1962).
14. LaGrone, A.H., "Forecasting Television Service Fields," *Proceedings of the IRE*, Vol. 48, pp. 1009-16, June 1960.
15. LaGrone, A.H., and Chapman, C.W., "Some Propagation Characteristics of High UHF Signals in the Immediate Vicinity of Trees," *IRE Transactions on Antennas and Propagation*, Vol. AP-9, pp. 487-91, September 1961.
16. Lagrone, A.H., "Height gain Measurements at VHF and UHF behind a Grove of Trees," *IRE Transactions on Broadcasting*, Vol. 8-9, pp. 37-54, 1962-63.
17. Matthews, P.A., *Radio Wave Propagation VHF and Above* (London: Chapman and Hall, Ltd., 1965).
18. McMahon, J.H., "Interference and Propagation Formulas and Tables Used in the FCC Spectrum Management Task Force Land Mobile Frequency Assignment Model," *IEEE Transactions on Vehicular Technology*, Vol. VT-23, November 1974.
19. Norton, K.A., "Transmission Loss in Radio Propagation," *Proceedings of the IRE*, Vol. 41, pp. 146-52, 1953.

20. Norton, K.A., "The Calculation of Ground-Wave Field Intensity over a Finitely Conducting Spherical Earth," *Proceedings of the IRE*, Vol. 29, pp. 623-39, December 1941.
21. Norton, K.A., "Transmission Loss of Space Wave Propagation over Irregular Terrain," *IRE Transactions on Antennas and Propagation*, Vol. Ap-3, pp. 152-66, August 1952.
22. Norton, K.A., "System Loss in Radio Wave Propagation, *Proceedings of the IRE,* Vol. 41, pp. 146-52, 1953.
23. Norton, K.A.; Rice, P.L.; and Vogler, L.E., "The Use of Angular Distance in Estimating Transmission Loss and Fading Range for Propagation through a Turbulent Atmosphere over Irregular Terrain," *Proceedings of the IRE*, Vol. 43, pp. 1488-526, October 1955.
24. Oliver, J.K., Jr., et. al., "LF/VLF Propagation Analysis Computer Program Documentation," Bell Aerosystems Co., RADC-TR-68-453, Final Report, December 1968.
25. Reed, H.R., and Russell, C.M., *Ultra High Frequency Propagation* (New York: John Wiley & Sons, Inc., 1953).
26. Rice, P.L.; Longley, A.G.; Norton, K.A.; and Barsis, A.P., "Transmission Loss Predictions for Tropospheric Communications Circuits," National Bureau of Standards Technical Note 101, Vols. I and II, May 7, 1965.
27. Saxton, J.A., *Basic Ground Wave Propagation Characteristics in the Frequency Band 50 to 8,000 MHz*, pp. 211-14 (London: IEEE, 1954).
28. Spogen, L.R., Jr., et. al., "HF and LF Propagation Models for Interference Prediction," Bell Aerosystems Co., RADC-TR-67-396, June 1967.
29. Volger, C.E., "Calculation of Ground Wave Attenuation in the Far Diffraction Region," *NBS Journal of Research*, Vol. 68D, 1964, pp. 819-827.
30. Volger, E.C., "Smooth Earth Diffraction Calculations for Horizontal Polarization," *NBS Journal of Research*, Vol. 65D, 1961, pp. 397-9.
31. Wait, J.R., "Electromagnetic Surface Waves," *Recent Advances in Radio Research*, Vol. I, p. 184 (New York: Academic Press, 1963).

Chapter 7

Operational Performance Models for EMC Analysis

This chapter discusses considerations relative to operational performance and system effectiveness as they apply to EMC analysis. Two basic techniques are presented for translating EMC analysis results into a form that is meaningful from an operational performance standpoint. The first technique is based on the concept of **performance threshold** which is defined as the signal-to-interference ratio that separates acceptable performance from unacceptable performance. The second technique is based on **performance scoring** and provides information which may be translated into grades of service. This chapter also discusses the overall system effectiveness problem and describes how EMC analysis results may be used to determine the electromagnetic effectiveness (EME) of a system.

EMC analysis techniques presented in previous chapters are used to eliminate those unintentional signals that have a low probability of interference, to identify potentially interfering signals and to provide information on the effective level of potentially interfering signals at the input to the demodulation. Consideration of desired signal level at the receiver input will provide information on signal-to-interference ratios and signal-to-noise ratios. Interpretation of these ratios in terms that relate to operational performance is an important final step in EMC analysis.

7.1 Operational Performance Considerations

Ideally, the end result of an EMC analysis would be expressed in a form that completely describes system performance. To accomplish this, mathematical models of system performance are required. However, many different system performance criteria exist. The best criteria to be used for a particular system in a specific application depends on a number of factors. One of the basic problems associated with extending EMC analysis to provide system performance answers is to determine exactly what type of operational performance measure should be used.

Much research has been directed toward operational performance evaluation. Basic performance measures that are widely used include:

1. Articulation score, which is the percentage of words received correctly and is a performance measure for voice communication systems

2. Bit error rate or the character error rate, which is the number of bits or characters received incorrectly in a specified length message (e.g., one per thousand) and is generally accepted as a performance measure for digital communication systems

3. Total failure of a digital communication system because of a loss of synchronization

4. Resolution, which defines the ability to distinguish objects visually and is a performance measure for television and facsimile

5. Probability of detection, probability of false alarm and scope condition, which are performance measures for radar systems

6. Errors in bearing angle, distance, latitude and longitude, altitude and the like as a percentage of total values, which are measures of navigation performance

Other measures of performance include acquisition time delays and break lock in radar systems or other systems that need to acquire and track a signal. Each of these is discussed in Section 7.2.

In evaluating the performance of a particular system, there are several alternatives of varying complexity and utility available. Several of these alternatives are identified below.

1. The simplest and perhaps most widely used operational performance evaluation is based on the concept of a performance threshold which represents the boundary between acceptable performance and unacceptable performance.

2. A slightly more complicated and useful technique for evaluating operational performance is to define the basic system performance measure (articulation score, error rate, resolution, etc.) for the specific signal and interference conditions.
3. The ideal goal for operational performance evaluation is to specify the overall system effectiveness in terms of the ability to accomplish an intended mission or missions.

All three are discussed in more detail in Sections 7.3 through 7.5.

7.2 Operational Performance Measures

This section describes operational performance measures that are often used for different types of systems. The section presents the necessary background and theory required to apply these performance measures to an EMC analysis. Communication systems, for which performance measures are provided, include analog and digital systems for voice transmission, written text and pictures. Other types of systems for which performance measures are provided include surveillance and tracking radars and navigation systems.

In order to assess the performance of a communication system, it is necessary to consider both the type of information being transmitted (voice, written text, pictures, digital data, etc.) and the signal format used to transmit the information (analog or digital). In general, the performance of analog systems (systems that use analog techniques to transmit analog data such as voice or video) tends to be related to the average interfering signal power level and the performance degradation occurs relatively gradually (over a range of 20 dB or more) as the interference level is increased. On the other hand, systems that use digital techniques to transmit digital data tend to experience a rapid transition (over a range of 10 dB or less) from acceptable performance to unacceptable performance as the interference level is measured. Also, digital systems tend to be more susceptible to impulsive or pulse-type signals than do analog systems. In some instances, digital systems will exhibit catastrophic failure as a result of a loss of synchronization when exposed to interference. The following sections describe some of the measures that are used to assess performance of communication systems transmitting various types of information.

7.2.1 Voice Communication Systems

The problem of specifying an operational performance measure for voice communication systems is complicated by the random nature of a received voice signal, variations in message content and differences in hearing and understanding abilities from one receiver operator to another.

7.2.1.1 Articulation Score

One performance measure used for voice systems is articulation score, which is found by using trained talkers and listeners to determine the percentage of words scored correctly by the listener out of the total number of words contained in the test.

The procedure used in an articulation test consists of a talker (or a standardized voice generator such as a tape-recorded voice) reading a set of selected words or syllables over a communication system (which may be subjected to interference). The listener panel interprets what it hears. Various levels of interference may be introduced into the receiver system along with the selected words. The percentage of words interpreted correctly by the listener indicates the intelligibility level or articulation score for the particular set of conditions tested.

Resulting empirical data can then be translated into suitable electrical characteristics (such as a signal-to-interference ratio) which in turn can be used in an EMI prediction process to determine system performance.

Figure 7.1 shows the relationship between signal-to-interference ratio and articulation score for different combinations of desired and interfering signal conditions. All of the cases illustrated are for co-channel interference conditions. One very significant factor evident in the figure is that there is an abrupt transition from good to poor performance.

7.2.1.2 Articulation Index

Another method for specifying voice system performance is an articulation index which provides a measure of the masking effects of noise or an interfering signal on voice intelligibility.[1] The procedure for determining an articulation index is to divide the audio

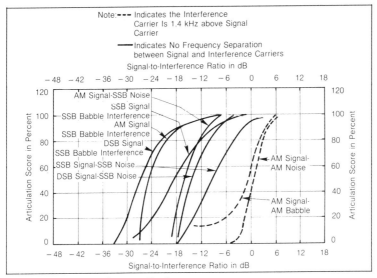

Figure 7.1—Voice System Performance

spectrum into bands that are weighted in frequency so that they all contribute equally to voice intelligibility, specify the signal-to-interference-plus-noise S/(I + N) ratio in each band, and assign each band a percentage of contribution to the total articulation index based on the signal-to-interference ratio in the band. A band is said to contribute in a maximum sense if the S/(I + N) is greater than +18 dB. If the S/(I + N) is less than -12 dB, the band does not contribute to intelligibility. For S/(I + N) between -12 dB and +18 dB, the contribution to intelligibility is defined by linear interpolation between endpoints.

The major advantages of the articulation index over articulation score are that it is: (1) well-defined and hence provides a good standard, (2) easily and quickly measured with repeatable measurements and (3) readily calculated from the receiver audio output spectrum. Relationships between articulation index and articulation score are available for a number of different types of interference.

Techniques which may be used to determine either articulation score or articulation index for voice communication systems operating in the presence of interference are presented in later sections of this chapter.

7.5

7.2.2 Digital Communication Systems

A typical state-of-the-art digital communication system is illustrated in Fig. 7.2. This type of system is capable of transmitting multiple channels of digital data which may be encoded or encrypted for error detection and correction as well as message security. A typical digital system such as the one depicted in Fig. 7.2 may use time-division multiplexing and any one of several modulation schemes, such as phase modulation or spread spectrum modulation techniques like frequency hopping or pseudo-random sequences. A given digital system may not provide all of the functions illustrated in Fig. 7.2.

Interference can cause any of several effects in a digital communication system. First, it can cause total failure of the system as a result of loss of synchronization at some point in the processing of the digital bit stream. Second, it can cause errors in the received message as a result of distortion, masking, automatic gain control action, etc. Both of these effects must be considered in assessing digital system performance in the presence of EMI.

The evaluation of performance for a digital system consists of calculating the probability or error. Two basic types of errors are false acceptance (mistaking interference or noise for the signal) and false dismissal (not recognizing the presence of the signal). For on-off binary transmission, false acceptance is equal to the probability of false alarm, and false dismissal is equal to one minus the probability of detection. Probability of false alarm is the conditional probability of deciding that a signal is present when no signal was transmitted. Probability of detection is the conditional probability of deciding that a signal is present, given that a signal was transmitted. The relative occurrence of false acceptance or dismissal can be determined from the probability densities for signal, interference and noise at the receiver output.

The relationship between the basic decision process and the two types of errors is illustrated in Fig. 7.3. The density function designated IN(x) refers to the output probability distribution density when interference and noise are present while SIN(x) is the output distribution density when a signal, interference and noise (S + I + N) are present. Decision regions are defined such that when the output exceeds a certain threshold T the decision is that the signal is present, whereas if the output is less than T the decision is that no signal is present.

Probability of false alarm (P_{FA}) is given by the probability that

7.6

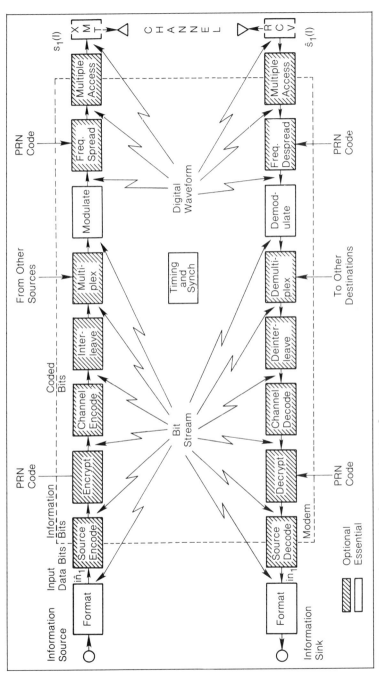

Figure 7.2—Typical Digital Communication System

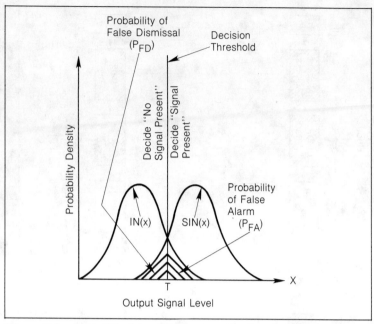

Figure 7.3—Binary Decision Process

interference and noise exceeds the decision threshold T. Probability of false dismissal P_{FD} is given by the probability that $S + I + N$ is less than the decision threshold. Probability of correct detection (P_{CD}) is given by the probability that $S + I + N$ exceeds the decision threshold.

Mathematically, these relationships can be expressed as:

$$P_{FA} = \int_{T}^{\infty} IN(x)dx \qquad (7.1)$$

$$P_{FD} = \int_{-\infty}^{T} SIN(x)dx \qquad (7.2)$$

$$P_{CD} = \int_{T}^{\infty} SIN(x)dx \qquad (7.3)$$

In order to predict the performance of this type of on-off binary

7.8

system in the presence of EMI, it is necessary to specify the probability density functions IN(x) and SIN(x).

The above discussion is helpful for illustrating probabilities of error for digital systems. However, most modern digital transmission systems are of a constant-power nature and do not use on-off carrier operation. Binary systems normally are designed so that the probability of a binary zero (space) and binary one (mark) are equal and the result of an error is identical in either case. This greatly simplifies the design and analysis. In a constant-power system, such as a frequency-shift or a phase-shift keyed system, the detector makes a decision as to whether the incoming information tends to indicate a zero or a one.

The probability of error is uniquely defined by the statistics at the output of the detectors under the hypothesis that a one is transmitted and under the hypothesis that a zero is transmitted. Thus, the problem in determining error characteristics of a digital system under any predetector input function is one of determining these statistics in sufficient detail.

Determination of the statistics which characterize the error rates of a digital system is not, however, a simple straightforward process. Despite the fact that Gaussian, band-limited white noise is used to test digital modems in the laboratory, it is rarely a factor in limiting performance in use over actual communication links such as HF or troposcatter links. In addition to simple signal-to-noise statistics, a complete statistical description of interference and channel-fading parameters is needed to ascertain performance of digital data modems. Since both parameters are important one should know both individual and joint probability distributions of these quantities.

Techniques are presented in later sections of this chapter for including performance predictions for digital data systems in the EMI process.

7.2.3 Picture Communication Systems

Television and facsimile systems transmit information that is eventually displayed in the form of a picture, an important form of communication. Aside from the many TV sets currently in use, this form of communication is experiencing increasing use by law-enforcement and criminal justice agencies for transmitting mugshots and line-ups to neighboring agencies. The picture phone is another example of picture communication which is expected to become widely used in the future.

Interference can degrade picture transmission by introducing dots, lines or bars, causing the picture to be blurred, or causing the receiver to lose sync and roll. Figure 7.4 shows typical effects of different types of interference to TV. Television receivers (particularly color TV receivers) are relatively sensitive to interference. For example, with pulse interference such as would be produced by a radar, a 15 dB ratio of peak signal to peak interference is required to avoid picture degradation in the form of snow in the picture.

Figure 7.4—Interference to TV Pictures

7.2.4 Surveillance Radar Systems

It has been estimated that over 12,000 high-power radars are currently operating in the continental United States. Many of these radars are situated in congested areas and because of real estate considerations are frequently co-located at specific sites such as airports, military bases and missile launch sites. There has been and will be an increased use of radar in airborne systems, navigational aids, weather observation, satellites and space probes. This trend toward greater spectrum usage and congestion has resulted in a mutual interference problem which is becoming increasingly complex.[2]

Surveillance radar systems are used in a wide variety of applications where it is necessary to monitor a relatively large area. The primary use of surveillance radars is to monitor marine and air traffic for the purpose of national defense and traffic control. A typical surveillance radar provides an operator with a scope display of both angular position and range of objects within the radar coverage area. The scope used for this type of display is referred to as a plan position indicator (PPI).

7.2.4.1 Pulse Interference

The most common form of interference is the appearance of interfering dots or spirals on the radar scope presentation caused by pulse interference from other radars. This type of interference is usually moving continuously and may cover a large portion of the scope face, making targets difficult to detect. Interference of this type is annoying to the operator and over a period of time causes fatigue which reduces effectiveness. If the interference sector contains a target, delayed detection is likely to result. If the interference is extreme, false target reports become likely.

One measure of operational performance which is used for this type of interference to surveillance radars is scope condition. Interference effects on radar PPI scopes have been classified into five scope conditions which are illustrated in Fig. 7.5.

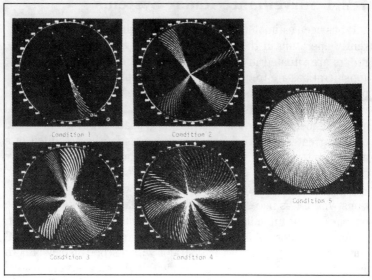

Figure 7.5—Typical Scope Conditions

7.2.4.2 Continuous Wave (CW) Interference

The presence of CW interference is not quite as obvious as pulse interference; however, the phenomenon is important in radar. A pulse radar operating in the vicinity of a CW transmitter can be rendered completely inoperative if the CW power level is sufficient to fire the transmit-receive (TR) tube continuously. In fact, lower levels of CW power may be sufficient to maintain a TR tube arc once the tube has been fired by its own transmitter. Some tubes remain in conduction when the CW power is reduced to 20 mW. If the CW power level is not high enough to maintain the TR tube arc, desensitization can still occur.

The presence of the CW signal at the radar mixer can affect the operation of the mixer crystal, thereby changing the noise level or conversion efficiency and reducing maximum range performance. One dB degradation in receiver response has been noted for CW power levels of 0.15 mW. Stronger signal levels tend to change bias levels in both the mixer and IF stages to a point where noise and desired signals disappear entirely due to receiver desensitization.

Other effects of CW interference include capture of the automatic frequency control circuits (which results in the radar receiver locking onto the wrong signal) and crystal deterioration or burnout as a result of severe overload conditions.

7.2.5 Tracking Radars

The primary function of a tracking radar is to provide continuous, accurate information on the position of a selected target. In addition to the tracking mode of operation, many tracking radars must also perform search and acquisition modes prior to locking onto a target. The radar may be subjected to interference during each of the modes, but it is most susceptible during the search or acquisition modes. Once the radar has locked onto a target, the tracking circuits (including range gates and correlators) provide a high degree of EMI protection.

7.2.5.1 Pulse Interference

During the search mode of operation, interference may cause the operator to pause momentarily on false targets (interference). These pauses reduce the time available for target searching, which results in a reduction in the probability of target detection and range performance. The performance measure which applies to this mode of operation is the probability of detection of a target; this is a function of the target range, velocity, size and other factors. For EMI prediction purposes, performance degradation may be expressed in terms of (1) the reduction in probability of detection at maximum range for specified targets or (2) the reduction in range for a given probability of detection and a specified target.

When a tracking radar is operating in the acquisition mode, interference may cause false lock-on, which results in an increase in the time required to identify and acquire the desired target. In certain military weapon system applications, the loss of a few seconds time in acquiring and locking on to the desired target may make the difference between success or failure of the mission. Performance measures which apply to this mode of operation are target acquisition time, probability of detection and probability of acquisition.

When the radar is in the tracking mode of operation, pulse interference may result in angle or range tracking errors. Tracking performance is measured in terms of rms angle or range errors. Under conditions of severe interference the radar may break track. As mentioned previously, radar susceptibility is significantly reduced by the tracking circuits. Usually, the interference must closely resemble the desired signal for performance degradation to occur.

7.2.5.2 CW Interference

Comments regarding the effects of CW interference to surveillance radars also apply to tracking radars. The primary effect is a reduction in the effective range of the radar because of CW desensitization.

7.2.6 Navigation Systems

Radio navigation systems are widely used in marine and aeronautical applications. Table 7.1 summarizes characteristics of some of the more widely used navigation systems. There are generally two important types of information that are required to use a radio-navigation system. First, it is necessary to correctly identify the station being received, and second, it is necessary to get the navigation information contained in the signal.

Interference can cause degradation in navigation systems by either causing incorrect identification or errors in the navigation. For example, in the case of VHF omnirange (VOR), interference could cause a VOR signal to be incorrectly identified so that the navigator or pilot would associate the signal with the wrong ground station, or it could result in errors in the heading and range information that is obtained.

7.3 Operational Performance Thresholds

In previous chapters, techniques were presented for modeling transmitters, receivers, antennas and propagation to determine whether a potentially interfering signal exceeds the receiver basic susceptibility threshold. Undesired signals that do not exceed this threshold may be dismissed from further EMI consideration. For those undesired signals that exceed the receiver susceptibility threshold, it is necessary to determine whether they result in unac-

Table 7.1—Radio Navigation Systems

System	Frequency	Range in km (Nautical Miles)	Propogation	Error = degrees or = meters			Comments
				Site	Instrument	System	
Direction finder Ground VHF/UHF Airborne: MF	Many	370 (200)	Negligible / Up to 25°	1° / 5°	1° / 2°	2° / Variable	Earliest radio navigation system; still in use as a backup system
Four-course low-frequency range	200 to 400 kHz	370 (200)	Up to 25°	1°	2°	Variable	Obsolescent and being replaced by VHF omni range
Nondirectional beacon	200 to 1,700 kHz	370 (200)					Worldwide use with airborne LF/MF direction finders
Marker beacons	75 MHz	370 (200)	Negligible	None	91.5 m	91.5 m	Used throughout U.S. as check points along airways and distance markers in instrument-landing systems
VHF omnidirectional range (VOR)	108 to 118 MHz	370 (200)	Negligible	3°	1°	3.5°	Successor to low-frequency range; accepted international standard
Decca	70 to 130 kHz	370 (200)	Up to 3,050 m	None	6.1 m	15 to 3,050m	Continuous-wave hyperbolic system used extensively in Europe by ships and fishing fleets
Ground-based radar	1,250 to 10,000 MHz	370 (200)	Negligible	None	1°/305 m	1°/305 m	Widely used
Loran-A	2 MHz	1,111 (600)	30.5 m	None	457 m	457 m	Long range
Tacan range bearing	960 to 1,215 MHz	370 (200)	Negligible / Negligible	None / 2°	61/610 m / 0.5°	610 m / 2°	Military short range omnibearing and distance measuring system
Distance-measuring equipment (DME)	960 to 1,215 MHz	(370) 200	Negligible	None	61 m to 2%	914 m or 3%	International standard often co-located with VOR to form a single site area-converge system.
Vortac							Co-location of VOR and Tacan to provide rho-theta navigation
Loran-C	100 kHz	2,222 (1,200)	152.5 m	None	30.5 m	30.5 to 366 m	Expected successor to Loran-A; longer range and improved accuracy obtained by cycle-matching techniques
Loran	100 kHz						Short range tactical system compatible with Loran-C
Omega	10 to 14 kHz	14,816 (8,000)	1,524 m	None	1,525 m	1,524 m	Hyperbolic system with longer range and less accuracy than Loran-C

ceptable operational performance. This section describes how the concept of operational performance thresholds may be used to translate the results of EMC analysis into a form that is meaningful to the user.

The concept of performance thresholds is based on the existence of a particular signal-to-interference ratio (S/I) at which the performance of a system suddenly changes in a step fashion from an acceptable to a unacceptable level as illustrated in Fig. 7.6a. In an actual system, the transition from acceptable to unacceptable performance does not occur at a discrete value of S/I. Instead, the transition is more gradual, involving grades of performance ranging from acceptable to marginal to unacceptable. An actual system performance function is illustrated in Fig. 7.6b.

Although the performance function does not exhibit a step transition from acceptable to unacceptable, in many applications the transition is rather abrupt (see Fig. 7.1) and the performance threshold concept provides a good approximation for EMC analysis.

In order to use performance thresholds for EMC analysis, select a specific point in the receiver which may be used as the reference for determining performance threshold levels. There are several points in the receiver such as RF input, IF input, IF output, detector input or detector output that could be considered as the location for specifying performance thresholds.

The primary factor that must be considered in establishing performance thresholds is the decision mechanism. This may be a part of the post-detection stage of the receiver or may be completely separated from the receiver (the decision mechanism of a voice communication system is the human listener). Therefore, for the purpose of EMI predictions using the performance threshold concept, receiver models are used to translate interfering signals to the decision mechanism or to the point where further translations of interference through the receiver becomes mathematically untractable.

For performance threshold models presented in this section, the detector input is selected as the threshold location. This makes it possible to use receiver models described in Chapter 4 to account for predetection receiver characteristics and to permit use of a performance threshold concept that is based on desired and interfering signal modulations. Where multiplexed receivers are involved, the detector input(s) are that of the final baseband. Where anti-jamming (AJ) post-detector circuits are used, families of performance thresholds are required to correspond to each AJ situation.

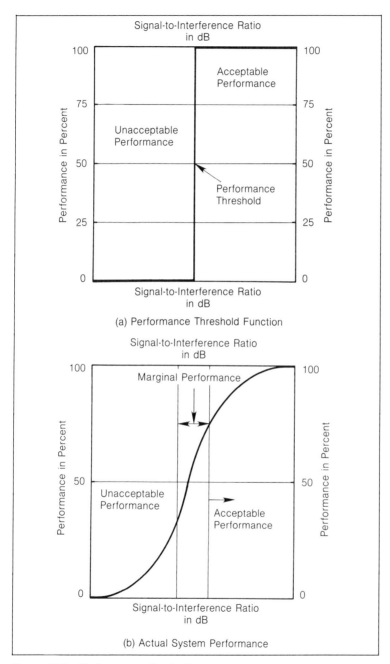

(a) Performance Threshold Function

(b) Actual System Performance

Figure 7.6—Performance Evaluation

Table 7.2 summarizes performance threshold values for 23 desired and undesired modulation types (529 cases).[3] Designations used for various desired and interfering signal types are defined in Table 7.3. Performance threshold values listed in this table represent the combined results of analysis and measurement. To use the table, it is necessary to know: (1) desired and interfering signal

Table 7.2—Performance Threshold Table
(Performance Thresholds in dB)

Interfering Signal Modulation*

	A1	A2	A3	A9	A3B	A3J	A4	A5C	A9	F1	F2	F3	F3	F4	F9	F9	P0	P9D	P9E	P9F	P9G	P9	P9
A1	8	6	7	7	7	7	7	7	7	7	7	7	7	7	7	7	8	7	7	8	7	7	7
A2	9	6	0	0	11	7	6	11	11	5	6	6	11	11	11	11	9	6	6	6	9	6	6
A3	-23	-13	-1	-5	4	0	0	0	2	-23	0	0	2	0	2	2	-23	-13	-13	-13	-23	-13	-13
A9	-19	-10	0	-4	7	3	3	3	5	-19	3	3	5	3	5	5	-19	-10	-10	-10	-19	-10	-10
A3B	-36	-24	-7	-7	-7	-7	-24	-24	-36	-36	-7	-7	-7	-7	3	3	-36	-24	-24	-24	-36	-24	-24
AJ	-36	-24	-7	-7	-7	-7	-24	-24	-36	-36	-7	-7	-7	-7	3	3	-36	-24	-24	-24	-36	-24	-24
A4	10	10	5	2	12	8	12	12	10	10	10	10	10	10	12	12	10	10	10	10	10	12	10
ASC	41	41	36	32	45	41	45	45	41	41	41	45	45	41	45	45	26	41	41	41	41	45	41
A9	10	10	5	2	12	8	8	8	16	10	8	8	10	8	10	10	10	10	10	10	10	10	10
F1	6	-6	-12	-16	-16	-6	-6	6	6	6	-6	-6	6	-6	6	6	6	-6	-6	-6	6	-6	-6
F2	6	16	16	16	16	16	16	16	16	6	16	16	16	16	16	16	6	16	16	16	6	16	16
F3	0	3	3	3	2	2	3	2	3	0	3	3	2	3	2	2	0	0	0	0	0	0	0
F3	0	0	0	0	-4	-4	0	-4	0	0	0	0	0	0	0	0	0	0	0	0	0	0	0
F4	12	12	10	10	10	10	10	10	12	12	12	12	12	12	10	10	15	12	12	12	12	12	12
F9	$22+n$	$22+n$	$22+n$	$22+n$	25	25	$22+n$	25	25	$22+n$	$22+n+n$	$22+n+n$	25	$22+n$	25	25	18	15	15	15	15	15	$22+n$
F9	10	$22+n$	$22+n$	$22+n$	25	25	$22+n$	25	25	$22+n$	$22+n$	25	25	25	25	25	18	15	15	15	15	15	$18+n$
P0	5	10	4	10	10	10	10	10	10	10	10	10	10	10	10	10	18	10	10	10	10	10	10
P9D	$18+n$	$18+n$	$18+n$	$18+n$	$18+n$	$18+n$	$18+n$	$18+n$	$18+n$	$18+n$	$18+n$	$18+n$	$18+n$	$18+n$	$18+n$	$18+n$	18	$18+n$	$18+n$	$18+n$	$18+n$	$18+n$	$18+n$
P9E	18	18	18	18	18	18	18	18	18	18	18	18	18	18	18	18	18	18	18	18	18	18	18
P9F	18	18	18	18	18	18	18	18	18	18	18	18	18	18	18	18	18	18	18	18	18	18	18
P9G	18	18	18	18	18	18	18	18	18	18	18	18	18	18	18	18	18	18	18	18	18	18	18
P9	$10-n$	$10-n$	$10-n$	$10-n$	$10-n$	$10-n$	$10-n$	$10-n$	$10-n$	$10-n$	$10-n$	$10-n$	$10-n$	$10-n$	$10-n$	$10-n$	$10-n$	$10-n$	n	$10-n$	$10-n$	$10-n$	$10-n$
P9	13	13	13	13	13	13	13	13	13	13	13	13	13	13	13	13	13	13	13	13	13	13	13

Desired Signal Modulation*

·See Table 7.3 for definition of signal modulation characteristics

Table 7.3—Designation of Modulation Types

Symbol	Modulation	Signal Characteristics	Perform.
A1	AM Pulse	$BW_S = 6$ kHz; $\delta_S = 0.5$; $P_{FA} = 10^{-4}$; $P_{FD} = 10^{-1}$	P_E 1%
A2	Pulse, AM, (2-Tone FSK)	$BW_S = 6$ kHz; $m_S = 1$; $P_{FA} = 10^{-4}$; $\delta_{m,s} = 0.5$	PE 1%
A3	AM Voice	$BW_S = 6$ kHz; $m_S = 0.5$; 1,000 word vocabulary	AS 50%
A3	AM Voice	$BW_S = 20$ kHz; $m_S = 0.3$; 1,000 word vocabulary	AS 50%
A3B	Ind. DSB-SC Voice/Analog	$BW_S = 6$ kHz; 1,000 word as per channel	AS 50%
AJ	SSB-SC Voice/Analog	$BW_S = 3$ kHz; 1,000 word vocabulary	AS 50%
A4	AM Facsimile	$BW_S = 6$ kHz; $m_S = 1$; $(S/I)_Q = 10$ dB	PER 90%
A5C	TV Video	$BW_S = 6.25$ MHz; $m_S = 0.7$; $(S/I)_Q = 33$ dB	PER 90%
A9	AM Analog	$BW_S \gg 6$ kHz; $m_S = 0.7$; $(S/I)_0 = 10$ dB	PER 90%
F1	FSK Pulse	$BW_S \leqslant 12$ kHz; $B_S = 1$; $(S/N)_I = 14$ dB	P_E 1%
F2	Pulse, FM, (2-Tone FSK)	$BW_S \leqslant 12$ kHz; $B_S = 1$	P_E 1%
F3	FM Voice	$BW_S = 12$ kHz; $B_S = 1$; 1,000 word vocabulary	AS 50%
F3	FM Voice	$BW_S = 60$ kHz, $B_S = 5$; 1,000 word vocabulary	AS 50%
F4	AM Facsimile	$BW_S \leqslant 12$ kHz; $B_S - 1$; $(S/N)_0 = 10$ db	PER 50%
F9	FDM	$n = $ No. of channels $n \geqslant 2$; n in dB	PER 90%
F9	PM Analog	$BW_S \geqslant 12$ kHz; $B_S = 1$; $(S/N)_0 = 10$ dB	PER 90%
P0	Pulse Wideband	$BW_S \gg 12$ kHz; $\delta = 1/30$; $P_{FA} = 10^{-4}$; $P_{FD} = 5$	P_E 1%
P9D	PAM	$n = $ No. of channels $n \geqslant 2$; n in dB	PER 90%
P9E	PWM	Threshold criteria single edge det.	PER 90%
P9F	PPM	Threshold criteria $(S/N)_0 - 12$ dB	PER 50%
P9G	Pulse Compression	Threshold criteria $(S/N)_0 = 12$ dB	PER 50%
P9	Matched Filter	$(BW_I/BW_0) = $ n n in dB: $(S/N)_0 = 10$ dB	PER 90%
P9	Phase Lock	22.5° Threshold criteria	PER 50%

modulations, (2) the equivalent interfering signal level (on-tune interfering signal level that would be required to produce an equivalent signal at the input to the detector) which may be determined by applying the EMI prediction process and (3) the desired signal level which is either determined from system considerations or is assumed to have a specific value. The use of Table 7.2 to determine whether system performance is acceptable or unacceptable in the presence of interference is best illustrated by an example.

Illustrative Example 7.1

Consider an airborne UHF AM voice receiver used for ground-to-air communications between air traffic controllers and pilots. The desired signal is double sideband AM (A_3) with a 6 kHz bandwidth and 50 percent modulation. The received signal level (S) is at least 20 dB above the receiver noise (N) of -110 dBm for ranges up to 160 km from the airport. Suppose that EMI prediction results indicate potential interference from another but similar transmitter located at a different airport approximately 640 km from the first. The undesired signal level I varies from $+7$ to $+12$ dB above receiver sensitivity for the 160 km area around the desired signal transmitter. Determine whether receiver performance is acceptable under these conditions.

In order to use Table 7.2 it is first necessary to determine the signal-to-interference ratio at the input to the detector. The signal-to-interference ratio can be determined from the desired and undesired signal levels relative to the receiver sensitivity, such as:

$$S/N = +20 \text{ dB}$$

$$I/N = +7 \text{ to } +12 \text{ dB}$$

$$(S/I)_{min} = S/N - (I/N)_{max}$$

$$= 20 \text{ dB} - 12 \text{ dB}$$

$$= 8 \text{ dB}$$

$$(S/I)_{max} = S/N - (I/N)_{min}$$

$$= 20 \text{ dB} - 7 \text{ dB}$$

$$= 13 \text{ dB}$$

From Table 7.2, the performance threshold level for the indicated types of modulation is a 0 dB S/I ratio. Thus, since the values calculated above exceed the performance threshold level, acceptable performance will result.

7.4 Operational Performance Models

Although the performance threshold models described in the previous section are quite useful for a wide variety of different types of interference prediction problems, there are applications which require operational performance results beyond the simple acceptable or unacceptable performance results. This section presents models for determining operational performance for various combinations of desired and interfering signals.

7.4.1 Voice Communication System Performance

As discussed in Section 7.2, there are two measures of performance that are often used for voice systems. The first is the articulation score which is given by the percentage of words scored correctly by a panel of listeners. The second is the articulation index which provides a measure of the masking effects of interference or noise on voice intelligibility (see Section 7.2.1).

Regardless of which method is used to specify performance of a voice communication system, the basic approach used in EMI prediction is the same. First, the receiver models presented in Chapter 4 are applied to account for various receiver characteristics and effects, such as noise, dynamic range, desensitization, selectivity (RF, IF and audio), adjacent-channel susceptibility, cross modulation, intermodulation and spurious responses. Second, the audio output of the receiver (the signal, interference and noise spectra) must be specified so that performance can be determined.

Because the human ear and brain serve as the decision mechanism for voice systems, it is helpful to summarize some of the major characteristics of human listeners.

7.4.1.1 Interference Effects on Human Listeners

The ear is an integrating device. The apparent loudness of a sound impulse, resulting from the integration of sound pressure over a 0.3 ms span, is valid for an unexpected or unfamiliar sound impulse. For many years the main interference concern was the degradation of radio performance as discerned by the human ear. Most electronic devices are not equivalent to the ear in terms of susceptibility of interference and interaction, and the characteristics of the hearing process are required to make comparisons. These characteristics are summarized below:

1. The ear responds to only a small portion of the energy of individual transients and spikes having durations of microseconds since it's cut-off frequency is about 15 kHz.
2. The ear's maximum sensitivity is from 1,000 to 3,000 Hz.
3. The ear responds logarithmically to impulse magnitude.
4. Recurrent sounds seem to be louder.
5. Sound impulse effects are negligible after one second.
6. The ear can detect a 10 percent change in intensity at low levels and a 25 percent change at high levels.
7. The ear will not hear noise 20 dB below signal level.
8. The ear normally notices 3 dB changes of noise in the presence of signals. However, up to 6 dB of noise variation can go unnoticed.

Three arbitrary thresholds have been established for identification of speech sounds. These are detectability, perceptibility and intelligibility. Detectability is the threshold for detection but not identification; it has a S/N ratio of -18 dB for an AM signal and white noise. Perceptibility is understanding the overall context and requires a S/N ratio of 0 to 5 dB. Intelligibility implies that nearly all words are understood, requiring a S/N ratio of 10 to 15 dB.

Masking is the degree of incomprehensibility of the desired information. A word articulation or sentence intelligibility test determines the percentage of words or sentences correctly received. For fewer syllables in a word, the number of words understood will be less. Masking occurs because of either noise intensity level or distortion caused by intermodulation products. The most important characteristic of the ear is its selectivity to certain frequency components and the rejection of others. In this respect, masking is the extent to which the ear is not perfect.

7.4.1.2 Performance Scoring

One method for specifying performance of voice communication systems is the articulation index (see Section 7.2.1). Figure 7.7 shows the relationship between articulation index and signal-to-

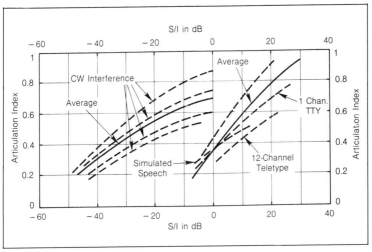

Figure 7.7—Measured Data, On-Tune Interference

interference ratio for a number of different types of interfering signals. The curves may be grouped into one of two classes: CW interference or modulated interference. Considering the many uncertainties that exist in an EMC analysis, the variations between the different curves within a group are relatively insignificant and all of the curves within a group may be approximated by the average curve shown in the figures.

Figures 7.8 through 7.13 show the relationship between articulation index, signal-to-interference and signal-to-noise ratio for different types of interference. Except for single frequency tones, which do not severely degrade performance, the articulation index relationships shown in the figures exhibit similar trends.

7.4.1.3 Performance Prediction

For interfering signals that result in audio outputs other than tones, the performance prediction should be based on the ratio of signal-to-average-interference-plus-noise in the audio passband, and the white noise curve should be used.

The EMC analysis process provides results in the form of interference-to-noise ratios (I/N) at the input to the detector. The signal-to-noise ratio (S/N) may also be specified at that point. For performance prediction, it is required to specify the signal-to-

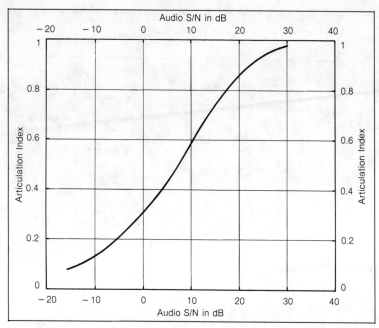

Figure 7.8—Audio Performance, White Noise Interference

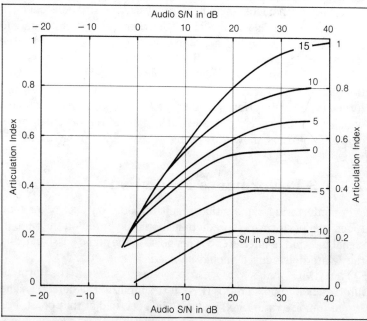

Figure 7.9—Audio Performance, White Noise, Simulated Speech Interference

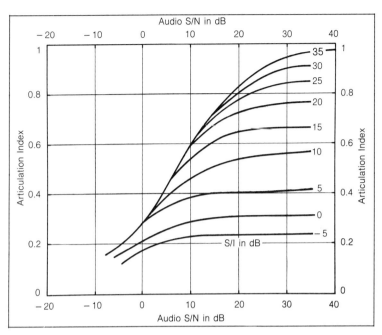

Figure 7.10—Audio Performance, White Noise, 12-Channel Multiplex

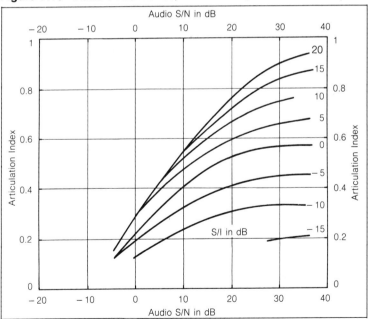

Figure 7.11—Audio Performance, White Noise, Single-Channel Teletype Interference

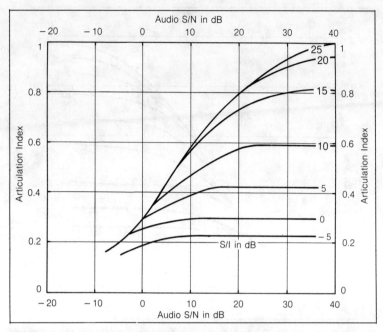

Figure 7.12—Audio Performance, White Noise, Pulse Interference, 200 pps

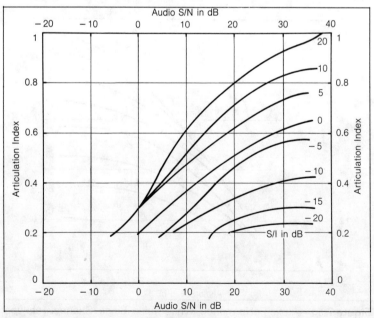

Figure 7.13—Audio Performance, White Noise, 500 Hz Tone Interference

interference-plus-noise S/(I + N), which is found by first determining (I + N)/N from Fig. 7.14 and then calculating S/(I + N):

Illustrative Example 7.2

Consider a VHF land-mobile voice receiver that is required to operate within an 80 km radius of the base station. The desired voice signal is at least 10 dB above receiver noise (S/N > 10 dB) within this operating region. Suppose that EMI prediction results indicate two potentially interfering signals within the desired operating region. One of the potentially interfering signals is from a P-band surveillance radar and the other is from a VHF TV station. Determine the operational performance when these signals are present.

P-Band Radar Interference

Assume that the P-band radar transmits a pulsed signal with a repetition rate of 400 pulses per second, and that EMI prediction has established that the average in-band undesired signal level is 10 dB above the receiver noise, i.e., I/N = 10 dB. The receiver noise can be neglected in this case because it is negligible compared to the undesired signal. This means that the signal-to-average-interference-plus-noise is 0 dB. From Eq. (7.4):

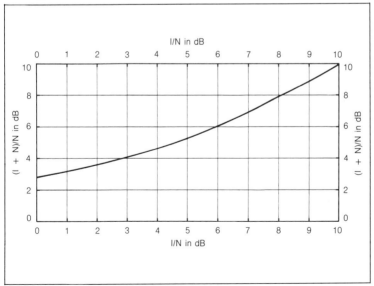

Figure 7.14—Relationship between Interference-Plus-Noise to Noise and Interference-to-Noise

$$\frac{S}{I+N} = \frac{S}{N} - \frac{I+N}{N} \qquad (7.4)$$

$$= 10 \text{ dB} - 10 \text{ dB}$$

$$= 0 \text{ dB}$$

Referring to Fig. 7.8, the articulation index resulting from this level of interference would be approximately 0.3. This value represents poor operational performance.

TV Station Interference

Assume that interference from the TV station results in an interference-to-noise ratio of 5 dB. Referring to Fig. 7.8, for I/N = 5 dB (I + N)/N = 6 dB. Thus, from Eq. (7.4):

$$\frac{S}{I+N} = \frac{S}{N} - \frac{I+N}{N}$$

$$= 10 \text{ dB} - 6 \text{ dB}$$

$$= 4 \text{ dB}$$

The articulation score and the articulation index resulting from TV interference are approximately 0.4 as derived from Fig. 7.8. This value represents marginal operational performance.

7.4.2 Digital Communication System Performance

A typical communication system was illustrated in Fig. 7.2. Although digital communication systems typically do not contain all of these elements, the illustration portrays the component chain of the receiver channel which contains numerous degradation mechanisms responsible for degrading communication performance during the reception of interfering signals. Possible sources of degradation in a typical digital receiver are:
1. Antenna adaptive array processor
2. Varactor filter nonlinearities
3. Automatic gain control
4. Diversity combiner

5. Demodulator
6. Acquisition and synchronization circuits such as:
   Carrier synchronization
   Clock or bit Synchronization
   Frame synchronization
   Codeword and node synchronization
   Network synchronization
   Coder/interleaver

A summary of the degradation mechanisms for a digital receiver is given in Table 7.4. In order to analyze performance, it is necessary to determine specific mechanisms causing the degradation of performance. A given interference will generally disturb several degradation mechanisms simultaneously within the receiver chain. Each mechanism produces disturbances affecting subsequent mechanisms in the chain, causing an accumulation of signal degradation that leads to the final degradation of system performance. The assessment of communication performance does not require a detailed analysis of the signal degradation process in a receiver (which is generally very complicated) but simply involves an overall performance evaluation at the information sink.

Interference can manifest itself in many ways from imperceptible perturbations to total disruption of service. Regardless of the way in which an interfering signal influences a degradation mechanism or circuit within the receiver, the fundamental questions to be asked are simply: "Will the system work? How well will it work? Will the communication center be able to talk to the field units at any time? What percentage of the time will I not be able to communicate?"

It becomes apparent that the criteria established for measuring system performance during interference degradation are very important, because system performance will be used in the final decision as to whether the radio system should be deployed or not. System performance should be defined in terms that are meaningful to the user. Many technical definitions of the performance measures can be given, such as bit-error rate, S/I, digital timing stability, etc. However, these criteria do not define the performance of the ultimate purpose of the communication system: to communicate information.

System performance should be evaluated at the points of the system where the receiver information is eventually used, displayed or presented to a user. For example, the measure of performance of voice transmission should be the intelligibility of the received

7.29

Table 7.4—Digital Receiver Degradation Mechanisms

Degradation Mechanism	Interference Waveform	Measure of Performance	Interference Margin
Antenna (Conventional)			
Overcome Attenuation Provided by Antenna Pattern	Any Waveform Within the Receiver BW	Antenna Pattern	Antenna Pattern
Receiver			
Mixer Preamplifier	1. Any Waveform 2. Signal at the Image Frequency 3. Two CW Tones Differ by the IF	IF Spectrum	Sufficiently High Power Level to Create Spurious Signal(s) in IF Output
Diversity Combiner			
1. Channel Weighting (AGC) 2. Adaptive Phasing	Noise Pulsed CW CW Within 30 kHz of 70 MHz	Output SNR Output SNR	Minimum to Degrade SNR Minimum to Degrade SNR
Demodulator			
1. Phase-Lock Loop 2. Receive Bit Synchronizer 3. Receive Clock Synthesizer	CW, NBAM, NBFM Pulsed CW Pulsed CW	Loss of Carrier Phase Lock Loss of Receive Bit Sync Loss of Receive Bit Sync	Minimum to Cause Loss of Phase Lock Minimum to Cause Loss of Sync Minimum to Cause of Sync
Second-Level Multiplexer			
Frame Control Synchronizer	Pulsed CW	Loss of Frame Sync Loss of Control Bit Loss of Control Bit Sync	Minimum to Cause Loss of Frame or Control Bit Synchronization
First-Level Multiplexer			
Frame Synchronizer	Pulsed CW	Loss of Sync	Minimum to Cause of Frame Synchronization

message. For teletype or printed text messages, the performance should be measured in terms of readability or intelligibility of the printed message. These kinds of communication data can tolerate a considerably high degree of error before they become unintelligible because of the redundancy of the English language. Thus, the radio system can be usable during periods of degraded performance, but only up to some point at which the degradation is severe enough to yield output information that is too garbled and difficult to comprehend.

Because the reception of voice and printed text requires interpretation by a human, the performance measure for these kinds of data is subjective. The interference level at which the information becomes usable will vary somewhat with each user's judgment. In order to avoid subjective evaluation of performance, it is desirable to determine a standard response of a measurable quantity, such as bit-error rate or S/I at which the performance degrades to an unacceptable level. Once the subjective level, such as articulation score or index for voice or character error-rate for text, is established and agreed upon for a given type of interference waveform, it would be related to a distinct measurable quantity of the signal. This can then be used to provide consistent measurements of the performance threshold for every test involving that same interference waveform. The subjective performance measure of information establishes a standard measure applicable to all receiving systems. However, the corresponding standard response generally varies with different types of receiver systems and must be determined separately for each.

The total performance measure of a receiving system having multiple types of information consists of a superimposition of the standard responses of all information devices. Figure 7.15 illustrates standard response levels for typical user terminal devices and their composite. The composite scale of standard response levels pertains to one type of interference waveform being received by the system under test.

As mentioned earlier, analog receivers tend to degrade gradually with increasing amounts of interference. On the other hand, digital receivers depend on pulse timing and synchronization of the received pulses to an internal clock. The presence of an interfering signal adds a noise component to the desired signal which may disturb the timing in the pulse waveform. As the level of interference increases, pulse synchronization becomes more difficult until synchronization is lost, at which time the system fails completely. The receiver circuits attempt to reacquire the signal by resynchronizing, which usually takes a long time. Thus, the performance of digital receivers can exhibit dramatic failure under certain interference conditions because of loss of signal synchronization. This loss properly accounts for distinct failure

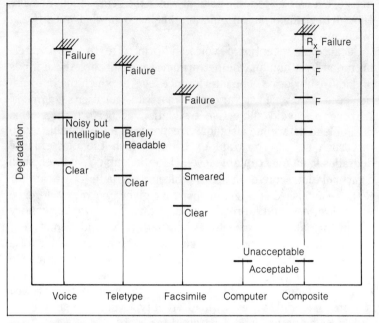

Figure 7.15—The impact of EMI on performance degradation depends on the type of information being received.

thresholds of receiver performance, representing the most severe type of degradation.

The potential interference effects of co-site equipment can severely degrade performance. One type of problem results from Automatic Gain Control (AGC) capture by a relatively strong signal radiated from a nearby transmitter. Co-site emitters can also desensitize receivers as a result of front-end saturation.

For the practical purpose of determining digital system performance, the effects of many types of interference can be approximated by representing the interference as if it were white noise. Although there are a number of different types of digital transmissions, two widely used are Frequency Shift-Keying (FSK) and Phase Shift-Keying (PSK). Figure 7.16 presents curves of error rate versus signal-to-noise ratio for FSK and PSK.[4]

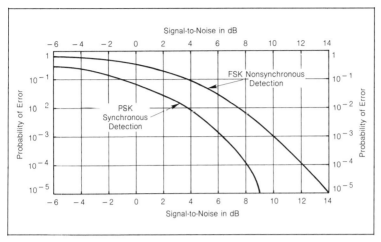

Figure 7.16—Digital System Error Rates

7.4.3 Picture Communication System Performance

The effects of interference on the performance of picture communication systems are somewhat subjective. One technique for rating television (TV) performance in the presence of interference is based on establishing six rating grades as follows: (1) excellent, (2) fine, (3) passable, (4) marginal, (5) inferior and (6) unusable. An extensive measurement program was conducted using the above rating scheme and approximately 38,000 ratings were gathered on color and monochrome TV pictures having different injected interference. Nearly 200 observers participated in these experiments.[5]

Representative results are shown in Figs. 7.17 and 7.18 for co-channel interference from another TV station and for random noise interference. For co-channel interference, the signal-to-interference ratios required for a passable score or better by 50 percent of the observers are tabulated in Table 7.5.

For random noise interference, the S/I requirement for at least a passable rating by 50 percent of the observers was +27 dB on the basis of root-mean-square (rms) sync amplitude to rms noise over the 6 MHz TV channel.

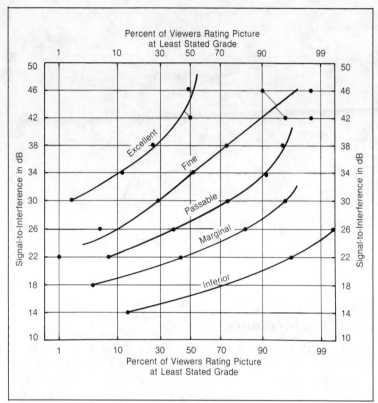

Figure 7.17—Co-channel Interference 604 Hz Carrier Separation

Table 7.5—S/I Required for at Least a Passable Score by 50 Percent of Observers

Interfering Signal Offset in Hz	Required S/I in dB
604	41
9,985	24
10,010	17
19,995	29
20,020	17

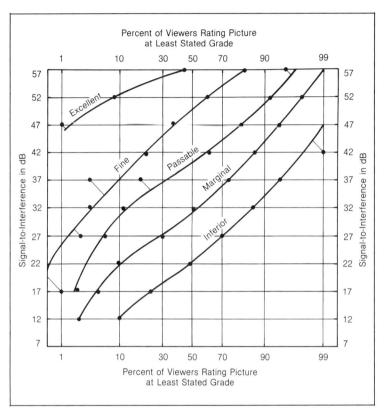

Figure 7.18—Random Noise Interference

7.4.4 Surveillance Radars

The basic approach for determining radar performance involves representing a radar receiver by a number of cascade stages, and then identifying the significant effects that influence performance for each stage. Figure 7.19 shows a typical representation for a radar receiver. The basic stages of the receiver and the major factors and effects that are considered for each of the stages are outlined in Table 7.6.

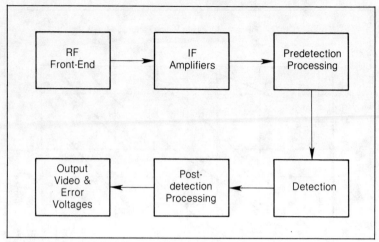

Figure 7.19—Typical Radar Receiver Representation

Table 7.6—Summary of Major Interference Effects			
Receiver Stage	Interference Effect	Result on Operational Performance	Important Factors
Output	Scope clutter error voltages	May mask desired signal; increase acquisition time; lose track	Type of output characteristics of interference at output
Post-detector processing	May reduce certain interference effects	May improve in presence of interference but may be reduced otherwise	Type of processing; interfering pulse level, width and rate out of detector
Detector	Production of interference at detector output	Interference appears on scope and may tend to obscure or mask desired signal	Desired signal pulse level, width and rate; interfering signal level, width and rate at IF
Pre-detector processing	May reduce certain interference effects	May improve in the presence of interference but may be reduced otherwise	Type of processing; interfering pulse level, width rate and frequency at IF
	AGC	Decrease range or probability of detection	AGC level and time constant interfering pulse level, width, rate and frequency at IF
IF	Saturation	Decrease range or probability of detection	IF saturation level and bandwidth; interfering pulse level, width, rate and frequency at IF
RF	Saturation	Decrease range or probabilty of detection	RF saturation level and interfering pulse level, width, rate and frequency at RF

The block diagram in Fig. 7.20 shows the basic elements of radar performance prediction. The three major receiver effects that must be considered are: (1) desensitization resulting from RF saturation, (2) desensitization resulting from IF saturation or unintentional AGC and (3) direct production of interference at the receiver output. The following sections present techniques for calculating surveillance radar performance measures for pulse and CW interference.

7.4.4.1 Pulse Interference

For surveillance radars operating in the presence of pulse interference, the primary interference effect that must be considered is the direct production of interference at the receiver output. Scope condition is used to specify surveillance radar performance in the presence of pulse interference.[6-8]

One technique for determining scope condition is based on the calculation of a numerical index for each of four possible combinations of antenna main beam and unintentional region orientation. The basic formula for calculating this numerical index N_i is:

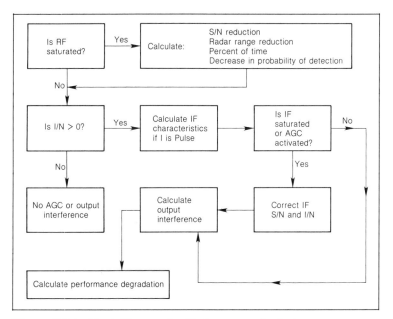

Figure 7.20—Block Diagram for Performance Analysis

$$N_i = 20 Q_{20} + \sum_{P_i} [Q_i (P_i - P_{mds})] \tag{7.5}$$

where, Q_{20} = number of pulses/scan with level
greater than $(P_{mds} + 20)$ dBm

P_{mds} = minimum discernible signal in dBm

Q_i = number of pulses/scan at level P_i
where $P_{mds} \leqslant P_i \leqslant P_{mds} + 20$

When N_i has been calculated, the scope condition can be evaluated according to the following rules:

1. If only those antenna orientations involving one or both of the antenna main beams result in an N_i greater than zero, then the scope condition will be one.
2. If antenna orientations involving unintentional region to unintentional region conditions result in a positive N_i, then the individual values of N_i are combined as (see Chapter 5):

$$N^* = 10^{-4} \sum_{i=1}^{4} N_i \tag{7.6}$$

Scope conditions from one to five are assigned based on the following:

$$
\begin{array}{ll}
0 \leqslant N^* \leqslant 3.7 & \text{Scope Condition 1} \\
3.8 \leqslant N^* \leqslant 9.4 & \text{Scope Condition 2} \\
9.5 \leqslant N^* \leqslant 14.7 & \text{Scope Condition 3} \\
14.8 \leqslant N^* \leqslant 25.2 & \text{Scope Condition 4} \\
25.3 \leqslant N^* \leqslant \infty & \text{Scope Condition 5}
\end{array}
$$

The scope conditions are defined such that degradation becomes more severe as the scope condition progresses from one to five.

If all or most of the interfering signal pulses are at least 20 dB above the minimum discernable signal level, Fig. 7.21 may be used directly to determine PPI scope condition. Time per scan is defined as the time in seconds that the interfering signal exceeds the minimum discernable signal level per revolution or sector scan of the receiving antenna. This may be determined directly from a con-

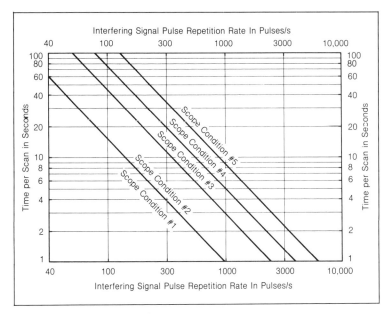

Figure 7.21—PPI Scope Conditions

sideration of time dependent statistics resulting from the rotation of the antennas (see Chapter 5).

Illustrative Example 7.3

Consider airport surveillance radars operating at two different airports that are separated by 16 km but situated within line of sight of each other. Calculate the scope conditions that would exist if the radars are tuned to 1,280 MHz and 1,300 MHz respectively, and each has the following operating parameters:

Transmitter power $P_T(f_{OR})$ = 1 MW peak = +90 dBm

Receiver sensitivity $P_R(f_{OR})$ = −90 dBm

Pulse width = 2 μs

PRF = 360 pulses/s

Antenna gain = 35 dB

Scan Rate = 6 rpm or the scan interval = 10 s/scan

7.39

First, calculate the fundamental interference margin (FIM) from Eq. 2.6. Assume antenna unintentional region conditions correspond to a mean gain of – 10 dB and a standard deviation of 14 dB (see Chapter 5):

$$FIM = P_T(f_{OR}) + G_{TR} - L + G_{RT} - P_R(_{OR})$$

$$= +90 \text{ dBm} + (-10) - (32 + 20 \log f_{MHz}$$

$$+ 20 \log d_{km}) + (-10) - (-90 \text{ dBm})$$

$$= 42 \text{ dB}$$

Next, correct for frequency separation between the transmitter and receiver. If it is assumed that the pulse is rectangular, the frequency separation correction for a 2 μs pulse and 20 MHz frequency separation is – 40 dB (see Fig. 3.25). Thus, the resulting mean Interference Margin (IM) is:

$$IM = FIM + \text{frequency correction} = 42 \text{ dB} - 40 \text{ dB} = 2 \text{ dB}$$

The antenna rotation is considered in terms of the resulting time-dependent standard deviation which is given by:

$$\sigma_D = \sqrt{\sigma^2_{GT} + \sigma^2_{GR}} = \sqrt{14^2 + 14^2} = 20 \text{ dB}$$

With a 20 dB standard deviation, a +2 dB mean margin will result in a positive interference (IM > 0 dB) approximately 50 percent of the time. This would result in approximately 180 pulses per second that exceed the receiver sensitivity. The resulting scope condition for a 10 s scan interval shown in Fig. 7.21 corresponds to scope condition #2.

7.4.4.2 CW Interference

The primary effect of CW interference on surveillance radars is to desensitize the RF or IF stages of the radar. This reduces receiver sensitivity to the desired signal. CW desensitization may be expressed directly in terms of a decrease in maximum range by using the radar range equation.

Techniques were presented in Chapter 4 for determining the effects of desensitization on receivers in terms of sensitivity reduction. When the effective sensitivity in the presence of interference has been determined, the maximum radar range R_{max} may be calculated from:[9]

$$R_{max} = \left[\frac{P_T \ G \ A_e \ a}{(4\pi)^2 \ S_{mds}} \right]^{1/4} \qquad (7.7)$$

where,

P_T = transmitter peak power in watts

G = transmitter antenna gain (ratio)

A_e = antenna effective aperture area in square meters

a = radar cross section of target in square meters

S_{mds} = minimum detectable signal in watts

The fractional range reductions resulting from a given sensitivity reduction is:

$$\text{Fractional Range} = \log^{-1} \left[\frac{\text{Sensitivity Reduction in dB}}{40} \right]$$

$$(7.8)$$

Figure 7.22 illustrates the relationship given by Eq. (7.8) and may be used directly to determine the range reduction resulting from a given sensitivity reduction.

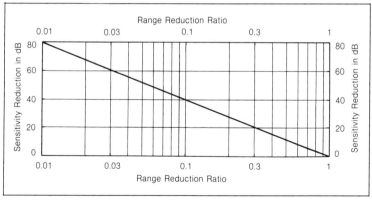

Figure 7.22—Range Reduction Resulting from Desensitization

Illustrative Example 7.4

Consider that an L-band surveillance radar with a normal range of 160 km is operating in the immediate vicinity (0.16 km) of a 1 kW L-band (1,000 MHz) CW illuminator used for missile tracking. Calculate the range reduction experienced by the surveillance radar when it is the main beam of the CW illuminator antenna which has a +30 dB gain. Assume that side and back lobe conditions (unintentional-radiation region) for the surveillance radar antenna correspond to a mean gain of −10 dB. From Eq. (2.2), the power available P_A at the surveillance radar is:

$$P_A = P_T + G_{TR} - L + G_{RT}$$

where, $\quad P_T = 1 \text{ kW} = +60 \text{ dBm}$

$\qquad\quad f = 1,000 \text{ MHz}$

$\qquad\quad d = 0.16 \text{ km}$

$\qquad\quad L = 32 + 20 \log f_{mHz} + 20 \log d_{km} = 76 \text{ dB}$

$\qquad\quad G_{TR} = 30 \text{ dB}$

$\qquad\quad G_{RT} = -10 \text{ dB}$

therefore, $\quad P_A = 60 \text{ dBm} + 30 \text{ dB} - 76 \text{ dB} - 10 \text{ dB} = +4 \text{ dBm}$

Assume that the techniques described in Chapter 4 are used to determine the sensitivity reduction resulting from a +4 dBm signal; it is found that the receiver sensitivity is reduced by 10 dB. Figure 7.22 may now be used directly to determine that the range is reduced to 0.55 of the maximum range. This means that the surveillance radar range now would be only 88 km instead of 160 km which would exist if no desensitization were encountered.

7.4.5 Tracking Radars

The basic approach for determining performance for tracking radars is similar to that used for surveillance radars in Section 7.4.4. The tracking radar receiver is represented by cascaded stages and the significant effects that influence performance are identified for each stage. The following sections present models for determining tracking radar performance for both pulse and CW interference.

7.4.5.1 Pulse Interference

Tracking radars provide a high degree of protection against pulse interference. If there are only a few potentially interfering pulse sources (only a few other radar transmitters), the major impact on operational performance may be expressed in terms of increased target acquisition time. On the other hand, if there are many potentially interfering sources, tracking errors may result. Techniques for determining each of these effects are described in the following paragraphs.

Tracking Radar Target Acquisition Time Model

Where there are only a few pulse interfering signal sources, the major interference effect to tracking radars is that target acquisition time is increased. The model for this provides a measure of the increase in acquisition time resulting from interference. One equation that is used for calculating target acquisition time in the presence of interference is:

$$t_s = \frac{\theta}{\omega_s} (1 + MT) \qquad (7.9)$$

where, t_s = average time required for angular sector search in seconds

θ = total angle searched by radar in degrees

ω_s = angular scan rate in degrees/s

M = average number of detected interference pulses/s

T = antenna dwell time upon detection

Individual sources of interference increase target acquisition time by an amount equal to $MT\theta/\omega_s$.

Tracking Radar RMS Error Model

Although individual sources of interference can cause degradation during the target tracking mode, the radar in general is less susceptible during this mode of operation. The major degradation during the target tracking mode results from an individual signal that is almost synchronized and in time coincidence with the desired signal.

Although individual interfering signals do not generally produce serious degradation during the target tracking mode, degradation may result when multiple interfering signal sources are present. Here interference tends to become random in nature and the effects are similar to those resulting from noise. Thus, this type of interference may be expected to affect the radar tracking functions in the same way as would a reduction in the signal-to-noise ratio resulting from desensitization. Thus, tracking degradation for multiple interfering signals may be expressed in terms of range reduction as described in Section 7.4.4.2.

7.4.5.2 CW Interference

The primary effect of CW interference on tracking radars is to reduce the sensitivity, which results in a decrease in the maximum effective range of the radar. Considerations regarding CW interference to tracking radars are the same as those that apply to surveillance radars. The reader is referred to the discussion in Section 7.4.4.2 for calculating range reduction resulting from CW interference.

7.5 System Electromagnetic Effectiveness Models

Previous sections presented models for determining system performance based on the concept of performance thresholds and performance scores. These models permit EMI prediction results to be expressed in terms of a quantitative measure of performance of a CE equipment or system which includes the performance of the human operator where applicable. System performance measures are technical parameters that must be interpreted in terms of their impact on the operational function or mission being performed by the system to measure the overall system's effectiveness.

System effectiveness is a measurement of the ability of a total CE system to provide the service required in support of a particular operational function or mission. Factors that influence system effectiveness are: the operational performance of each equipment or subsystem; the operational requirements each equipment or subsystem must satisfy to accomplish its part of the overall mission;

and the relative importance of the particular equipment or sub-system in the overall mission. One definition of system effectiveness E is:[10]

$$E = A \, D \, C \qquad (7.10)$$

where,   A = measure of availability

D = measure of dependability

C = measure of capability

EMC is more closely related to the measure of capability, C. The EME of a system is one factor that must be included in determining overall capability of a system. EME is a measure of the ability of the system to satisfy those operational requirements that depend on or are influenced by the electromagnetic spectrum.

Figure 7.23 shows a flow diagram for performing an evaluation of the EME of a system. The evaluation starts by selecting a particular mission for which a system EME evaluation is to be performed. The next step is to identify the functions that are required to complete the mission. Each of these functions is weighted in terms of its importance to the mission and the equipments that are

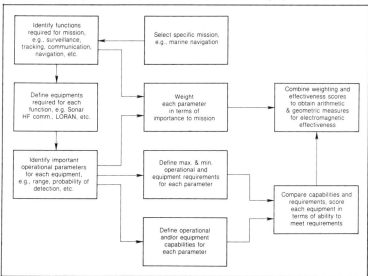

Figure 7.23—Flow Diagram for System Electromagnetic Effectiveness Evaluation

used to accomplish the function are specified. Next, it is necessary to identify the important operational parameters for each equipment.

When the operational parameters are identified, the next step is to define maximum and minimum usable operational requirements for each parameter. For example, if the parameter being considered is the range of an HF communication set, it may be that the maximum usable range is 1,600 km. Ranges in excess of 1,600 km are never encountered and are therefore of no additional consequence. The minimum usable range may actually be 800 km. Here, if the HF communication set does not provide ranges greater than 800 km it is of no practical value for the application considered.

Next, it is necessary to define operational capabilities (operational performance) for each equipment in terms of operational parameters described above. At this point, the capabilities are compared to the requirements and each equipment is scored in terms of its ability to satisfy the requirements. If the operational capability exceeds the maximum operational requirement, a perfect score (1.0) is assigned. If the operational capability fails to satisfy the minimum requirement, a zero score is assigned.

After each equipment has been assigned scores that reflect its ability to meet the operational requirements, individual scores for all equipments are combined in a weighted manner that accounts for the importance of each operational requirement on the overall mission. The resulting weighted combination provides a measure of the electromagnetic effectiveness of the total system.

There are two basic techniques that are used for combining individual scores. They may be combined arithmetically to determine a weighted arithmetic system EME:

$$\text{Arithmetic EME} = \frac{\displaystyle\sum_{i=1}^{N} w_i C_i}{\displaystyle\sum_{i=1}^{N} w_i} \qquad (7.11)$$

where, w_i = weight assigned to i^{th} operational parameter
based on its importance to the mission
(range 0 to 1)

$$C_i = \text{capability to satisfy operational requirements of ith operational parameter (score 0 to 1)}$$

$$N = \text{number of operational requirements defined}$$

The arithmetic EME measurement provides an overall indication of the ability of a system to satisfy requirements of a specific mission. However, it is relatively insensitive to individual instances of poor performance. Thus a high arithmetic effectiveness score would be gained if most of the important operational requirements were satisfied, but a high score does not guarantee that all important operational requirements are satisfied.

A second method for combining individual performance scores is to weight them exponentially and find a multiplicative EME:

$$\text{Multiplicative EME} = \left[\prod_{i=1}^{N} (C_i)^{w_i} \right]^{1/N} \tag{7.12}$$

The multiplicative EME is sensitive to individual instances of poor performance. Thus, a high score guarantees that all important operational requirements are satisfied.

By comparing the EME scores from Eqs. 7.11 and 7.12 it is possible to assess the overall system effectiveness. The results are illustrated in Fig. 7.24. For example, if both scores were high, it would imply that all important operational requirements are satisfied. If the arithmetic EME were high and the multiplicative EME were low it would imply that the system met most of the operational requirements well but some low scores existed. Low arithmetic and multiplicative EME scores would indicate that the system was poor in most requirements.

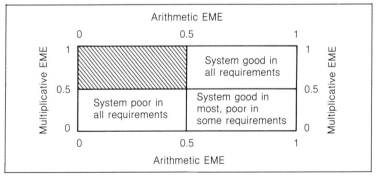

Figure 7.24—System Effectiveness Scores

7.6 References

1. French, N.R. and Steinberg, J.C., "Factors Governing the Intelligibility of Speech Sounds," *Journal of the Acoustical Society of America*, Vol. 19, January 1949, pp. 90-119.
2. "Electromagnetic Compatibility DH 1-4, *Air Force Systems Command Design Handbook*.
3. "Basic Performance Thresholds," ECAC, December 1966.
4. White, D.R.J. and James, W.G., "Digital Computer Simulation for Prediction and Analysis of Electromagnetic Interference," *IRE Transactions on Communications Systems*, Vol. CS-9, No. 9, June 1961.
5. Dean, C.E., "Measurements of the Subjective Effects of Interference in Television Receivers," *Proceedings of the Institute of Radio Engineers*, 1960, pp. 1,035-49.
6. Katz, L., "The San Diego Problem—Phase I, L-Band Signal Density Prediction Model Validation," Armour Research Foundation of the Illinois Institute of Technology, ECAC TDR 63-3.
7. Katz, L.; Parlow, R.; and Singer, A., "The San Diego Problem—Phase II, L-Band Radar Interference Prediction and Validation," IIT Research Institute, ECAC TDR 64-2.
8. Hudson, Capt. C.L. and Limburg, Lt. W.R., "Loss of System Effectiveness Due to Electromagnetic Interference," Tenth Tri-Service Conference on Electromagnetic Compatibility, November 1964.
9. Slolnick, M.I., *Introduction to Radar Systems* (New York: McGraw Hill Co., Inc., 1962).
10. Weapons System Effectiveness Industry Advisory Committee (WSEIAC), "Final Report of Task Group II, Prediction Measurements," System Effectiveness Division, Air Force Systems Command, AFSC-TR-65-5, January 1965.

7.7 Bibliography

1. American National Standards Institute, "Methods for Calculations of the Articulation Index," ANSI Standard 53.5-1969.
2. Duff, W.G., and Heisler, K.G., Jr., et. al., "Voice Communication Degradation Study," RADC-TR-67-556, February 1968.
3. Duff, W.G., et. al., "Radar EMI to Voice Communications Receivers," *1972 IEEE EMC Symposium Record* (New York: IEEE, 1972).
4. French, N.R., and Steinberg, J.E., "Factors Governing the Intelligibility of Speech Sounds," *Journal of the Acoustical Society of America*, Vol. 19, January 1949, pp. 90-119.
5. Goldman, J., "Multiple Error Performance of PSK Systems with Co-channel Interference and Noise," *IEEE Transactions on Communication Technology*, August 1971, pp. 420-30.
6. Kryter, K.D., "Methods for the Calculation and Use of the Articulation and Index," *Journal of the Acoustical Society of America*, Vol. 34, No. 11, November 1962, p. 1689.
7. Mayher, R., "Basic Performance Thresholds," ESD-TR-66-9, December 1966.
8. Mayher, R., "Introduction to the Analysis of Interference to the Performance of Communication Systems," ECAC-TR-65-1, ESD-TR65-16, May 1965.
9. Schwartzlander, H., "Intelligibility Evaluation of Voice Communications," *Electronics*, May 1958.
10. Thompson, A.S., "The Application of the Voice Analysis Interference System to the Prediction of Voice Intelligibility," U.S. Army Electronic Proving Ground Publication No. USAEPG-DR-433.

Chapter 8

System Analysis
for EMC Design

Previous chapters of this handbook have introduced basic concepts and models used in EMI prediction and analysis. This chapter describes the overall analysis process as it relates to CE system design. Methods and techniques used to combine transmitter, receiver, antenna and propagation models in various phases of EMC analysis are presented. Specific examples are presented to help the reader understand applications of each phase of the analysis process to various types of problems.

There are many situations for which EMC analysis techniques are applicable. However, several important factors must be resolved before the actual analysis may be performed. For example, specific analysis requirements may not be clearly defined. Problem definition must be recognized and regarded as an important and necessary step in the overall analysis process. Major considerations that must be applied during this stage are identified in Section 8.1.

Before an EMC analysis may be performed, it is necessary to gather information on equipments being considered. Since this is vital to analysis, results depend directly on the ability to find valid information. Section 8.2 identifies major sources of data for use in EMC analysis. It presents several alternatives that may be used when specific data are not available.

Sections 8.3 through 8.6 describe how models for transmitters, receivers, antennas and propagation are combined in the amplitude, frequency, detailed and performance phases of EMC analysis. Specific examples are given to illustrate basic techniques used in each phase of analysis. Results are presented in summary form for typical situations.

8.1 Problem Definition

The first step in EMC analysis is problem definition. During this stage, it is necessary to define the analysis frequency range, geographical area, equipment involved, relative geometry, prediction detail, sources of input data, output results required and related considerations.

Although each problem is different and requires separate consideration, there are certain generalizations that can be made. For example, regarding frequency range limitations, the **fundamental interference margin (FIM)** is usually considered for situations in which the transmitter and receiver frequencies are separated by 20 percent or less. FIM refers to situations resulting from the transmitter fundamental emission interfering with the receiver fundamental response (see Chapter 2).

Significant transmitter spurious outputs and significant receiver spurious responses are generally limited to a frequency range from 0.1 to 10 times the operating frequency. Hence consideration of **transmitter interference margin (TIM)** and **receiver interference margin (RIM)** is usually limited to cases for which the transmitter and receiver fundamental frequencies are separated by more than 20 percent but less than one decade. TIM refers to situations resulting from the transmitter fundamental interfering with receiver spurious, and RIM refers to situations resulting from transmitter spurious emission interfering with the receiver fundamental response.

Spurious interference margin (SIM) is usually considered in cases for which transmitter and receiver fundamental frequencies are separated by more than one octave but less than two decades. SIM refers to situations involving a transmitter spurious emission interfering with a receiver spurious response.

The geographical area that must be considered in an EMI intersystem prediction problem is a function of operating frequency, transmitter power output, antenna gains and receiver susceptibility threshold. However, general criteria may be developed. For example, fundamental interference (transmitter fundamental to receiver fundamental including adjacent channels) must be considered over a relatively large geographical area which includes line-of-sight conditions. Typically, for ground-based systems, the FIM is considered for all potential emitters or receptors within 80 to 160 km (50 to 100 mi.) of the equipment under investigation.

The separation for which it is necessary to consider TIM and RIM is defined in Fig. 8.1 as a function of radio frequency and **effective power margin (EPM)** in dB which is:

$$EPM = P_T + G_{TR} + G_{RT} - P_R \qquad (8.1)$$

where,

P_T = transmitter power in dBm

G_{TR} = transmitting gain in direction of receiver in dB

G_{RT} = receiving antenna gain in direction of transmitter in dB

P_R = receiver sensitivity in dBm

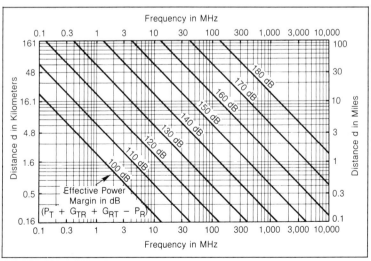

Figure 8.1—Distance Separation Criteria for RIM and TIM

Relationships in Fig. 8.1 are based on rejection levels of 60 dB for transmitter and receiver spurious emissions and responses. In EMC analysis it is necessary to consider RIM and TIM cases for distances less than those specified by the appropriate relationships in Fig. 8.1. SIM separation distances that must be considered are illustrated in Fig. 8.2.

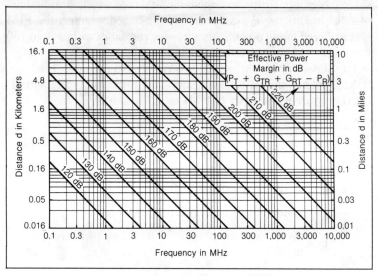

Figure 8.2—Distance Separation Criteria for SIM

When the geographical area of consideration has been defined, the next step is to define specific emitters and receptors within that area that must be considered. This information may be obtained from various sources such as the FCC files on licensees and applicants for a license to use the spectrum, the Electromagnetic Compatibility Analysis Center (ECAC) environmental files, and the National Technical Information Agency (NTIA) of the Department of Commerce. If the antennas associated with the emitters and receptors are high-gain, directional antennas, it is necessary to define whether a main beam or unintentional-radiation region condition exists. The reader is referred to Chapter 5 for a discussion of antenna techniques to be used.

There are certain transmitter-receiver frequency relationships that are more likely to produce interference than others. For example, if it is of interest to analyze EMI to a receiver having an operating frequency (f_{OR}), the environmental transmitters of primary interest are: (1) those that have operating frequencies approximately equal to f_{OR}/N where N is an integer from 1 to 10 and (2) those that have operating frequencies approximately equal to $pf_{LO} \pm f_{IF}$ where f_{LO} is the receiver local oscillator frequency, f_{IF} is the receiver intermediate frequency and p is an integer from 1 to 10. If $f_{IF} \ll f_{LO}$, the above relationship is approximately pf_{OR}.

Conversely, if transmitter EMI to environmental receivers must be analyzed, the most susceptible receiver frequencies are: (1) those that have operating frequencies approximately equal to Nf_{OT} where f_{OT} is the transmitter operating frequency and N is an integer from 1 to 10 and (2) those that have operating frequencies given by $[f_{OT} \pm (p - 1) f_{IF}]/p$ and p is an integer from 1 to 10. If $f_{IF} \ll f_{OT}$, the above relationship is approximately f_{OT}/p. When the EMC analysis problem is defined, particular attention should be directed toward identifying transmitters and receivers that have the above frequency relationships.

It is also necessary to identify sources of input data to be used for analysis. For example, identify whether interference characteristics are to be specified by measured data, EMI standards or summary models and determine the type of results desired.

Illustrative Example 8.1 is used throughout this section. Various phases of EMC analysis are applied to the problem in latter sections dealing with specific stages of analysis.

Illustrative Example 8.1: Problem Definition

Consider the EMC analysis problem shown in Fig. 8.3. This problem involves a UHF (270 MHz) AM voice receiver used for air-to-ground communications. (The UHF band covers 300 MHz to 3 GHz. However, the 225 to 400 MHz communication band is referred to as a UHF communication band.) The receiver antenna is located on top of the air traffic control center (ATCC) with a UHF transmitting antenna which has two UHF (280 MHz and 291 MHz) AM voice transmitters multicoupled to it. These transmitters are used for military ground-to-air communications. Also located on top of the ATCC is a civil VHF antenna driven by a 130 MHz transmitter used for ground-to-air communications. Each of the three transmitters has 100 W (+50 dBm) output and operates into a vertical colinear array antenna having a 10 dB gain. The antenna has a 360° horizontal coverage and a 10° vertical beamwidth.

8.5

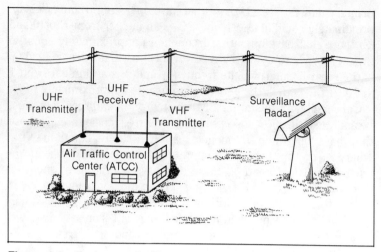

Figure 8.3—Equipment Configuration for Illustrative Example 8.1

The receiver, operating at 270 MHz, has a sensitivity of –110 dBm. It also uses a vertical colinear array antenna with a 10 dB gain. Separations between the UHF and VHF transmitting antennas and the UHF receiving antenna are 15 m (approx. 50 ft.) or more in distance. For these situations, the EPM is given by:

$$\text{EPM} = P_T + G_{TR} + G_{RT} - P_R \text{ dB}$$
$$= 50 \text{ dBm} + 0 + 10 - (-110 \text{ dBm}) \qquad (8.2)$$
$$= 170 \text{ dB}$$

For the TIM and RIM cases, it is necessary to recognize that one antenna will realize its design gain and the other antenna will be operating at a nondesign frequency. Thus, its gain will be reduced to the level given later in Table 8.7.

Figure 8.1 shows that for an EPM of 170 dB, it is necessary to consider the TIM and RIM cases for UHF transmitters if they are within 26 km (16 mi.) of the receiver. An even greater range of consideration 56 km (35 mi.) would be obtained for the VHF transmitter TIM case at 130 MHz. The maximum distance separation criteria for the SIM case is obtained from Fig. 8.2 by using the minimum spurious frequency which in this case is 0.1 times the receiver frequency, i.e., 0.1 (270 MHz) = 27 MHz. For the SIM case it is necessary to use antenna gains at nondesign frequencies for both antennas, hence $G_{TR} = G_{RT} = 0$ and EPM = 160 dB.

From Fig. 8.2 the distance separation is found to be less than 0.1 km (0.06 mi.), i.e., less than 91 m. Therefore, the SIM case must also be considered for this problem.

Further definition of potential EMI sources in the vicinity of the ATCC indicates that there is also a surveillance radar located 61 m (200 ft.) from the receiver. The radar operates at 2,900 MHz, has a peak power output of 1 MW (90 dBm) and an antenna gain of 30 dB, and the antenna main beam illuminates the receiver antenna when it scans by. For this case it is not necessary to consider FIM, TIM or RIM because the fundamental frequency separations are greater than a decade. Thus, EPM = 90 + (31 − 13) + 0 − (−110) = 217 dB. For the SIM case it is necessary to use antenna gains at nondesign frequencies for both antennas since G_{TR} = (30 − 13) dB and G_{RT} = 0 dB (see Chapter 5). For the minimum spurious frequency of the radar 2,000 MHz (determined by waveguide cutoff), Fig. 8.2 indicates that the SIM must be considered for distances less than 0.8 km (0.5 mi.).

The next section discusses the problem of data collection for EMC analysis and continues with an illustrative example.

8.2 Data Collection

A second step in preparing for an EMC analysis is collecting the required data. There are two types of data used in EMC analysis.

The first type, which is referred to as required problem input data, consists of nominal equipment characteristics and specific problem data. Nominal characteristics data include transmitter bandwidth and fundamental power output, receiver bandwidth and sensitivity and antenna gains, polarization and beamwidths. Specific problem data refers to assigned frequencies, equipment locations and antenna direction of transmission or reception. Table 8.1 is a sample data form which identifies required problem input data.

Table 8.1—Required Problem Input Data

Characteristic ↓ / # →	1	2	3	4	5
Transmitter: Nomenclature Frequency-Upper (MHz)　Lower Power (dBm) Type Modulation Bandwidth (kHz)					
Antenna: Type Gain (dB) Polarization Location (X m) (Y m) (H m) Beamwidths (°AZ) (°EL) Direction (°/North)					
Receiver: Nomenclature Frequency-Upper (MHz)　Lower Sensitivity (dBm) Type Modulation Bandwidth (kHz) LO Frequency (MHz) 1st IF (MHz) Sign of IF					
Antenna: Type Gain (dB) Polarization Location (X m) (Y m) (H m) Beamwidths (°AZ) (°EL) Direction (°/North)					

The second type of data used in EMC analysis is referred to as interference characteristics. Although it is best to get these data for all equipments considered in an analysis, this is not always possible. To provide data for use in analysis problems for which specific information is not available, statistical interference characteristics summaries have been presented for various equipment types. If specific interference characteristics data are not available, an EMC analysis may still be performed based on the summary models. Thus, specific interference data are not required for EMC analysis in the same sense as is the required problem input data. Table 8.2 serves as a sample data form for the interference characteristics data.

Table 8.2—Interference Characteristics Data
(Amplitude and Frequency Analysis)

Transmitter		1	2	3	4	5
Harmonic A (dB/Decade) B (dB) (f > f_{OT}) σ (dB) Maximum Frequency (MHz)						
Spurious A' (dB/Decade) B' (dB) (f < f_{OT}) σ' (dB) Minimum Frequency (MHz)						
Modulation Δf_0 (kHz) Envelope M_0 (dB/Decade) Δf_1 (kHz) M_1 (dB/Decade) Δf_2 (kHz) M_2 (dB/Decade)						
Antenna		**1**	**2**	**3**	**4**	**5**
Main Beam	Harmonic C (dB/Decade) D (dB) (f > f_O) σ (dB)					
	Spurious C' (dB/Decade) D' (dB) (f < f_O) σ' (dB) Waveguide Cutoff (MHz)					
Side and Back Lobe	Mean G[p($\theta \neq \theta_0$)] Gain (dB/Isotrope) σ (dB)					

Table 8.2—Interference Characteristics Data*
(Amplitude and Frequency Analysis)

Receiver	1	2	3	4	5
Spurious I (dB/Decade) (f > f_{OR}) J (dB) σ (dB) Maximum Frequency (MHz)					
Spurious I' (dB/Decade) J' (dB) (f < f_{OR}) σ' (dB) Minimum Frequency (MHz)					
Selectivity B_{R20} (kHz) B_{R60} (kHz)					
Adjacent Δf_{max} (MHz) Signal Allowable FIM (dB)					

Antenna		1	2	3	4	5
Main Beam	Spurious C (dB/Decade) D (dB) (f > f_O) σ (dB)					
Main Beam	Spurious C' (dB/Decade) D' (dB) (f < f_O) σ' (dB) Waveguide Cutoff (MHz)					
Side and Back Lobe	Mean G[p($\theta \neq \theta_O$)] Gain (dB/Isotrope) σ (dB)					

Data for an EMC analysis problem may be found from a number of sources. For example, nominal characteristics data may be obtained from equipment operating manuals or specifications, design specifications, ECAC's nominal characteristics files, direct solicitation of equipment users or other sources (see Chapter 10). Information on specific equipment locations, antenna directions, frequencies, etc. can be obtained from operational plans, system deployment plans, frequency, assignments and schedules, ECAC's environmental files, FCC applications for frequency assignments and direct solicitation of users.

Specific interference characteristics data is generally not as readily available as nominal data and specific problem input data. However, there are still a number of possible sources for these types of data such as: MIL-STD-449 measurement results, equipment limits provided in specifications and standards, FCC rules and regulations governing spurious emissions and responses and design test evaluation results. In the event that specific interference characteristics data are available from one of these sources, it is used as the basis for the equipment models for EMC analysis. If specific interference data are not available, summary models presented in Chapters 3 through 8 are used.

Illustrative Example 8.2: Data Collection

Continuing with the illustrative problem described in the previous section, show the process of data collection. It is assumed that all pertinent required problem input data was either given in the statement of the problem or could be determined from operational information and equipment operation manuals. The resulting data are tabulated in Table 8.3. For interference characteristics data, it is assumed that there are no measured data or other specific data available. Thus, the statistical summary data presented in previous chapters of this volume are used. The resulting data are given in Table 8.4, and sources for each type of data are given in Tables 8.3 and 8.4.

Table 8.3—Required Problem Input Data

Characteristic ↓ / # →	1	2	3	4	Source
Transmitter:					
Nomenclature	T−1	T−2	T−3	T−4	
Frequency-Upper	130	280	291	2,900	
(MHz) Lower	130	280	291	2,900	
Power (dBm)	50	50	50	90	
Type Modulation	AM Voice	AM Voice	AM Voice	Pulse	
Bandwidth (kHz)	10	25	25	1,000	
Antenna:					
Type	Colinear Array	Colinear Array	Colinear Array	Parabolic	
Gain (dB)	10	10	10	30	
Polarization	Vertical	Vertical	Vertical	Horizontl	
Location (X m)	12	−12	−12	6	
(Y m)	12	−12	−12	0	
(H m)	6	0	0	0	
Beamwidths (°AZ)	360°	360°	360°	4°	
(°EL)	10°	10°	10°	10°	
Direction (°/North)	--	--	--	Rotating	
Receiver:					
Nomenclature	R−1				
Frequency-Upper	270				
(MHz) Lower	270				
Sensitivity (dBm)	−110				
Type Modulation	AM Voice				
Bandwidth (kHz)	25				
LO Frequency					
(MHz)	230				
1st IF (MHz)	40				
Sign of IF	+				
Antenna:					
Type	Colinear Array				
Gain (dB)	10				
Polarization	Vertical				
Location (X m)	0				
(Y m)	0				
(H m)	0				
Beamwidths (°AZ)	360°				
(°EL)	10°				
Direction (°/North)	---				

Source column: Statement of Problem

Table 8.4—Interference Characteristics Data
(Amplitude and Frequency Analysis)

Transmitter	1	2	3	4	Data Source
Harmonic A (dB/Decade)	−80	−80	−80	−60	Table
B (dB)	−30	−30	−40	−40	8.7
(f> f_{OT}) σ (dB)	15	20	20	20	
Maximum Frequency (MHz)	1,300	2,800	2,900	29,000	
Spurious A' (dB/Decade)	20	20	20	20	
B' (dB)	−80	−80	−80	−80	
(f < f_{OT}) σ' (dB)	10	10	10	10	Equipment
Minimum Frequency (MHz)	13	28	29	2,000	Manual
Modulation Δf_0 (kHz)	0.01	0.01	0.01	100	Table
Envelope M_0 (dB/Decade)	0	0	0	0	8.9
Δf_1 (kHz)	0.1	0.1	0.1	1,000	
M_1 (dB/Decade)	0	0	0	−20	
Δf_2 (kHz)	1	0.1	1	10,000	
M_2 (dB/Decade)	−60	−60	−60	−40	

Antenna	1	2	3	4	5
Main Beam Harmonic C (dB/Decade)	0	0	0	0	Table
D (dB)	−10	−10	−10	−13	8.7
(f > f_0) σ (dB)	3	3	3	3	
Spurious C' (dB/Decade)	0	0	0	0	
D' (dB)	−10	−10	−10	−13	
(f < f_0) σ' (dB)	3	3	3	3	Equipment
Waveguide Cutoff (MHz)	--	--	--	2,000	Manual
Side and Back Lobe Mean G[p($\theta \neq \theta_0$)]					Table
Gain (dB/Isotrope)	0	0	0	−10	8.7
σ (dB)	6	6	6	14	

8.13

8.3 System Amplitude Analysis

Problems associated with analyzing EMC between equipments were introduced in Chapter 2. The basic EMC analysis equation, which may be applied to communication system problems, involves the independent variables frequency (f), time (t), distance (d) and direction (p) as follows:

$$IM(f, t, d, p) = P_T(f, t) + C_{TR}(f, t, d, p) - P_R(f, t) \qquad (8.3)$$

where,

$$IM(f, t, d, p) = \text{interference margin in dB}$$

$$P_T(f, t) = \text{source emitting power in dBm}$$

$$C_{TR}(f, t, d, p) = \text{transmission coupling in dB}$$

$$P_R(f, t) = \text{susceptibility threshold in dBm}$$

For applications involving potential EMI coupled between antennas associated with transmitters and receivers, Eq. (8.3) becomes:

$$IM(f, t, d, p) = P_T(f, t, d, p) + G_{TR}(f, t, d, p) - \qquad (8.4)$$
$$L(f, t, d, p) + G_{RT}(f, t, d, p) -$$
$$P_R(f, t)$$

where,

$$G_{TR} = \text{transmitter antenna gain in direction of receiver in dB}$$

$$G_{RT} = \text{receiver antenna gain in direction of transmitter in dB}$$

$$L = \text{propagation loss in dB}$$

This is abstracted from Chapter 2.

Although the basic analysis equation appears to be simple, Chapter 2 identified several problems that occur when Eq. (8.4) is applied to an EMI problem. One problem is that the functions represented in the equation are complicated, and the equation must be applied to each of a number of transmitter output-receiver response pairs. To overcome this difficulty and simplify calculation procedures for problems involving many transmitters and receivers, a multilevel analysis philosophy is used.

During the first stage of EMC analysis, the amplitude analysis, some simplifying assumptions are made about each function in Eq. (8.4). A simple, quick calculation is performed and the obviously noninterfering cases are eliminated from further consideration.

Four interfering cases are considered separately in the amplitude analysis. They are: (1) FIM is the interference margin that exists if the receiver is tuned to the transmitter fundamental output, (2) RIM is the interference margin that exists if the receiver fundamental is tuned to the nearest transmitter spurious output, (3) TIM is the interference level that exists if the nearest receiver spurious response is tuned to the transmitter fundamental output and (4) SIM is the interference margin that exists if a receiver spurious response is tuned to the nearest transmitter spurious output.

These four cases were introduced and discussed in Chapter 2 and a short-form EMC analysis process was introduced for calculating the interference margin for each case. However, the amplitude analysis portion of the short-form prediction process is based on using transmitter spurious emission levels and receiver spurious-response levels that are constant with frequency. In certain applications, particularly when a computer is to be used in the prediction, it is best to use more realistic amplitude frequency relations at the beginning for the amplitude analysis such as those described in Chapters 3 through 5. Table 8.5 summarizes general EMC analysis models used for the amplitude analysis.

A second problem that arises in applying Eq. (8.4) for EMC analysis is that it is necessary to specify each function in the equation in a form that is consistent with the overall requirements of the process. Chapters 3 through 6 presented amplitude models for each function and these models are summarized in Table 8.5 for a range of frequencies above and below fundamental emission and reception. Table 8.6 presents the resulting system amplitude models for the FIM, RIM, TIM and SIM cases. Although the models appear to be relatively complicated, they are easily programmed and implemented on a digital computer. All parameters required for the models have been discussed previously in Chapters 3 through 6.

A third problem that occurs when applying Eq. (8.4) is that sufficient information about equipment interference characteristics is not always available. Because of this problem, equipment summary characteristics, which may be used in the absence of specific data, were presented. These summary characteristics were also provided in earlier chapters and are summarized in Table 8.7.

Table 8.5—Amplitude Analysis Models

Parameter	Frequency	Average Level (dB)	Standard Deviation (dB)
Interference Margin	f	$P_T(f) + G_{TR}(f) - L(f) + G_{RT}(f) - P_R(f)$	$\sigma_{IM}(f)$
FIM	$f_{OT} = f_{OR}$	$P_T(f_{OT}) + G_{TR}(f_{OT}) - L(f_{OT}) + G_{RT}(f_{OT}) - P_R(f_{OR})$	$\sigma_{IM}(f_{OT} = f_{OR})$
RIM	$f = f_{OR}$	$P_T(f_{OR}) + G_{TR}(f_{OR}) - L(f_{OR}) + G_{RT}(f_{OR}) - P_R(f_{OR})$	$\sigma_{IM}(f_{OR})$
TIM	$f = f_{OT}$	$P_T(f_{OT}) + G_{TR}(f_{OT}) - L(f_{OT}) + G_{RT}(f_{OT}) - P_R(f_{OT})$	$\sigma_{IM}(f_{OT})$
SIM	$f \neq f_{OT}, f_{OR}$	$P_T(f) + G_{TR}(f) - L(f) + G_{RT}(f) - P_R(f)$	$\sigma_{IM}(f)$
Transmitter, P_T	f	$P_T(f)$	$\sigma_T(f)$
Fundamental	f_{OT}	Nominal Power (dBm)	~2
Harmonic	$f > f_{OT}$	$P_T(f_{OT}) + A \log f/f_{OT} + B$	$\sigma_T(f)$
Spurious	$f < f_{OT}$	$P_T(f_{OT}) + A' \log f/f_{OT} + B'$	$\sigma_T{}^1(f)$
Antenna, G	f	$G(f)$	$\sigma_G(f)$
Main Beam	$f = f_O$	Nominal Gain (dB)	~2
	$f > f_O$	$G(f_O) + C \log f/f_O + D$	$\sigma_G(f)$
	$f < f_O$	$G(f_O) + C' \log f/f_O + D'$	$\sigma_G{}^1(f)$
Side and Back Lobe	f	$G(f) + \Delta G(f, \Theta \neq \Theta_0)$	$\sigma_G(\Theta)$
Propagation, L	f	$L(f)$	$\sigma_L(f)$
Free Space	f	$32 + 20 \log f_{MHz} + 20 \log d_{km}$	0
Receiver, P_R	f	$P_R(f)$	$\sigma_R(f)$
Fundamental	$f = f_{OR}$	Nominal Sensitivity (dBm)	~2
Major Spur.	$f > f_{OR}$	$P_R(f_{OR}) + I \log f/f_{OR} + J$	$\sigma_R(f)$
Other Spur.	$f < f_{OR}$	$P_R(f_{OR}) + I' \log f/f_{OR} + J'$	$\sigma_R{}^1(f)$

The propagation model that is most often used for the amplitude analysis is the free-space propagation model. Figure 8.4 illustrates the resulting propagation loss L that results from free-space propagation.

The interference margin calculated in the amplitude analysis is a normally distributed random variable with mean value and standard deviation as given in Tables 8.5 and 8.6. The probability distribution associated with the interference margin must be considered in selecting an interference criteria level. The interference criteria level must be low enough so that situations that result in mean interference margins below the interference criteria level have almost no chance of causing EMI.

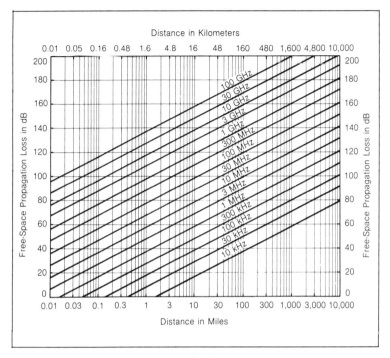

Figure 8.4—Free-Space Propagation Loss

Although the interference criteria level is somewhat optional, there are some tradeoffs. For example, if a low level is used, the probability of eliminating potentially interfering situations is low, but it is at the expense of analysis efficiency. On the other hand, large interference criteria levels increase the analysis efficiency at the risk of eliminating potential EMI situations. This relationship between interfering criteria level and analysis errors is illustrated in Fig. 8.5.

Table 8.6—System Amplitude Models

(Mean Interference Margin Level)
FIM $(f_{OT} = f_{OR}) = P_T(f_{OT}) + G_{RT}(f_{OT}) - 37 - 20 \log (f_{OT})_{MHz} - 20 \log$ $d_{mi} + G_{RT}(f_{OR}) - P_R(f_{OR})$
RIM $(f = f_{OR} > f_{OT}) = P_T(f_{OT}) + G_{TR}(f_{OT}) + (A + C_T) \log (f_{OT}/f_{OR}) + (B + D_T)$ $- 37 > - 20 \log (f_{OR}) \text{ MHz} - 20 \log d_{mi}$ $+ G_{RT}(f_{OR}) - P_R(f_{OR})$
RIM $(f = f_{OR} < f_{OT}) =$ Same as above Except A', B', C_T', D_T', Replace A, B, C_T, D_T
TIM $(f = f_{OT} > f_{OR}) = P_T(f_{OT}) + G_{TR}(f_{OT}) - 37 - 20 \log (f_{OT})_{MHz} - 20 \log$ $d_{mi} + G_{RT}(f_{OR}) - P_R(f_{OR}) + (C_R - I)\log$ $(f_{OR}/f_{OT}) + (D_R - J)$
TIM $(f = f_{OT} < f_{OR}) =$ Same as above Except C_R', D_R', I', J' Replace C_R, D_R, I, J
SIM $(f < f_{OT}, f_{OR}) = P_T(f_{OT}) + G_{TR}(f_{OT}) + (A' + C_T') \log (f/f_{OT}) + (B' + D')$ $- 37 - 20 \log (f)_{MHz} - 20 \log d_{mi} + G_{RT}(f_{OR})$ $- P_R(f_{OR}) + C_R' - I') \log (f/f_{OR}) + (D' - J')$
SIM $(f_{OT} < f < f_{OR}) =$ Same as above Except A, B, C_T, D_T Replace A', B', C_T', D_T',
SIM $(f_{OR} < f < f_{OT}) =$ Same as above Except C_R, D_R, I, J Replace C_R', D_R', I', J'
SIM $(f > f_{OT}, f_{OR}) =$ Same as above Except A, B, C_T, D_T, C_R, D_R, I, J Replace A', B', C_T', D_T', C_R', D_R', I, J
(Standard Deviation for Interference Margin)
FIM $\sigma_{IM}(f_{OT} = f_{OR}) = [\sigma_T^2(f_{OT}) + \sigma_{GT}^2(f_{OT}) + \sigma_L^2(f_{OT}) + \sigma_{GR}^2(f_{OR}) + \sigma_R^2(f_{OR})]^{1/2} \cong 4 \text{ dB}$
RIM $\sigma_{IM}(f = f_{OR} > f_{OT}) = [\sigma_T^2(f > f_{OT}) + \sigma_{GT}^2(f > f_{OT}) + \sigma_L^2(f) + \sigma_{GR}^2(f_{OR})$ $+ \sigma_R^2(f_{OR})]^{1/2}$ $\cong [\sigma_T^2(f > f_{OT}) + \sigma_{GT}^2(f > f_{OT}) + 8]^{1/2}$ $\sigma_{IM}(f = f_{OR} < f_{OT}) =$ Same as above Except $\sigma_T(f < f_{OT})$ and $\sigma_{GT}(f < f_{OT})$ Replace $\sigma_T(f > f_{OT})$ and $\sigma_{GT}(f > f_{OT})$
TIM $\sigma_{IM}(f = f_{OT} > f_{OR}) = [\sigma_T^2(f_{OT}) + \sigma_{GT}^2(f_{OT}) + \sigma_L^2(f) + \sigma_{GR}^2(f > f_{OR}) + \sigma_R^2(f > f_{OR})]^{1/2}$ $\cong [8 + \sigma_{GR}^2(f > f_{OR}) + \sigma_R^2(f > f_{OR})]^{1/2}$ $\sigma_{IM}(f = f_{OT} < f_{OR}) =$ Same as above Except $\sigma_{GR}(f < f_{OR})$ and $\sigma_R(f < f_{OR})$ Replace $\sigma_{GR}(f > f_{OR})$ and $\sigma_R(f > f_{OR})$
SIM $\sigma_{IM}(f < f_{OT}f_{OR}) = [\sigma_T^2(f < f_{OT}) + \sigma_{GT}^2(f < f_{OT}) + \sigma_L^2(f) + \sigma_{GR}^2(f < f_{OR})$ $+ \sigma_R^2(f < f_{OR})]^{1/2}$ $\sigma_{IM}(f_{OT} < f < f_{OR}) =$ Same as above Except $\sigma_T(f > f_{OT})$ and $\sigma_{GT}(f > f_{OT})$ Replace $\sigma_T(f < f_{OT})$ and $\sigma_{GT}(f < f_{OT})$ $\sigma_{IM}(f_{OR} < f < f_{OT}) =$ Same as above Except $\sigma_R(f > f_{OR})$ and $\sigma_{GR}(f > f_{OR})$ Replace $\sigma_R(f < f_{OR})$ and $\sigma_{GR}(f < f_{OR})$ $\sigma_{IM}(f > f_{OT}f_{OR}) =$ Same as above Except $\sigma_T(f > f_{OT})$, $\sigma_{GT}(f > f_{OT})$, $\sigma_{GR}(f > f_{OR})$ and $\sigma_R(f > f_{OR})$ Replace $\sigma_T(f < f_{OT})$, $\sigma_{GT}(f < f_{OT})$, $\sigma_{GR}(f < f_{OR})$ and $\sigma_R(f < f_{OR})$

Table 8.7—Summary of Equipment Characteristics for Amplitude Analysis

Equipment Fund. Frequency	Transmitters							Receivers				
	A dB/Decade	B dB/Fund	σ dB	A' dB/Decade	B' dB/Fund	σ dB	I dB/Decade	J dB/Fund	σ dB	J' dB/Decade	J' dB/Fund	σ dB
Equipment Combined	−70	−30	20	20	−80	10	35	75	20	−20	80	10
Below 30 MHz	−70	−20	10	20	−80	10	25	85	15	−20	80	10
Between 30 MHz and 300 MHz	−80	−30	15	20	−80	10	35	85	15	−20	80	10
Above 300 MHz	−60	−40	20	20	−80	10	40	60	15	−20	80	10

Antenna Type	Frequency Condition	Intentional-Radiation Region					Unintentional Radiation Region	
		$\alpha°$	$\beta°$	C and C' dB/Decade	D and D' dB/G_o	σ and σ' dB	C dB/Isotrope	σ (dB)
High Gain > 25 dB	Design						−10	14
	Nondesign	4α	4β	0	−13	3	−10	14
Medium Gain 10 ≤ G ≤ 25 dB	Design						−10	11
	Resonant Nondesign	3α	3β	0	−10	3	−10	10
	Nonresonant Nondesign	α	β	0	0	3	−10	10
Low Gain G < 10 dB	Design						0	6
	Nondesign			0	$-G_o$	2	−3	6

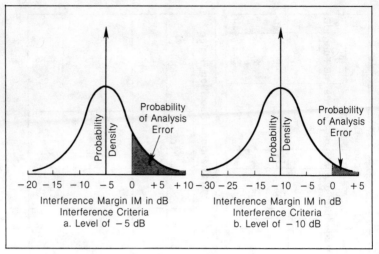

Figure 8.5—Relationship between Interference Criteria Level and Analysis Error

If the interference criteria level is set at 2.33 standard deviations below a 0 dB interference margin, there is only a 1 percent probability of eliminating a source of EMI under the somewhat worst-case assumptions of the amplitude analysis. An interference criteria level of 1.36 standard deviations below zero results in a 10 percent probability of eliminating a source of EMI under worst-case conditions. Similar probabilities can be associated with other interference criteria levels, e.g., one standard deviation below zero results in a 16 percent probability.

The amplitude analysis is applied to Illustrative Example 8.1 in the following pages.

Illustrative Example 8.3: Amplitude Analysis

The models presented in the previous pages will be applied to the EMC analysis example involving a UHF receiver, a VHF transmitter, two UHF transmitters and a radar transmitter. The amplitude analysis calculations for the mean interference margin are illustrated graphically in Figs. 8.6 through 8.8. The amplitude analysis results identify the potential magnitude of EMI situations and define the frequency range and interfering cases that must be considered further in the frequency and detailed analyses.

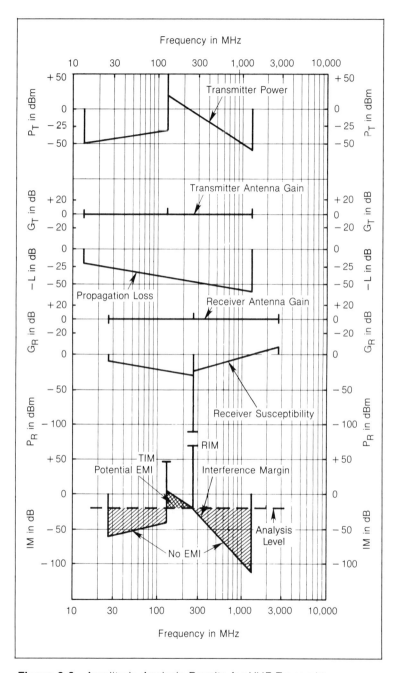

Figure 8.6—Amplitude Analysis Results for VHF Transmitter

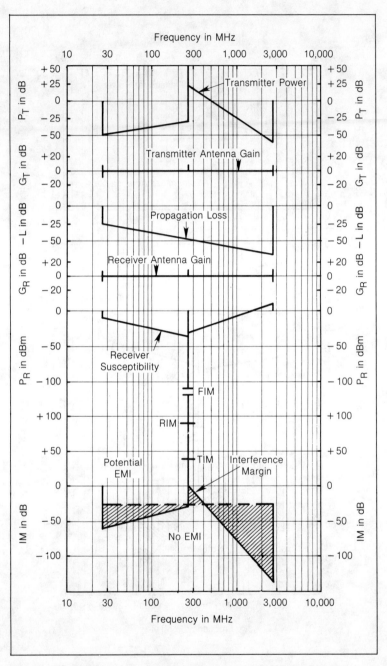

Figure 8.7—Amplitude Analysis Results for UHF Transmitter

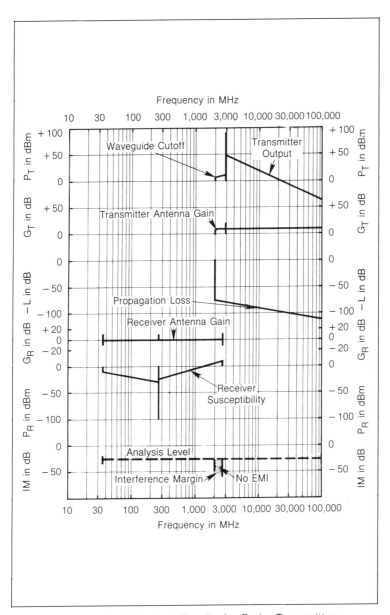

Figure 8.8—Amplitude Analysis Results for Radar Transmitter

Illustrative Example 8.3: Amplitude Analysis

The models presented in the previous pages will be applied to the EMC analysis example involving a UHF receiver, a VHF transmitter, two UHF transmitters and a radar transmitter. The amplitude analysis calculations for the mean interference margin are illustrated graphically in Figs. 8.6 through 8.8. The amplitude analysis results identify the potential magnitude of EMI situations and define the frequency range and interfering cases that must be considered further in the frequency and detailed analyses.

Although the amplitude analysis models for the mean interference margin presented in Table 8.6 may appear to be complicated, they are easily implemented graphically. All that is required is to plot each of the functions and apply Eq. (8.4) to the matching frequency points of each line segment as shown in Figs. 8.6 through 8.8.

Referring to Fig. 8.6, the amplitude analysis results indicate that it is necessary to consider the TIM, RIM and SIM cases further for the VHF transmitter. For the SIM case, it is only necessary to consider spurious outputs and responses that occur over the frequency range from 130 MHz to approximately 270 MHz.

Figure 8.7 presents amplitude analysis results for the UHF transmitter. For these transmitters all cases must be considered further, but the frequency limits for SIM are 270 MHz to approximately 400 MHz.

The amplitude analysis results show that the radar transmitter does not need to be considered further.

To define the interference criteria level to be used, it is necessary to determine the resulting standard deviations. These are determined by applying the equations for standard deviations presented in Table 8.6. Individual standard deviations for the applicable cases are obtained from Table 8.7 and the results are presented in Table 8.8.

If the interference criteria level is set at −1.0 standard deviation ($-\sigma$) there is only a 16 percent probability of eliminating a potential interference situation even with worst-case assumptions used in the amplitude analysis. Hence, for this problem a cull level of $-\sigma$ is used.

Figures 8.6 through 8.8 indicate that some potential EMI situations are possible for the UHF receiver being considered. These are summarized in Table 8.9. These cases must be considered further in the frequency and detailed analyses.

Table 8.8—Standard Deviations for Sample Problems

| Interference | Transmitter Type | | |
Case	VHF (dB)	UHF (dB)	Radar (dB)
FIM		4	
RIM	16	20	
TIM	16	20	
SIM	2?	25	25

Table 8.9—Summary of Amplitude Analysis Results

| Interference | Transmitter Type | | |
Case	VHF	UHF	Radar
FIM	No	Yes	No
RIM	Yes	Yes	No
TIM	Yes	Yes	No
SIM	Yes	Yes	No
(Frequency Range of SIM)	130 to 270 MHz	270 to 400 MHz	

8.4 System Frequency Analysis

The frequency analysis stage of EMC analysis accounts for (1) differences in the bandwidths associated with transmitter emissions and receiver responses and (2) signal rejection resulting from frequency separation between a potentially interfering signal and a receiver response. Frequency analysis results in a correction factor which modifies the interference margin determined in the previous amplitude analysis process. The models used in the frequency analysis are summarized in Table 8.10.

The first step in frequency analysis is to determine the frequency separation between: (1) transmitter and receiver FIM case, (2) transmitter closest spurious frequency and the receiver fundamental frequency (RIM case), (3) transmitter fundamental frequency and closest receiver spurious frequency (TIM case) and (4) transmitter spurious frequency and closest receiver spurious frequency (SIM case).

These frequency separations are then used to calculate the correction factors used to modify the amplitude analysis results for the FIM, RIM, TIM and SIM cases.

8.25

Table 8.10—Frequency Analysis Models

Frequency Separation (Δf)

General $\quad \Delta f = \left| Nf_{OT} - \left| \dfrac{pf_{LO} \pm f_{IF}}{q} \right| \right|$

FIM $\quad \Delta f = |f_{OT} - f_{OR}|$

RIM $\quad \Delta f = |N\, f_{OT} - f_{OR}|_{min}$

TIM $\quad \Delta f = \left| f_{OT} - \left| \dfrac{pf_{LO} \pm f_{IF}}{q} \right| \right|_{min}$

SIM $\quad \Delta f = \left| Nf_{OT} - \left| \dfrac{pf_{LO} \pm f_{IF}}{q} \right| \right|_{min}$

Frequency Correction

On Tune: $\qquad CF = K \log (B_R/B_T)$

$\Delta f \leqslant (B_T + B_R)/2$

Off Tune: $\qquad CF = K \log (B_R/B_T) + M(\Delta f)$

$\Delta f > (B_T + B_R)/2 \qquad$ or $-S(\Delta f)$ $\qquad \Big\}$ Select Maximum

---

Identification of Adjacent Channel

FIM Frequency Separation $|f_{OT} - f_{OR}| < \Delta f\ max$

FIM Interference Margin FIM $(f_{OT} = f_{OR}) > FIM\ max$

Transmitter Models

Bandwidth $(B_T) =$ Nominal Value

Modulation Envelope, $M(\Delta f) = M(\Delta f_i) + M_i \log (\Delta f/\Delta f_i)$

Receiver Models

Bandwidth $(B_R) =$ Nominal Value

Selectivity $S(\Delta f) = S(\Delta f_i) + S_i \log (\Delta f/\Delta f_i)$

The above frequency separations are found as follows:

FIM Frequency Separation

$$\Delta f = |f_{OT} - f_{OR}| \qquad (8.5)$$

where,

f_{OT} = transmitter fundamental emission

f_{OR} = receiver main response

RIM Frequency Separation

Calculate $N = f_{OR}/F_{OT}$ and round off to nearest integer.

then, $\quad \Delta f = |N\, f_{OT} - f_{OR}| \qquad (8.6)$

TIM Frequency Separation (based on q = 1, the most likely case)

$$\text{Calculate } (p + \Delta p) = \frac{f_{OT} \pm f_{IF}}{f_{LO}} \qquad (8.7)$$

where, $\qquad p$ = an integer and $-0.5 \leqslant \Delta p \leqslant 0.5$

f_{IF} = receiver intermediate frequency

f_{LO} = receiver local oscillator

For example, if $(p + \Delta p) = 3.45$, then $p = 3$ and $\Delta p = 0.45$. Had the decimal part of $(p + \Delta p)$ been greater than 0.5, e.g., $(p + \Delta p) = 3.55$, then p would equal 4 and Δp would equal -0.45. The frequency separation Δf can be calculated from Δp:

$$\Delta f = \Delta p\, f_{LO} \qquad (8.8)$$

SIM Frequency Separation (Based on q = 1)

$$\text{Calculate } (p + \Delta p) = \frac{N\, f_{OT} \pm I_{IF}}{f_{LO}} \qquad (8.9)$$

Repeat Eq. (8.9) for integer values of N $\geq$ 2 over the frequency range of interest (p is an integer and $-0.5 \leq \Delta p \leq 0.5$). The frequency separation is:

$$\Delta f = \Delta p \, f_{LO} \qquad (8.10)$$

When the frequency separation has been determined for each case of interest, the frequency correction factor is calculated from the appropriate equation (on-tune or off-tune situation) presented in Table 8.10. If the frequency separation and interference margin for the FIM case satisfy the conditions given for adjacent-channel interference, the case is retained for further consideration in the detailed analysis.

As indicated earlier, one of the main problems encountered in performing an EMC analysis is finding the information required to apply the models. In recognizing this problem, this volume has presented data that can be used in the EMC analysis models if specific data are not available. Chapters 3 and 4 contain the details of these transmitter and receiver frequency models. Table 8.11 presents a summary of equipment characteristics that may be used in applying the frequency-cull models to various EMC problems.

Application of the frequency analysis to Illustrative Example 8.1 is presented in the following pages.

Table 8.11—Summary of Equipment Characteristics for Frequency Analysis

Transmitters				
Type of Modulation	**Constants for Modulation Envelope Model**			
	i	$\|\Delta f_i\|$	$P_T(\Delta f_i)$ (dB above Fundamental)	M_i (dB/ Decade)
AM Communication and Radar	0 1 2	$0.1\ B_T$ $0.5\ B_T$ B_T	0 0 -40	0 -133 -67
AM Voice	0 1 2 3	1 Hz 10 Hz 100 Hz 1,000 Hz	-28 -28 0 -11	0 28 -7 -60
FM	0 1 2	$0.1\ B_T$ $0.5\ B_T$ B_T	0 0 -100	0 -333 0
Pulse	0 1 2	$1/10\tau$ $1/\pi(\tau + \Delta\tau)$ $1/\pi\Delta\tau$	0 0 $-20 \log\left(1 + \dfrac{\tau}{\Delta\tau}\right)$	0 -20 -40

Receivers					
Type of Modulation	**Constants for IF Selectivity Model**			**Constants for Adjacent-Signal Model**	
	i	$\|\Delta f_i\|$	$P(\Delta f_i)$ (dB above Fund.)	S_i (dB/ Decade)	$\Delta f\text{max}$	FIM max dB
Any	0 1	$0.1\ B_R$ $0.5\ B_R$	0 0	0 100	Fig. 4.8 $0.2\ f_{OR}$	80

Illustrative Example 8.4: Frequency Analysis

To illustrate the application of frequency analysis models summarized in preceding pages, the sample EMC analysis problem introduced earlier in this chapter is continued here.

VHF Transmitter

Consider the amplitude analysis results for the UHF receiver and the VHF transmitter (see Example 8.3). It was determined that potential EMI problems could result from the RIM, TIM and SIM cases. To determine whether these cases really represent a potential EMI threat, it is now necessary to consider the additional rejection provided because of bandwidth differences and emission-response frequency separations.

Receiver Interference Margin (RIM)

For the VHF transmitter, the **RIM** frequency separation is:

$$\Delta f = |N\, f_{OT} - f_{OR}|$$

where, $N = f_{OR}/f_{OT}$ rounded to the nearest integer.

For the VHF transmitter, $F_{OT} = 130$ MHz and $f_{OR} = 270$ MHz. Thus, $N = 2$. Therefore,

$$\Delta f = |2(130 \text{ MHz}) - 270 \text{ MHz}| = 10 \text{ MHz}$$

The frequency analysis correction factor is given by the smaller of case (1) or (2).

Case 1:

$$10 \log(B_R/B_T) + M(\Delta f) = 10 \log(B_R/B_T) + M(\Delta f_i) + M_i \log (\Delta f/\Delta f_i)$$

$$= 10 \log(25/10) - 11 -$$

$$60 \log(1{,}000 \text{ kHz}/1 \text{ kHz})$$

$$= 4 - 11 - 180 = -187 \text{ dB}$$

8.30

Since this exceeds the maximum allowable correction (−100 dB), this contribution to the frequency analysis correction is limited to −100 dB.

Case 2:

$$-S(\Delta f) = -[S(\ \Delta f_i\ +\ S_i\ \log\ (\Delta f/\Delta f_i)]$$

$$= -[0\ -\ 100\ \log(10{,}000/25)\ =\ -260\ dB$$

Since this also exceeds the maximum allowable correction of −100 dB, it is limited to −100 dB. Thus, for the VHF transmitter RIM case the amplitude analysis interference margin (RIM = 70 dB) is corrected by −100 dB, and the RIM case is eliminated from further consideration.

Transmitter Interference Margin (TIM)

For the VHF transmitter the **TIM** frequency separation is:

$$\Delta f\ =\ \Delta p\ f_{LO}$$

where, Δp is determined from the following:

$$(p\ +\ \Delta p)\ =\ \frac{f_{OT}\ \pm\ f_{IF}}{f_{LO}}$$

$$\frac{130\ \pm\ 40}{230}\ =\ 0.74$$

Therefore,

$$\Delta p\ =\ -0.26 \text{ and } \Delta f\ =\ (0.26)\ (230)\ \approx\ 58\ MHz$$

Because this case results in an even greater frequency separation than the RIM case, the frequency analysis correction will again be −100 dB.

Applying the −100 dB correction to the amplitude analysis TIM = 50 dB, the transmitter interference case is also eliminated from further consideration.

Spurious Interference Margin (SIM)

The **SIM** frequency separation is given by Eq. (8.8):

$$\Delta f = \Delta p \, f_{LO}$$

where,

$$(p + \Delta p) = \frac{N f_{OT} \pm f_{IF}}{f_{LO}}$$

For N = 2:

$$(p + \Delta p) = \frac{2(130) \pm (40)}{230} = \frac{220}{230} = 0.956$$

Therefore, $\Delta p = 0.044$ and $\Delta f = (0.044)(230) = 10$ MHz

This again results in a correction of −100 dB. When this is applied to the amplitude analysis interference margin, the SIM case is eliminated.

UHF Transmitter

Fundamental Interference Margin (FIM)

The **FIM** frequency separation is given by Eq. (8.5):

$$\Delta f = |f_{OT} - f_{OR}| = |280 - 270| = 10 \text{ MHz}$$

From the previous calculations for the VHF transmitter, the 10 MHz frequency separation results in the maximum frequency analysis correction of −100 dB. When this correction is applied to the amplitude FIM = 130 dB, the resulting FIM = 30 dB and there is still a potential EMI problem. The UHF transmitter at 291 MHz has a frequency separation of 21 MHz and the resulting FIM will again be 30 dB.

Note that the two UHF transmitters fall within the frequency limits of the receiver adjacent-signal region, i.e., $\Delta f < \Delta f_{max} = 0.1$ (270 MHz) = 27 MHz. Also, the amplitude analysis FIM = 130 dB which exceeds the FIM_{max} = 80 dB for adjacent signals. Hence, the UHF transmitters must be subjected to further considerations during detailed analysis.

Radar Transmitter

The radar transmitter was eliminated during the amplitude analysis and hence does not have to be considered during the frequency analysis.

8.5 System Detailed Models

During the third step of EMC analysis, frequency analysis results are corrected further to account for additional factors associated with transmitting and receiving antennas, propagation media and receiver adjacent-signal effects. Finally, after all corrections have been applied, the probability of a positive interference margin is calculated. This is used as an input to the performance analysis.

8.5.1 Antenna Considerations

The antenna effects that are introduced during the detailed analysis include polarization, near-field gain reduction and time dependence resulting from rotating antennas. These effects are described in Chapter 5 where models were presented for each. A brief summary of these considerations is presented below.

If EMC analysis involves an antenna configuration where each antenna is in the intentional-radiation region of the other and a potential fundamental interference problem exists (FIM is above the interference criteria level), then it is necessary to consider the relative polarization of the two antennas. If both transmitting and receiving antennas have the same polarization (vertical-to-vertical or horizontal-to-horizontal) no polarization correction is required. When the two antennas have orthogonal polarization (one vertical and the other horizontal) then it is necessary to correct the frequency-cull results to account for polarization discrimination. The correction is determined by the antenna offering the least polarization discrimination. If specific data are not available, the polarization corrections shown in Table 8.12 may be used.

Antenna near-field considerations (if applicable) are also included in the detailed prediction. For low-gain antennas the transition distance is $\lambda/2\pi$; whereas, for high gain antennas, the transition-distance on main axis is $L^2/2\lambda$, where L is the largest antenna aperture dimension. For off-axis situations, the transition distance is much less as given in Fig. 5.17. For high gain on-axis situations, the near-field gain reduction was given in Figs. 5.18 through 5.21. For low-gain antennas and for off-axis high gain antennas, near-field situations usually occur at and below HF only. Chapter 5 presents a discussion of the math models to use in this case.

Antenna rotation is also considered in the detailed EMC analysis. If one or both antennas involved are rotating, the results are expressed in terms of a time-dependent statistic, i.e., percentage of time that various interference margin levels are exceeded. Figure 5.23 shows the percentage of time (or the probability) that a main-beam-to-main-beam antenna orientation exists if both antennas are rotating. The antenna considerations discussed in this section do not apply to the continuing illustrative example discussed in previous sections because all polarizations are vertical and no antenna is in the near field of the others.

Table 8.12—Correction for Transmitter and Receiver Polarization

Transmitter \ Receiver		Horizontal		Vertical		Circular
		G < 10 dB	G > 10 dB	G < 10 dB	G > 10 dB	
Hor	G < 10 dB	0	0	−16	−16	−3
	G > 10 dB	0	0	−16	−20	−3
Ver	G < 10 dB	−16	−16	0	0	−3
	G > 10 dB	−16	−20	0	0	−3
Circular		−3	−3	−3	−3	0

8.5.2 Propagation Considerations

EMC calculations performed during amplitude and frequency analysis were based on free-space propagation assumptions. Although free-space propagation is a primary mode of coupling for a large percentage of actual EMI problems, during the detailed analysis it is necessary to examine each potential transmitter-receiver EMI problem to determine the actual mode of coupling involved. The selection of the applicable propagation mode(s) is made easy in Fig. 6.2.

One of the major factors that influences the propagation mode for a particular desired signal or interfering emission path is whether a line-of-sight condition prevails or whether the receiver antenna is either beyond line-of-sight or the propagation path is blocked. The latter includes masking of intervening terrain. If terrain profiles are available for the desired and interfering signal path of interest, path profiles and antenna elevations may be plotted as shown in Fig. 8.9. This determines whether line-of-sight conditions exist or not between the antennas. The profile chart is constructed to account for atmospheric refraction so that signals propagate along straight lines. Figure 8.9 shows that a line-of-sight path exists between antennas 1 and 2, but line-of-sight between antennas 3 and 4 is blocked by the intervening hill.

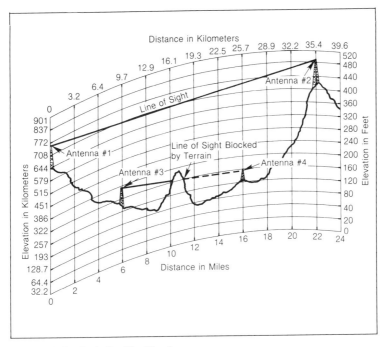

Figure 8.9—Path Profile Chart

The propagation models described in Chapter 6 may be used to calculate propagation loss and the results may be used to modify the frequency-cull results. An alternate procedure that works well

8.35

for beyond line-of-sight paths is to apply a beyond-line-of-sight (BLOS) correction to the free-space loss:

$$\text{BLOS correction} = 60 \log(d_{TX}/d) \qquad (8.11)$$

where,

d_{TX} = distance from transmitter to terrain obstacle

d = distance from transmitter to receiver

8.5.3 Adjacent-Signal Considerations

Receiver adjacent-signal effects resulting from nonlinear interactions between two or more interfering signals or between an interfering signal and the desired signal are considered a part of the detailed EMC analysis. Adjacent-signal effects include intermodulation, desensitization and cross modulation. These effects and the resulting detailed EMC analysis models were discussed in Section 4.3, and Table 8.13 summarizes the most significant adjacent-signal models. Summary values for parameters that appear in the models were presented in Section 4.3.

Table 8.13—Adjacent Signal Models

Intermodulation			
Frequency $\quad \left| \, \lvert mf_n \pm nf_F \rvert - f_{OR} \right| \leqslant B_{R60}$			
Amplitude— Third Order Intermodulation			
Case #	AGC	RF Saturation	Equivalent Input signal, P_E, in dBm
I	No	No	$2P_N + P_F + P_R(f_{OR}) - 3P^*(f_N, f_F)$
II	Yes	No	$2P_N + P_F + P_R(f_{OR}) - 3P^*(f_N, f_F) + 2\Delta \, G_{RF}$
III	No	Near Signal	$2P_N + P_F + P_R(f_{OR}) - 3P^*(f_N f_F) - 2[P_N - P_{SAT}(f_N)]$
IV	No	Far Signal	$2P_N + P_F + P_R(f_{OR}) - 3P^*(f_N, f_F) - [P_F - P_{SAT}(f_F)]$
Desensitization			
$S/N = P_D - P_{REF} + (S/N)_{REF}$			
$(S/N)' = S/N - (P_A - P_{SAT})/R$			
Cross Modulation			
$S/I = -2P_A + CM$			

8.5.4 Probability of Interference

As discussed in Chapter 2, a number of variations that contribute to an EMC analysis problem exist. These variations are best accounted for by representing the final analysis result in probability terms. The probability of potential interference is simply the probability that the interference margin exceeds zero, i.e., the probability that the power available exceeds the receiver susceptibility threshold. In the final analysis, the probability that an EMI problem exists is based on the $S/(I + N)$ ratios existing at the equivalent output terminals of the receptor. The rationale for not considering the intended signal level until the very end is that many situations must operate with marginal signals such as the radar maximum range, fringe area of land-mobile communications, etc. Figure 8.10 expresses the probability of potential EMI in terms of the resulting interference margin (IM) normalized to a standard deviation (σ).

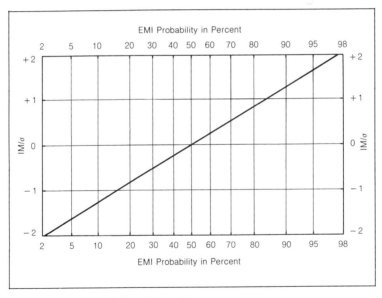

Figure 8.10—Probability of Interference

Illustrative Example 8.5: Detailed Analysis

To illustrate the application to the detailed analysis models summarized in preceding pages, the sample EMC analysis problem introduced in earlier sections is continued here.

8.37

Detailed Antenna Considerations

From the results of frequency analysis, it was determined that the potential EMI problems resulted from the two UHF transmitters (see Example 8.4). The first factors considered in the detailed analysis are associated with the antennas. For the case of the UHF transmitter interfering with the UHF receiver, the following observations are made.

1. Both transmitting and receiver antennas are vertically polarized; thus, no polarization correction is required.
2. Both transmitting and receiving antennas are low gain and are separated by more than $\lambda/2\pi$; thus, near-field considerations do not apply.
3. The antennas do not rotate; thus, it is not necessary to consider time dependence.

Detailed Propagation Considerations

The second factor considered in the detailed analysis is associated with propagation. The antennas associated with the UHF transmitters and the UHF receiver are only about 17 m (57 ft.) apart. Therefore, they are within line-of-sight of each other. It is not necessary to introduce any propagation corrections.

Adjacent-Signal Effects

A third factor that must be considered during the detailed analysis is receiver adjacent-signal effects. Because the frequency separations between the receiver and the potentially interfering transmitters are 10 MHz and 21 MHz respectively (see Example 8.4), the signals are within the frequency limits ($\Delta f_{max} = 0.1 f_{OR} = 27$ MHz) of the adjacent-signal region. For this example, UHF receiver models are used because this receiver is considered to be in the UHF band even though it operates below 300 MHz. See Section 4.3 for a discussion of the adjacent-signal frequency limits.

Furthermore it was shown that the FIM resulting from the amplitude analysis was 130 dB which exceeds the $\text{FIM}_{max} = 80$ dB allowed for the adjacent-signal region (see Section 4.2.1). Hence, adjacent-signal interference effects must be considered during the detailed analysis.

Intermodulation

Intermodulation is one of the adjacent-signal effects that is to be considered. In order for a significant third-order intermodulation product to be present, it is necessary that the frequency relations satisfy:

$$\left| \, |2f_N - f_F| - f_{OR} \, \right| \leqslant B_{R60} \qquad (8.12)$$

where,

f_N = 280 MHz = near interfering signal frequency

f_F = 291 MHz = far interfering signal frequency

f_{OR} = 270 MHz = receiver operating frequency

B_{R60} = 100 kHz = receiver 60 dB overall bandwidth

Substituting the above in Eq. (8.12) yields:

$$\left| \, |2(280) - (291)| - 270 \, \right| = 1 \text{ MHz}$$

which is greater than the 100 kHz receiver 60 dB bandwidth. Hence, third-order intermodulation need not be considered.

Desensitization

Another adjacent-channel effect which must be considered is **desensitization**. The desensitized signal-to-noise (S/N)' ratio in dB is (see Section 4.3):

$$(S/N)' = S/N - (P_A - P_{SAT})/R \qquad (8.13)$$

$$S/N = P_D - P_{REF} + (S/N)_{REF} \qquad (8.14)$$

where,

$$P_D = -80 \text{ dBm} = \text{assumed value for desired signal level in dBm}$$

$$P_{REF} = -110 \text{ dBm} = \text{receiver sensitivity in dBm}$$

$$(S/N)_{REF} = 5 \text{ dB} = \text{signal-to-noise ratio for standard response in dB}$$

$$P_A = 20 \text{ dBm} = \text{potentially interfering power available in dBm}$$

$$P_{SAT} = P_B + 10 \log \Delta f(\%), \text{ where } P_B = 1 \text{ dBm from Fig. 4.12}$$

$$R = 0.95 \text{ from Fig. 4.11}$$

For the potentially interfering signal at 280 MHz, $\Delta f(\%)$ = 10 MHz/270 MHz = 3.7 percent. For this case:

$$P_{SAT} = 1 \text{ dBm} + 10 \log 3.7 \text{ (\%)}$$
$$= 7 \text{ dBm}$$

and,

$$(S/N)' = (S/N) - (P_A - P_{SAT})/R$$
$$= [-80 - (-110) + 5] - (20 - 7)/0.95$$
$$= 35 \text{ dB} - 14 \text{ dB} = 21 \text{ dB}$$

For the potentially interfering signal at 291 MHz, $\Delta f(\%)$ = 21 MHz/270 MHz = 7.8 percent. For this case:

$$P_{SAT} = 1 \text{ dBm} + 10 \log 7.8 \text{ (\%)}$$
$$= 10 \text{ dBm}$$

and,

$$(S/N)' = (S/N) - (P_A - P_{SAT})/R$$
$$= [-80 - (-110) + 5] - (-20 - 10)0.95$$
$$= 35 \text{ dB} - 11 \text{ dB} = 24 \text{ dB}$$

From the above results, notice that the signal-to-noise ratio is reduced because of desensitization. The nearest interfering signal results in a 14 dB reduction in the signal-to-noise-ratio and the other interfering signal results in an 11 dB reduction in the signal-to-noise ratio.

Cross Modulation

The final adjacent-signal effect that must be considered is **cross modulation**. The relationship used to examine cross modulation effects is:

$$S/I = -2 P_A + CM \qquad (8.15)$$

where,

CM = cross modulation parameter from Fig. 4.19.

From that figure,

CM = −20 for Δf = 3.7 percent (i.e., 10 MHz)

and,

CM = −15 for Δf = 7.8 percent (i.e., 21 MHz)

The resulting cross modulations effects are;
For I at 280 MHz,

$$CM = 34 \text{ and}$$
$$S/I = -2(20) - 20$$
$$= -60 \text{ dB}$$

For I at 291 MHz,

$$CM = 30 \text{ and}$$
$$S/I = -2(20) - 15$$
$$= -55 \text{ dB}$$

As mentioned in Chapter 4, the cross modulation relationship is such that negative values of S/I do not have much quantitative significance. Severe masking and signal distortion may result from interfering signal conditions that result in these negative values. This occurs because the interfering signal is considerably above the level required for cross-modulation effects to be significant.

8.6 System Performance Models

The final step in an EMC analysis problem is to express the results in a form that relates to system performance. Chapter 7 was dedicated to operational performance considerations and models including performance measures, performance thresholds, performance scoring and system effectiveness.

For voice systems, one method for specifying operational performance is the articulation index. To apply performance calculations to an EMI prediction problem, it is necessary to either calculate or assume a desired signal margin, (SM), i.e., the amount by which the desired signal exceeds the receiver sensitivity. Calculate an equivalent signal-to-interference (S/I) ratio at the detector input (S/I = SM – IM) and use Figs. 7.8 and 7.9 to determine the articulation index. The calculations are illustrated in the continuing example below.

Illustrative Example 8.6: Performance Prediction

As a result of applying the amplitude, frequency and detailed analysis to the continuing illustrative example involving a UHF receiver, a VHF transmitter, two UHF transmitters and a radar transmitter, it has been determined that the only potential problem results from the two UHF transmitters. Furthermore, the potential EMI problem results from desensitization and cross modulation.

First, in considering the problem of desensitization it was determined that a desired signal of –80 dBm would result in a 35 dB signal-to-noise ratio without interference. The potentially interfering signal at 2 MHz would reduce this signal-to-noise ratio to 21 dB. Referring to Fig. 7.8, an articulation index of approximately 0.85 would result. This is good performance for a voice system.

Second, concerning the problem of cross modulation, the results of a detailed analysis indicated that a large negative S/I ratio developed. From Fig. 7.9 this would result in very low values of articulation index and hence unacceptable performance. However, as described in Section 8.5, negative values of S/I resulting from cross modulation do not have much quantitative significance. Severe masking and distortion may be expected to result in very poor performance, but it is difficult to assign a value to the resulting articulation index.

To provide acceptable performance with a voice system, it is necessary to maintain positive S/I ratios. For the case of cross modulation effects, it would be necessary to provide sufficient interfering signal rejection to ensure that the S/I ratio will increase. Referring to Eq. (8.15), the cross modulation S/I ratio will increase from −60 dB to 0 dB if the interfering signal power available is reduced from +20 dBm to −10 dBm. It is therefore necessary to provide 30 dB more interfering signal rejection at the receiver front end to eliminate the cross modulation problem. This rejection could be provided by using a better preselector in the receiver.

Another approach to eliminating the EMI problem is to choose different UHF ground-to-air transmission frequencies. To reduce the cross-modulation levels to insignificant amounts, frequency separations of about 10 percent or more should be used (see Section 4.3). Thus, each UHF transmitter should be retuned to a frequency that is 10 percent or more above or below 270 MHz. For example, the transmitters should be operated below approximately 240 MHz or above approximately 300 MHz.

A third approach is to separate the UHF receiver antennas on top of the ATCC building. By separating the antennas from 17 m (57 ft.) to about 0.8 m (0.5 mi.) 30 dB of additional free-space propagation loss will result. However, such a move would require hard wiring or telemetering the received signal back to the tower.

It is important to realize that statistical summary models were used throughout this continuing illustrative example. If the particular type of receiver being used in this problem was designed to provide significant RF selectivity, the cross modulation problem would be avoided. Hence, for this example, the results can best be summarized by saying that there is a potential for EMI, and the particular equipment interference characteristics should be considered.

Chapter 9

Control of EMI in
Telecommunication Systems

The previous chapters have presented techniques that may be used for designing communication systems for EMC. The standard techniques for controlling EMI include frequency management, time management, location management and direction management, which were identified and discussed briefly in Chapter 1. In addition to the standard EMI control techniques that have been presented, there are a number of other techniques available as a result of new trends and new technologies.

Some of the more significant new trends and technologies include the use of the cellular systems concept in mobile telephone applications; the use of trunked systems in land mobile applications; the more widespread use of cable for fixed point-to-point communication applications; the increased use of fiber optics and optical signals for fixed point-to-point communication applications; the increased emphasis on spread-spectrum systems for military applications; the more widespread use of digital signals, signal processing and coding; and the use of phased arrays and adaptive antennas to control antenna radiation and reception patterns. The use of these new trends and technologies to control EMI in communication systems is discussed in this chapter.

9.1 Cellular Systems[1]

Cellular systems provide more efficient use of the radio frequency spectrum for mobile telephone service. The cellular system concept is based on dividing an area into a number of congruent cells and limiting the radiation within each cell so that the same frequency can be used simultaneously by users in other cells. The concept of cellular systems and the improvement in spectrum use resulting from it are described below.

Consider the radio link in today's mobile radio communication system. Not knowing where the mobile station is, the base station sends out a nominally omnidirectional signal, strong enough to cover all or almost all locations where the vehicle could be. Clearly, however, only the area around the mobile station needs to be irradiated by the RF signal. If only the dispatcher had some way of knowing where the vehicle was and could transmit an RF signal only into that area, more traffic could be handled because the same frequency could be reused simultaneously in another section of the city. This is the basic principle of cell systems.

The urban area is divided into many congruent cells, or zones, as shown in Fig. 9.1. In connection with this figure showing hexagonally shaped cells, note that only three regular polygons—the hexagon, the square and the triangle—can be tightly packed in a plane so that no gaps or overlaps occur. The hexagon's shape is closest to the nominally circular coverage pattern of the cell. At the center of each zone is a base station that can communicate with mobile stations in the zone. Each base station is also connected by land lines (or point-to-point microwave links) to a central processing unit (CPU).

The CPU is a computer-controlled switching center. In telephone applications, this CPU would be connected by trunk circuits to other switching centers and then to the land telephone network. In dispatch-type mobile radio applications, each dispatcher belonging to this common-user system would be connected to the CPU by a land line. The communication path, in any case, proceeds by land lines from the fixed station through the switch of the CPU. From there it travels by land lines (or microwave link) to the local cell's base station and from there by low-power radio to the mobile station. The base stations (and the mobile stations) require only low power because the reliable range needed (cell radius) is only a fraction of the range needed for reliable coverage of the whole urban area (all the cells). This is especially desirable in the 900 MHz band, where it is expensive to develop high-power transmission.

As far as traffic-carrying capability is concerned, the advantage of this scheme is that the low-power communication on a given RF channel in a certain zone allows the same channel to be reused in different zones simultaneously so long as there is sufficient geographical separation between the zones. In effect, one RF channel can act as more than one server or can handle more than one erlang (a unit for measuring traffic intensity).

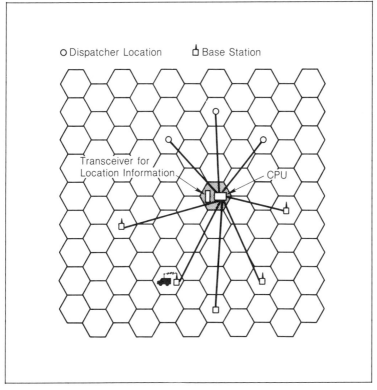

Figure 9.1—Typical Layout of a Metropolitan Area Employing a Small-Cell System (Courtesy *IEEE Spectrum*)

Another, not-so-obvious advantage is the easing of the adjacent-channel interference problem. The difficulty in mobile radio today in rejecting adjacent channels occurs because mobile stations can roam. Thus, they can sometimes be located much closer to the adjacent-channel base station than to their own base station. As a result, the adjacent-channel output is sometimes many decibels above that of the desired channel. This problem does not occur in a small-cell system since the adjacent-channel signal is coming from the same base station or from the base station in the adjacent zone.

It should be pointed out that in one form or another a vehicle-location subsystem is needed to allow a small-cell system to function. This is an additional expense which must be shared by the users. It has nothing to do with the communications but rather allows the communication system to function. For dispatch service, however, this subsystem in itself is desirable since some present-day communications are involved in finding out just where the vehicle is. In order for the cellular system concept to function, all that is required of the vehicle-location system is that it determine the cell in which the vehicle is located. This can be done by receiving the signal from the vehicle in a number of adjacent cells and using the received signal level to determine the cell in which the vehicle is located.

For communication between base and mobile stations in any cell to be reliable, it must be recognized that the RF energy cannot be confined to that cell and will spill over to neighboring cells, as shown in Fig. 9.2. It is assumed that a two-ring buffer provided around any cell using a channel is sufficient. If more than a two-ring buffer is needed, the details are different but the principles remain the same. If a frequency is used in a cell, it may not be used simultaneously in that cell or in any of the 18 cells forming the two-ring buffer. Nevertheless it can be used in many cells simultaneously outside this forbidden region. An important question is: how many cells can use the same frequency simultaneously?

To answer the above question, realize that there are a number of methods of operating such systems and each is capable of providing increased traffic capacity. Some are more suitable for telephony, others for dispatch-type service. Two such methods are described here, starting with what is probably the simplest.

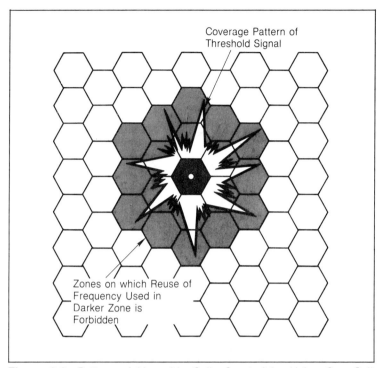

Figure 9.2—Pattern of Unusable Cells Created by Using One Cell
(Courtesy *IEEE Spectrum*)

Fixed-Frequency Method

The difference between the two techniques to be discussed is
the way in which the reuse of a frequency is forbidden in the zone
in which it is used and in the 18 surrounding zones. In the fixed-
frequency-allocation method, the total number of frequencies
available is divided into m separate frequency groups, each of which
contains j frequency channels. A cell is assigned to one of the m
groups. Each base station can communicate with j mobile units in
its cell simultaneously, using the j different channels in its group.
The number of groups, m, is chosen as the smaller number that
satisfies the interference-buffering requirements. It is easy to show
that m need never be larger than 7 for 19-zone or 2-belt buffering.
This is presented graphically in Fig. 9.3. Each number corresponds
to a group of j frequencies. For example, 1 might correspond to
frequencies 1 through 10, 2 to frequencies 11 through 20, 3 to frequencies 21 through 30, etc.

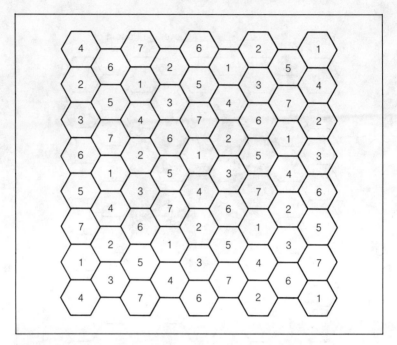

Figure 9.3—Reuse Arrangement for Two-Ring Buffer (m = 7) (Courtesy *IEEE Spectrum*)

It is easily verified that no frequency may be reused within the area forbidden by its use in any one cell. An obvious advantage of this scheme is that each base station need only be equipped to communicate on j of the mj frequencies, rather than all mj. A clear disadvantage is that each mobile station must be equipped for at least m frequencies to guarantee the ability to communicate in any zone even if no other traffic is present. Giving mobile stations m frequencies will give only one channel in each cell, i.e., anywhere in the urban area. To provide lower blocking and to give equal service in all parts of the city require equipping mobile units with channels in groups of m; giving km channels to a mobile unit implies that it has k possible channels to try anywhere in the city.

This technique has been mentioned in connection with telephony.[2] Its ability to carry increased traffic, as compared with a standard radiotelephone system, is simple to explain. From the traffic point of view, the analysis is quite straightforward; if each vehicle is able to communicate on C channels (where C is a multiple of 7), it can communicate on C/7 channels in any given zone. Because of the way the frequency groups are allotted to cells, each zone can be considered independent of any other zone and can handle 1/N of the traffic of the entire urban area. Furthermore, if the total traffic generated in the urban area is A erlangs, the traffic per channel in any given zone is 7A/CN. If C channels are used without the cellular structure, the number of erlangs per channel is, of course, A/C. If C-channel capability is given to each mobile station in a cellular arrangement, only C/7 can be used at any one location. Hence, with a cellular structure of N cells, the nature of the blocking is as if the erlangs per frequency were reduced by a factor of N/7, whereas the effective number of trunked channels is divided by 7. In other words, although the effective number of trunked channels per vehicle is reduced by a factor of 7, the maximum erlang load that can be handled by any one frequency, citywide, is increased by a factor of N/7. At all but extremely low traffic intensities, the second effect is more important, and thus there is an increased spectrum efficiency, as shown in Fig. 9.4.

Dynamic-Frequency Assignment

The second method takes advantage of the fact that mobile-unit and base-station communication and control are effected through the CPU, where signals from all dispatchers and base stations terminate. The CPU, therefore, remembers which frequencies are in use by which base stations and mobile units, and it can assign channels on a dynamic basis. Accordingly, each base station is equipped to operate on all channels. A mobile unit can operate on one channel only or, for better service, with C-channels for trunking. The CPU will permit communication to a mobile station in a given cell at a given frequency only if that frequency is not currently in use in the cell or in any of the surrounding 18 cells.

An advantage of this scheme is that a mobile unit need only be equipped with capability on one channel to provide communication capability anywhere in the city. Furthermore, if trunking is desired, any number of channels can be added; they need not be in multiples of some number as in the fixed-frequency-assignment scheme. On the other hand, each base station must be equipped for communication on all channels.

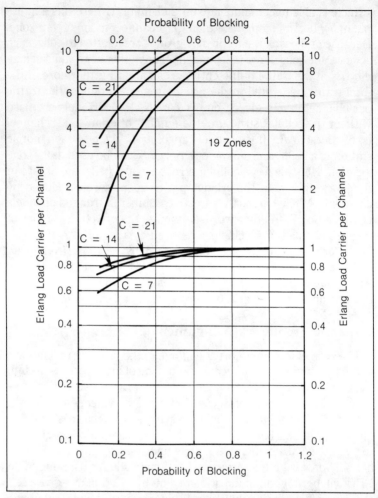

Figure 9.4—Comparative Traffic Improvement with Trunking Techniques (top curves) and Fixed-Frequency Assignment Techniques (bottom curves) (Courtesy *IEEE Spectrum*)

This method has been proposed in connection with dispatch service, mainly because of the potential cost advantage of one frequency per mobile station operation. The increase in traffic capacity is not as easily arrived at as in the fixed-frequency assignment technique. An approximate analysis has been carried out and is reproduced in Fig. 9.5. One can gain an intuitive understanding of the increased traffic-carrying capacity by the following sort of argument.

9.8

The system can obviously reuse the same frequency many times simultaneously. The tightest packing pattern is still just as shown in Fig. 9.3. Hence N/7 simultaneous users are possible just as in the fixed-frequency scheme. But since calls arrive at random, the system may not always find itself in this tightest packing configuration.

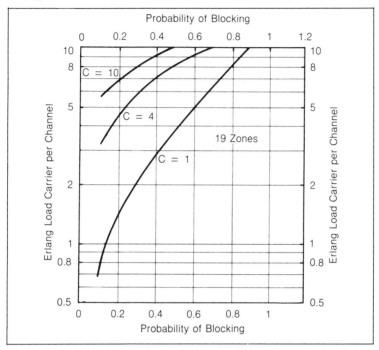

Figure 9.5—Traffic Improvement through the Use of Dynamic-Frequency Assignment (Courtesy *IEEE Spectrum*)

On the other hand, the number of times a frequency may be used at the same time can certainly be lower-bounded. Each cell that uses a certain frequency makes 19 cells unusable at that frequency (that cell plus the 18 surrounding cells forming two rings). As long as 19 multiplied by the number of cells in progress on a given frequency is less than N (the total number of cells) a new call can be placed on that frequency in at least one other zone. Therefore, even in the most adverse situations a given frequency may be used about N/19 times.

An Evolutionary Cellular System

Another type of system that has been proposed for dispatch service is one that takes advantage of the zonal approach in a partial sense. In its early stages, this type of system would not use the cellular approach at all.

In the previous two systems discussed it was intrinsically assumed that the communication path between base and mobile stations consisted of a pair of frequencies: one to be used for base-to-mobile, the other for mobile-to-base communications. The spectrum savings accrue for both base-to-mobile and mobile-to-base frequencies. Another idea is a common-user system in which all dispatchers are brought together to a common base station (via land lines), but in which a cellular structure is not used. In this situation it is also possible to get some increased spectrum efficiency on the fixed-station transmission part of the channel. This is because one of the great practical problems, adjacent-channel interference, is substantially reduced.

As already mentioned, in traditional dispatch-service mobile radio the mobile station can roam into an area where the strength of the adjacent-channel station is much larger than the desired signal, i.e., it can be much closer to the adjacent-channel transmitter. But if all signals come from the same source, the problem is reduced and one should be able to reduce channel spacing. This naturally results in some spectrum improvement. Of course, this savings accrues only to those frequencies used for dispatcher-to-vehicle transmission. It has been estimated that the traffic on these frequencies can be increased between 100 and 150 percent. Since this is true one way only, however, the system traffic can be increased only between 50 and 75 percent. On the other hand, cellular systems can give improvements by a factor of 10 and 100 zones or so. For even larger zonal systems the traffic intensity would increase directly as the number of cells.

Although it might be feasible to build a fixed station with enough power to cover the urban area in the 900 MHz band, it would be difficult to have the mobile station develop enough RF power to reach a central station. Hence this common-base-station plan provides for a distributed group of receive-only stations over the urban area that receive from relatively low-powered mobile transmitters and relay to the central point. This is similar in principle to methods already used in mobile radio. The mobile station needs to generate only enough power to transmit reliably to one of the receive-only stations. At the central point, the strongest signal from the receive-only stations is selected. As mentioned earlier, the only spectrum efficiency gained is one-way and barely significant compared with what a cellular system can ideally give. However, when system load is increased and a vehicle-location system is provided, it is possible to gain spectral efficiency on the mobile-to-base frequencies. Each receive-only station can be imagined as the center of a cell or zone and different mobile stations can transmit on the same frequency simultaneously if they are in cells sufficiently far removed One can imagine either fixed- or dynamic-frequency operation.

Comparison of Systems

Note that all the cellular system ideas for spectrum conservation that have been discussed involve two essential features: small zones and common-user operation. Although one can increase system spectrum efficiency by many techniques (such as trunking, decreased channel spacing, etc.), the common-user cellular system can give increases in efficiency on top of the other increases. Of course, this improved efficiency does not necessarily come cheap. The reader will recognize that all zonal systems need some kind of vehicle-locator subsystem.

Which, if any, of the ideas discussed can be applied to a specific system depends on detailed economic trade-offs that can only be hinted at here. For example, in fixed-frequency cellular systems one must have mobile stations that operate on any one of a number of channels (multiples of seven), but each base station need only be equipped for one-seventh the total number of channels. In dynamic-frequency assignment, it is just the other way around. A vehicle can get by with one channel but each base station has all. The basic economics ultimately depends on the number of base and mobile stations.

Over and above the types of trade-offs suggested by the previous examples, note that, so far as cellular systems are concerned, there is a major difference between radiotelephony and dispatch service that has not yet been pointed out. In telephony, because the conversation length is on the average of 3 or 4 minutes and often much longer, provision must be made for transferring control to a new base station once a vehicle crosses a zone boundary. In fact, many crossings may occur during one call. On the other hand, in dispatch service with an average call length of 15 seconds, it is unlikely for a zone crossing to occur during the call and, even if it does occur, the signal is unlikely to decay drastically in so short a period of time. The fact that "handover" from zone to zone is not necessary in a dispatch service implies significant cost reductions, at least in comparison with radiotelephone service. Details aside, the major difference between the small-cell, common-use mobile radio systems and the large-area, private-user systems are: (1) substantial capital investment to implement a high-capacity, common-use system, (2) reduced cost per vehicle when enough vehicles join the system and (3) new uses for mobile radio, since the mobile equipment which requires low power (a few watts at most) can be made very compact and portable.

9.2 Trunked Systems[3]

A trunked communications system is one in which two or more links are time-shared by the users of the system. The trunked system uses an access subsystem through which a user gains access to a "pool" of available links and "seizes" one for his own use. It is similar in concept to the modern telephone system, except that radio waves are the transmission path instead of the wires used in most of the telephone systems. Just as in the telephone system, the user must dial or otherwise generate the "address" of the unit or units he is calling. Typically, dialing will generate a frequency-coded signal which, when received by the switching center, translates this into the "address" of the user for which the call is intended. The equipment automatically makes the connection, and the call proceeds as in present radio systems until the user has finished the conversation and terminated the cell. The user hears only those messages intended for him because of the selective signaling built into the system. Individual users or groups of users can be addressed by selection of proper codes. Each user in a link-sharing system can use the system to address only the desired party without "opening up" the receivers of other users.[4]

Frequently used addresses, especially group addresses, can be preset into the equipment and sent by using a push button. This is not only time-saving because the caller does not have to dial the number, but it is also almost a matter of necessity in mobile units where the distraction of dialing numbers could be hazardous.

It may be that the short delays which might be incurred in a trunking system would be intolerable for some messages of extreme emergency, in which case provision could be made for priority calls within the system. This would preempt a busy link and allow the user to go on a link immediately if one is not otherwise available. Another way of implementing this function is to have a nontrunked priority link available between base and mobile stations.

The main advantage of a trunked system is the reduced queuing times for users of the system. This results in a higher probability of success of finding a vacant link as compared to a system in which users are assigned to dedicated links. The basic reason for this characteristic is that, given a set of links which are each occupied a certain percentage of the time (say 50 percent), the probability of all of them being occupied at any given instant is less than 50 percent. How much less depends on the number of links being considered. For a dedicated link with 50 percent occupancy, the probability of finding a clear link is 0.50.

To calculate the probability of finding a clear link in a trunked system requires several assumptions about the message lengths and the signaling duration. If average message length is 10 seconds and signaling takes two seconds, then link occupancy of 50 percent for dedicated links becomes 60 percent for the 180 messages per hour for the same information content. The probability of finding a clear link in a two-link trunked system is 56 percent, while in a four-link trunk system it rises to 72 percent. Clearly, if the average message length is greater, the improvement over dedicated links increases. If signaling durations increase, however, the improvement will decrease or may actually become worse in link availability.

With trunking, the average delay in getting on the air may therefore be reduced. Trunked links offer the greatest improvement over nontrunked links if the separate links are loaded somewhere between 30 percent and 70 percent; for more heavily loaded links, trunking offers little improvement in terms of delay in getting on the air.

Another important advantage of trunking is the fairly even loading of all links within the system. Since all users have access to all links and whenever possible idle links are accessed, the uneven loading which can occur in a nontrunked system does not exist. For example, the uneven loading caused on one link in a zoned system by an emergency in that zone would tend to be distributed over the entire system with a trunking system.

A further advantage of trunking is that the selective signaling which takes place to reach the unit being called allows only those units whose codes are dialed to hear the message. By having group as well as individual addresses, the audience can be tailored to suit the need of the moment. This might be desirable for certain command and control functions. Aside from the internal privacy and security offered by such a system, there is also a large degree of external security because of the trunking. This occurs because the random use of the links by any given user in time would make it difficult for someone listening in to find the right link at the right time and to follow that particular user through the links if he wanted to. It is most likely that anyone listening to one particular link would not gain much usable information because of the intermixing of messages from all parts of the system. Thus, while the selective coding technique does not prohibit anyone from listening to a link, it does prohibit a listener from monitoring all of the conversations between certain users as is possible with nontrunked systems. In order to do so, the listener would have to have a multichannel receiver identical to that used in the trunking system.

An additional benefit of trunked systems is that, since they will have some digital circuitry and access equipment, the inclusion of a computer access capability is entirely possible. It is possible that a mobile unit could address the computer (that is an information retrieval system) via a code just as the unit reaches other users, and by use of a simple keyboard, the unit can request information, e.g., license plate checks. The computer could then return the information via the link to a teleprinter in the mobile unit. Since it seems probable that the use of a keyboard in a mobile unit would present operational problems, a more likely setup would be for the mobile station to call an information center with a particular code and have the operator there enter the request on a computer terminal. The reply could still be automatically sent to the mobile unit and printed on a teleprinter.

At first glance, it appears that trunking could be of great use in most mobile communications systems; however, there are several disadvantages of trunking which will have to be weighed against the advantages in each situation to decide if it is justified.

The first problem is that because of the fairly short messages found in some mobile communication and the fact the reliable signaling may take up to two seconds, the percentage of air time spent in signaling may be a significant percentage of the total air time.[5] It is especially bothersome that this signaling time is in no way shortened by congestion on the air, as nontrunked messages are. The signaling time will always remain a constant (except for failures) and is not subject to the self-organization effect and time reductions in message length found in periods of high congestion on dedicated links.

Another problem which must be considered is if the signaling reliability attainable in the mobile environment is high enough to use in the emergency services. It is possible, however, that this problem could be circumvented to some extent by the use of a dedicated "urgent" emergency link or by manual override of the signaling equipment to seize a channel. The additional cost of such an option would have to be carefully evaluated.

A further limitation of a trunking system in some networks is the large area of coverage which is necessary to serve all of the users of the system. The coverage must extend over all possible areas of usage of all possible users. Since all links must cover the entire area, higher transmitter power and greater antenna height will be required than if the same links were used like dedicated links, each covering a separate geographical zone. Therefore, the minimum distance at which a frequency can be repeated will be greater for trunked system use of a channel than for dedicated-channel systems. Thus, some or all of the spectrum savings that may result from a trunked system in one network will be lost to the larger area as a whole.

The practice of monitoring a link or links to be acquainted with events which are occurring (a capability which is included in present dedicated-link systems) would only be available to predetermined address groupings in a trunked system. This is done by having the dispatcher address that group of cars which he wants to have on the link. The exact groupings would have to be determined in the system makeup and would not be subject to control by the dispatcher. He would, however, have the option of addressing a single user or any address grouping available in the system. Thus, if a four-link trunked system serves 100 cars, there could be 100 single-user addresses, 20 addresses for groups of five users each, four addresses for groups of 25 users each and one all-network address.

Another allied effect which could make a trunked system inefficient is that the lack of monitoring by individuals of what is going on in the system would lead to the users regarding the system as infinite in capacity. Essentially what happens is that, as in a telephone system, the user does not know if the system is busy and so would not tend to compensate as on a monitored link by shortening messages and eliminating nonessential ones. Thus, the system would tend to operate at the low efficiencies that are typical of low-occupancy links in conventional systems. During congestion this could be disastrous.

Another effect which is present on the conventional links and would probably not occur in trunking is overlapping of messages. There would undoubtedly be a tendency to hold a link until a message is completed, even if many seconds of dead time exists in the message. The extent to which this would affect the efficiency of the system would have to be determined from an analysis of message traffic to determine to what extent overlapping of messages occurs and to what extent users would be likely to hold onto a link for a complete, though discontinuous, message.

Trunked systems have a negligible advantage over conventional systems at high link occupancies. At high occupancies, the only way to have significantly improved probability of finding a clear link is to have a large number of trunked links. However, a large number of links means a large number of users, and the resulting necessity for a unique code for each user requires several digits or letters to identify each user. This in turn increases the signaling time required and adds to link congestion, with the result that efficiency is impaired.

The spectrum requirements of a trunked system depend on the number and types of links which are included in the system. Assuming that conventional voice channels are used and the links are all one-channel, the requirement is simply the number of links (N) times the individual channel bandwidth. For systems involving two-channel links, the bandwidth requirement is of course higher. Although trunking techniques do not alter the amount of bandwidth required for a given number of links as compared to present systems, the use of a trunked system may lead to spectrum requirements different from the present ones. For example, if users now having 10 dedicated simplex links (one-channel each) were to pool their links in a trunked system and adequate service could be obtained through the use of only 8 of the original links, the savings in spectrum space has been achieved by trunking. Of course, the opposite could also happen.

9.3   Cable Systems

There are certain applications where cable systems can be and have been used to provide EMI-free communication services in otherwise congested electromagnetic environments where spectrum crowding and saturation posed a problem. Some of the widely used applications of broadband cable systems include the telephone, cable television and local area networks. In each of these applications the use of cable systems provides communication without adding to the requirements for the radio frequency spectrum and thus avoids many potential EMI problems.

In the future, it is expected that the requirements for communications in home and office environments will increase significantly. The increased use of the computer will result in extensive requirements for electronic transfer of data between various locations. The home of the future will use computers to control and manage energy use and to transact business. Extensive communications will be required for home entertainment, electronic transfer of mail and news and other applications. The office of the future will make extensive use of computers, and communications will be required for electronic transfer of data, networking computers, video and teleconferencing, etc.

One means of providing for the increased communications requirements in the future without significantly increasing EMI problems will be the use of networks of broadband cable systems. These cable networks already exist in most urban areas and currently provide cable television service to residential areas. The coaxial cable networks offer the potential for providing a number of services in addition to the home entertainment services for which they were originally intended. We can expect to see significant expansion in the use of cable systems.

9.4 Fiber Optics and Optical Systems[6]

A tremendous expansion of fiber-optic cable networks is planned in the telecommunications industry over the next several years. This trend is expected to create new communication services. Additionally, the increased use of fiber optics should result in a radical lowering of prices for data, voice and video transmission, making a host of services like electronic mail and teleconferencing more available. It will also stimulate the growth of digital networks.

One reason for the shift to fiber-optic systems is that they are much less susceptible to noise and EMI from outside sources than are copper cable or satellite links. Furthermore, no electromagnetic radiation leaks from the fiber cable, making fiber more secure because optical signals cannot be easily intercepted or tapped.

Another plus for fiber optics in long-distance, point-to-point communications is that there is no noticeable delay in signal propagation, as there is when a signal is sent to and from a communications satellite. The majority of these satellites are in geosynchronous orbits about 36,000 km above the earth; the quarter-second delay in signal propagation for a single-hop circuit—and proportionately more for two or more transits—can cause problems in both voice and data circuits.

Some of the major problems associated with fiber-optic networks are now being overcome. Near-term advances will enhance fiber systems as point-to-point medium, but future technology may put some point-to-multipoint applications within their reach.

Recent advances are opening larger and larger portions of the huge potential bandwidth of systems. Single-mode optical fiber, first field-tested in 1983, drastically reduces the dispersion that limits the performance of multimode fibers. With core diameters of about 50 mm, multimode fibers convey signals along many internal paths or modes.

This results in modal dispersion which causes pulses to spread and limits the rate and the distance at which they can be transmitted without regeneration. The most widely used multimode optical fiber—graded index fiber—compensates for modal dispersion with an evenly varying index of refraction that is greatest at the center axis of the core and smallest at the edges. Therefore, modes at high angles of incidence which must travel longer in the lower-refraction, outer edges of the core propagate faster than modes traveling down the higher-refraction center of the core, and the effect of the dispersion is greatly reduced.

With single-mode fiber, however, intermode dispersion is eliminated altogether. Single-mode fibers have a core only about 5 to 8 μm in diameter, so only a single mode is propagated down the center of the cable. Because of their small cores, however, the joining and splicing of the cables requires more precision than in the multimode case, and the laser source must be able to transmit at high intensity in a small cross section. Nonetheless, the higher bit rates and longer distances between repeaters that are possible with single-mode fiber strengthen the economic argument for using fiber-optic links, particularly for long-distance communications.

For example, AT&T's multimode fiber links which were installed in 1983 can transmit 90 Mb/s, or the equivalent of 1,344 voice circuits. The single-mode fiber systems now being installed transmit 565 Mb/s, and engineers expect to increase such systems to 2.4 Gb by 1991. In a recent test of a prototype system, a group of researchers from AT&T Bell laboratories are reported to have demonstrated 4 Gb transmission over 117 km without the use of a repeater.

Other distance and bit-rate milestones are being set with dispersion-shifted optical fiber. In conventional single-mode optical fiber, different wavelengths travel at different velocities. This chromatic dispersion is typically at a minimum in a narrow band of frequencies with wavelengths centered near 1,300 nm. In dispersion-shifted fiber, the fiber core is fabricated to shift the region of minimum chromatic dispersion near the wavelength of minimum attenuation.

Researchers at Corning Glass Works in Corning, New York, recently announced a fiber with minimum attenuation at 1,575 nm and with chromatic dispersion of +1.5 ps delay per nm of wavelength per km of fiber for wavelengths between 1,520 and 1,560 nm. In comparison, for that band, regular single-mode fiber typically has chromatic dispersion of about 17 ps between wavelengths separated by 1 nm over a distance of 1 km.

Dispersion-shifted fiber is expected to make practical transmission rates that exceed 1 Gb/s over distances as great as 150 km. Such capabilities will be particularly important for the long-distance applications in which fiber-optic lines will compete directly with satellite-based systems. Besides Corning, two other centers of development of the fiber are British Telecom in Martlesham Heath, England, and AT&T Bell Laboratories in Norcross, Georgia.

9.5   Spread-Spectrum Systems

A spread-spectrum system is one in which the transmitted signal is spread over a wide frequency band, much wider in fact than the minimum bandwidth required to transmit the information being sent. A voice signal, for example, can be sent with amplitude modulation in a bandwidth only twice that of the information itself. Other forms of modulation, such as low-deviation FM or single side-band AM, also permit information to be transmitted in a bandwidth comparable to the bandwidth of the information itself. A spread-spectrum system, on the other hand, often takes a baseband signal (say a voice channel) with a bandwidth of only a few kilohertz and distributes it over a band that may be many megahertz wide. This is accomplished by modulating with the information to be sent and with a wideband encoding signal.

The most familiar example of spread-spectrum modulation is seen in conventional frequency modulation in which deviation ratios greater than one are used. Bandwidth required by an FM signal is a function not only of the information bandwidth but of the amount of modulation. As in all other spread-spectrum systems, a signal-to-noise advantage is gained by the modulation and demodulation process.

Although FM could be classified as a spread-spectrum technique from the standpoint that the RF spectrum produced is much wider than the transmitted information, the term **spread spectrum** is usually applied only to those techniques in which some signal or operation other than the information being sent is used for broad-banding (or spreading) the transmitted signal.

Three general types of modulation used in spread spectrum are:

1. Modulation of a carrier by a digital code sequence whose bit rate is much higher than the information signal bandwidth. Such systems are called "direct-sequence" modulated systems.
2. Carrier frequency shifting in discrete increments in a pattern dictated by a code sequence. These are called "frequency hoppers." The transmitter jumps from frequency to frequency within some predetermined set; the order of frequency usage is determined by a code sequence.
3. Pulse-FM or "chirp" modulation in which a carrier is swept over a wide band during a given pulse interval.

Closely akin to the frequency hoppers are "time hopping" and "time-frequency-hopping" systems whose chief distinguishing feature is that their time of transmission (usually of low duty cycle and short duration) is governed by a code sequence. In time-frequency hoppers it follows that the code sequence determines both the transmitted frequency and the time of transmission.

An obvious question that must be addressed in a discussion of spread-spectrum systems is: "Why consider spread-spectrum systems when we already have an overcrowded situation with too little spectrum to accommodate the ever increasing demand?" One answer to this question is that spread-spectrum systems, under certain circumstances, can provide improved performance in a severe interference environment.

The improvement provided by spread-spectrum systems exists from both a transmitting and recovery viewpoint. First, from a transmitting standpoint the wideband signal spectrum generated by code modulation is such that the power transmitted is low in any narrow frequency band. Thus, the spectral density of a spread-spectrum signal is considerably less than that of a conventional signal in which all of the transmitted power is concentrated within a narrow band of frequencies that are comparable with the baseband information bandwidth. For this reason, spread-spectrum systems are less likely to cause interference to other conventional systems that may share the same bands.

Second, from a receiving standpoint a spread-spectrum system is able to reject certain types of interference so that the system may be able to provide almost error-free operation in a noisy signal environment. The spread-spectrum system accomplishes this function by providing for a trade-off between bandwidth and signal-to-interference level.

A spread-spectrum system develops a processing gain as a result of the signal bandwidth spreading and despreading operation. The transmit part of the process may be accomplished with any one of the band-spreading modulation methods. Despreading is accomplished by correlating the received spread spectrum signal with a similar local reference signal. When the two signals are matched, the desired signal collapses to its original bandwidth before spreading, whereas any unmatched input is spread by the local reference to its bandwidth or more. A filter then rejects all but the desired narrowband signal; that is, given a desired signal and its interference (atmospheric noise, receiver noise or jamming), a spread-spectrum receiver enhances the signal while suppressing the effects of all other inputs. Thus, spread-spectrum systems are able to provide significantly enhanced performance in certain interference environments.

9.6 Digital Technology

The basic information to be transmitted by a communication system may exist in either analog or digital format. Analog information would be continuous in nature and all signal levels are possible. Voice is an example of analog information. Digital information is defined in terms of discrete levels. Numerical data or printed text would represent examples of digital information. Although the basic information is either analog or digital, it is possible to approximate analog information digitally or vice versa. For example, an analog signal such as voice may be quantified into discrete steps so that the signal is approximated by a digital signal.

In a typical communication system, the information to be transmitted is processed onto an RF carrier. This processing may include multiplexing a number of sources of information and then modulating the multiplexed information onto the carrier. Either analog or digital techniques may be used for the multiplexing and modulation process. In the past, analog techniques were typically used for both multiplexing (frequency-division multiplexing) and modulation (amplitude or frequency modulation). However, with the recent advances of digital technology, digital techniques are now being more widely used for multiplexing (time-division multiplexing) and modulation (phase shift keying). Digital communication systems offer some decided advantages over analog communication systems from the standpoint of their ability to operate in the presence of EMI. However, digital systems also have some problems that are not exhibited by analog systems. Therefore, it is important to understand the relative advantages and disadvantages of both analog and digital communication systems.

With analog systems, noise and interference are additive and will affect the quality of performance. Because noise and interference are additive, the system performance will gradually degrade if it is transmitted over long paths that require amplifiers or repeaters. This occurs because each amplifier or repeater adds noise to the signal and therefore the signal-to-noise ratio is reduced each time the signal is amplified. The same is true of interference. That is, if the signal is relayed over several links, interference may enter into the receivers associated with each of the links and the interference at the last receiver (which represents the receiving end for the message) will be the result of the combined additive effects of the interference at all of the receivers.

In general, analog communication systems require a relatively high signal-to-interference plus noise level to achieve good performance. As the signal-to-interference plus noise level degrades, the system performance will also degrade. However, analog systems will tend to fail gracefully in the presence of noise and interference. Thus, there is a range of signal-to-interference plus noise levels over which it is possible to maintain some degree of communication even though the quality is degraded.

With digital systems, the signal is defined in terms of discrete levels. Because of this, high-quality performance is possible in the presence of interference or noise as long as it is possible to determine which discrete level exists. Thus, it is possible to achieve excellent performance with a relatively low signal-to-interference plus noise. Furthermore, digital signals may be relayed over many links without degradation (as long as the signal-to-interference plus noise is adequate over each link). This is possible because the digital signal is reconstructed at each relay point and the interference and noise are removed. Thus, the effects of interference and noise are not additive as they are with analog systems.

The performance of digital systems may also be improved through the use of error detection and correction coding. Some of these, such as the Bose-Chaudhuri-Hocquenghem codes and convoluted codes, are capable of detecting and correcting multiple random errors in the block of data. Of the convoluted codes, the Viterbi algorithm seems to be gaining in popularity. Variations of Viterbi coder-decoders now in use effectively double the throughput in comparison with uncoded data for a given error rate.

These codes, however, are considerably more complex and generally require more bits in the block of data than simpler codes capable only of correcting random single errors in multiple burst errors. Thus, they further reduce the efficiency of transmission.

Although error detecting and correcting codes will improve the performance of digital systems, it is important to recognize that in order for these coding techniques to be effective, it is necessary to have relatively good performance initially. Thus, error detection and correction coding might be used in an application where the bit-error rate is one error in 10^4 bits and may result in essentially error-free performance. On the other hand, error detection and correction coding would not usually be effective in an application where the bit-error rate is greater than one error in 10 bits.

Unlike analog communication systems, digital communication systems tend to fail catastrophically. That is, digital receivers tend to exhibit a sharp threshold where they transition from good performance to complete failure in performance. The reason for this abrupt transition is that digital receivers depend on pulse timing and synchronization of the received pulses to an internal clock. The presence of an interfering signal adds a noise component to the desired signal which may disturb the timing in the digital waveform. As the level of interference increases, time synchronization becomes more difficult until synchronization is lost, at which time the system fails completely. The receiver circuits attempt to reacquire the signal by resynchronizing, which usually requires a larger signal-to-interference ratio and a long time. Thus, the performance of digital receivers can exhibit dramatic failure under certain interference conditions because of loss of signal synchronization. This loss properly accounts for distinct failure thresholds of receiver performance, representing the most severe type of degradation.

A digital receiver tends to be more immune to interference during the time it is synchronized with the signal. Thus, an interfering signal that might not disturb the receiver during normal signal reception could provide serious degradation if present during the time when the receiver is attempting to synchronize with the desired signal.

Another type of problem results from automatic gain control (AGC) capture by a relatively strong signal radiated from a nearby high-power interference or jamming source. High-power emissions also desensitize receivers or produce distortion of the desired signal as a result of saturating the front end of the receiver.

9.7 Phased Arrays and Adaptive Antennas

Arrays of antenna elements provide an attractive solution to many otherwise severe interference problems. By properly phasing the individual elements, it is possible to control the antenna pattern so that radiation or reception of signals in certain directions is significantly enhanced while radiation or reception of signals in other directions is minimized. Phased arrays are particularly useful for providing significant rejection against the radiation or reception of signals because it is possible to create nulls in the antenna pattern in certain directions, and these nulls will selectively reject signals in the direction of the nulls.

The phased-array concept has been used for years by the broadcast industry to control the radiation pattern of radio and television broadcast antennas to eliminate interference within other stations' coverage areas. More recently, the advent of highly compact, inexpensive digital computers has made it possible to develop array antenna systems that have the capability of steering one or more beams or nulls over wide areas of coverage.

For certain applications (such as radar) the ability of phased array antennas to electronically steer a beam quickly over a wide area is a desirable feature. However, from the standpoint of interference rejection, the ability of phased array antennas to electronically control and steer the direction of nulls is the capability of interest. Phased array antenna systems that automatically respond to a changing signal environment have also been developed. This self-adjusting or adaptive capability results in flexible and reliable systems that offer improved reception and performance in the presence of interference or jamming. These "adaptive" antenna systems offer a very effective method for suppressing interference.

Adaptive arrays are currently the subject of extensive investigation as a means for reducing the vulnerability of the reception of desired signals to the presence of interference signals in radar, sonar, seismic and communication systems. The main reason behind this widespread interest in adaptive array systems derives from their ability to sense automatically the presence of interference noise sources and to suppress these noise sources while simultaneously enhancing desired signal reception without prior knowledge of the signal/interference environment. Adaptive arrays can be designed to complement other interference suppression techniques so the actual suppression achieved is greater than that which can be obtained solely through more conventional means, e.g., by use of spread-spectrum techniques or the use of a highly directive sensor device.

An adaptive array is a system consisting of an array of sensor elements and a real-time adaptive signal receiver-processor that automatically adjusts the array beam sensitivity pattern so that a measure of the quality of the array performance is improved. An adaptive array offers enhanced reliability compared to that of a conventional array. When a single sensor element in a conventional array fails, the sidelobe structure of the array sensitivity pattern may be significantly degraded because the sidelobe increases. With an adaptive array, however, the response of the remaining operational sensors in the array can be automatically adjusted until the array sidelobes are reduced to an acceptable level. Adaptive arrays, therefore, fail gracefully compared to conventional arrays, and increased reliability results.

Frequently an array beam pattern is determined more by nearfield scattering effects than by its own inherent pattern in free space. For example, if a very low sidelobe antenna is placed on an aircraft, the tail and wings of the aircraft will completely change the antenna directional sensitivity pattern. An adaptive array will often yield successful operation even when antenna patterns are severely distorted by near-field effects.

The operation of an adaptive array can be most easily visualized by considering the response in terms of the array beam sensitivity pattern. Interference signal suppression is obtained by appropriately steering beam pattern nulls and reducing sidelobe levels in the directions of interference sources, while desired signal reception is maintained by preserving desirable main lobe (or signal beam) features. An adaptive array system therefore relies heavily on spatial characteristics to improve the output SNR. Since it is possible to form deep sensitivity pattern nulls over a narrow bandwidth region, strong interference suppression can be realized. This exceptional interference suppression capability is a principal advantage of adaptive arrays compared to waveform processing techniques, which generally require a large spectrum-spreading factor to obtain comparable levels of interference suppression. Sensor arrays possessing this key automatic response capability are sometimes referred to as "smart" arrays since they respond to far more of the signal information at the sensor outputs than do more conventional array systems.

The capabilities provided by the adaptive array techniques offer practical solutions to the realistic interference problems mentioned above by virtue of their ability to sort out and distinguish the various signals in the spatial domain, in the frequency domain and in polarization. At the present time adaptive nulling is considered to be the principal benefit of the adaptive techniques employed by adaptive array systems, and automatic cancellation of sidelobe jamming provides a valuable electronic counter-countermeasure (ECCM) capability for radar systems. Adaptive arrays can be designed to incorporate more traditional capabilities such as self-focusing on receive and retrodirective transmit. In addition to automatic interference nulling and beam-steering, adaptive imaging arrays may also be designed to obtain microwave images having high angular resolution. It is useful to call self-phasing or retrodirective arrays **adaptive transmitting arrays** to distinguish the principal function of such systems from an **adaptive receiving array**.

Figure 9.6 shows the principal system elements that an adaptive array must possess if it is to successfully achieve the twin objectives of enhancing desired signal reception and rejecting undesired interference signals. The main adaptive array system elements consist of the sensor array, the pattern-forming network and the adaptive pattern control unit or adaptive processor that adjusts the variable weights in the pattern-forming network. The adaptive pattern control unit may also be conveniently subdivided into a signal processor unit and an adaptive control algorithm. The way in which these elements are actually implemented depends on the propagation medium in which the array is to operate, the frequency spectrum of interest and the user's knowledge of the operational signal environment.

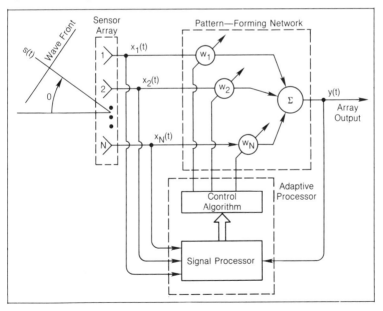

Figure 9.6—Functional Diagram of an N-Element Adaptive Array

Adaptive arrays offer a promising solution to many types of EMI problems, and they may be expected to be more widely used in future applications. One of the obvious advantages of adaptive arrays over other methods of suppressing EMI is that they may be added to an existing system without having to modify the remainder of the system.

9.8 References

1. Staras, H. and Schiff, L., "Spectrum Conservation in the Land Mobile Radio Sources," *IEEE Spectrum*, July 1971.
2. Frankiel, R.H., "A High Capacity Mobile Radiotelephone System Model Using a Coordinated Small-Zone Approach," *1969 IEEE Communication Conference Record*, p. 31.
3. Church, Dr. J.; Ebstein, B.; et. al., "Initial Development of Implementation Plans," Illinois Police Communication Study, Phase 2, Vol. 2, APCO, 1969.
4. "Task Force Report: Science and Technology," a report to the President's Commission on Law Enforcement and Administration of Justice, 1967, Appendix D, pp. 30-32.
5. Cohn, J.; Braun, W.; and Bruckert, E.J., "Evaluation of Trunking for Use in Land Mobile Radio Services," Motorola document, p. 4.
6. Guteri, F. and Zorpetti, G., "Fiber Optic: Poised to Displace Satellites," *IEEE Spectrum*, August 1985.

9.9 Bibliography

1. Duff, W.G., et. al., "A Neglected Dimension of EMC," *1971 IEEE EMC Symposium Record* (New York: IEEE, 1971).
2. Skolnik, M.I., *Introduction to Radar Systems* (New York: McGraw-Hill Book Co., Inc., 1962).

Chapter 10

Survey of EMC Analysis Computer Programs

The previous chapters describe EMC analysis techniques that may be used for a variety of applications involving EMC design of telecommunication systems so they may be compatible with their RF environments. Section 10.1 highlights some of the general uses of the EMC analysis techniques presented in this volume, and Sections 10.2 through 10.9 summarize some of the available computer programs, routines and services.

Although this volume is mainly concerned with EMC analysis techniques, it is important to realize that EMC analysis is a special area of systems analysis. Hence, many of the methods and techniques described in this handbook for use in EMC analysis may also be applied to other areas of systems analysis. For example, propagation is an important element of both systems analysis and EMC analysis. Therefore, comprehensive propagation models developed for one of these applications may often also be used for the other applications. Another example is that the tradeoffs involved in allocating the power budget between transmitter, receiver, antenna and propagation are the same for system design as for EMC analysis. The only difference is that in the system design problem, the desired signal level at the receiver must be large enough to ensure reception; whereas, in the EMC analysis problem, the interfering signal must be small enough to ensure compatibility. There are many other system design, planning, installation and operational problems (such as frequency allocation, frequency assignment and scheduling and siting) that require consideration of EMI and hence rely heavily on the prediction techniques described in this volume.

10.1 Applications for EMC Analysis Techniques

The models and techniques presented in this volume may be used for many applications which are directly or indirectly related to EMC analysis. Figure 10.1 illustrates some of the major functions that may be supported by EMC analysis models and techniques. Because of the many supplemental applications of EMC analysis methods, it is suggested that special consideration be given to the development of EMC analysis routines (especially those which are to be programmed for computers) so that the resulting software may be applied to systems analysis and design as well as EMC analysis.

As described in Chapter 1, EMC analysis is applicable to each of the three basic phases (definition and planning, hardware design and development and operation) in the life cycle of an equipment or system. Table 10.1 identifies the major EMC technical problem areas that must be addressed and relates them to the particular phase in the system life cycle for which they are applicable. Also, Table 10.1 identifies the type or types of analysis (intersystem, intrasystem or environment) that are appropriate for each problem area. The following sections describe individual problem areas and how EMC analysis techniques may be used to help ensure EMC.

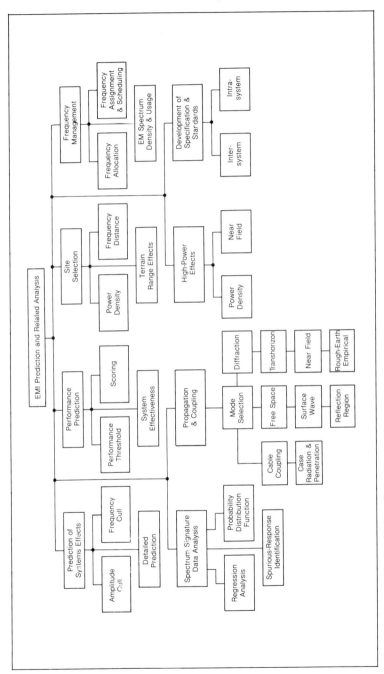

Figure 10.1—EMI Prediction Functions

Table 10.1—EMI Problem Area

General Problem Area	Specific Problem Area	Life-Cycle Phase			Intra-system	Inter-system	Environment
		Definition and Planning	Design and Development	Operation			
Frequency Management	Allocation	✓				✓	✓
	Assignment and Scheduling			✓	✓	✓	✓
	EMI Spectrum Density	✓		✓	✓	✓	
Site Selection	Frequency Distance Separation Criteria	✓				✓	
	Terrain Effects			✓	✓	✓	✓
	Power Density	✓				✓	✓
System Effects	Emissions and Response		✓	✓	✓	✓	
	Intermodulation			✓	✓	✓	
Performance Prediction	Performance Thresholds	✓			✓	✓	
	Performance Scoring			✓	✓	✓	✓
	Systems Effectiveness	✓		✓	✓	✓	✓
Development of Specifications and Standards	Intersystem	✓	✓			✓	
	Intrasystem		✓		✓		
Propagation and Coupling	Cable Coupling		✓		✓		
	Case Radiation and Penetration		✓		✓	✓	
	Antenna Coupling	✓		✓	✓	✓	
High-Power Effects	Power Density	✓	✓		✓		✓
	Near Field	✓	✓			✓	

10.1.1 Analysis of System Effects

In order to make the best use of the frequency spectrum and ensure EMC, it is often necessary to predict the effects of systems in a specific environment in which the system is required to operate. Results of these predictions are used by system planners for the (1) preparation of system or equipment requirements and specifications, (2) definition of EMI suppression or control techniques required for compatibility or (3) evaluation of the effects of new systems on the use of the spectrum. Typical problems for which EMC analysis may be required include:

1. Examine the impact of adding a new system to an existing environment.
2. Examine the EMC and frequency management consideration for several different new systems.
3. Provide information about the adequacy of EMI specifications for a proposed system.
4. Provide information about the best frequency band to use for a new system.
5. Determine existing equipments or systems which are likely to interfere with or be interfered with by a new system.

EMC analysis of systems effects is an engineering tool that may be used in analyzing problems of the type identified above. The analysis techniques described in this volume are directly applicable to problems of this type.

10.1.2 Performance Prediction

Many applications require prediction of the effects of EMI on operational performance or effectiveness of an equipment or system. EMC analysis techniques presented in this volume may be used to determine performance thresholds, i.e., the signal and interference conditions that represent the boundary between acceptable and unacceptable performance. Alternately, EMC analysis techniques can be used to provide a quantitative measurement of system performance such as voice articulation score, radar scope conditions, error rates for communications systems, maximum effective range and angular or range errors. Once performance measures have been found for individual equipments or systems, they may be combined to provide overall measures related to mission effectiveness.

10.1.3 Site Selection

Many factors exist that must be considered in selecting a site for installation of an equipment or system. Some of the primary considerations are: (1) power density or field strengths in the vicinity of the site as a result of RF emitters in the environment, (2) RF coverage or radio line-of-sight in the vicinity of the site as a result of the surrounding terrain and (3) frequency-distance separations that must be maintained between the equipments being considered for installation and existing equipments or systems in the immediate area.

EMC analysis techniques presented in this volume may be used for evaluation, comparison and selection of sites. Additionally, once a site has been selected, EMC analysis techniques may be used to optimize equipment installation on the site and to define operational limitations and constraints that must be imposed to ensure EMC. Frequency distance separation criteria may be found by using the prediction equations to determine separations required to ensure EMC.

10.1.4 Frequency Management

Electromagnetic spectrum density is an important consideration in the evaluation of spectrum usage for frequency allocation or assignment studies. In general, information on electromagnetic spectrum density may be used to provide a measurement of frequency congestion and to identify potential EMI problems. Spectrum density considerations are particularly useful during system planning because the results may be used to indicate potential EMI problems without consideration of specific frequency schedules. Prediction techniques may be used to evaluate electromagnetic spectrum density, to optimize frequency allocations and identify potential problem areas.

In order to use the frequency spectrum effectively and ensure compatibility, it is necessary to give careful attention to frequency assignment and scheduling. EMC analysis techniques presented in this handbook may be used to find clear channels for frequency assignment, to check proposed frequency assignments for potential EMI problems and to assist frequency coordination personnel in making effective and efficient use of the spectrum.

One problem that arises in frequency assignment problems is that there are often so many equipment-frequency combinations that must be considered that a detailed analysis of each combination is prohibitive. In order to reduce the problem to a manageable size, analysis techniques are used to eliminate those interactions that are not likely to produce interference.

A procedure that may be used is as follows. Equipments whose frequencies fall outside of an "RF acceptance range" are eliminated. Of those equipments that remain, only combinations that produce intermodulation products in the "IF acceptance range" are retained. The reduced list is then subjected to a quick amplitude analysis, and additional analysis is performed. Finally, those equipment-frequency combinations that remain are analyzed in detail.

One approach used in frequency assignment problems is to first identify from a list of existing frequency assignments those transmitters and receivers that fall within certain criteria of frequency, antenna orientation and distance with respect to the equipment being considered for assignment. Each potentially interfering transmitter and its associated receiver are assumed to deny the use of a band of frequencies about their assigned frequency. Frequencies not denied are therefore available for assigning to other transmitter-receiver pairs.

The transmitter-receiver pair which has the smallest number of frequencies available for assignment is the first to be considered. A frequency is assigned and checked against the remaining equipment-frequency combinations to determine compatibility. Available frequencies for remaining equipments are updated using the same criteria as employed in evaluating the existing assignment. After the available frequencies are updated, a frequency is assigned for the remaining transmitter-receiver pair which has the smallest number of available frequencies. The process is continued until all frequencies have been assigned. For the particular situation where there are a small number of equipment-frequency combinations to be considered, it is possible to examine all combinations so that an optimum selection can be determined.

10.1.5 High-Power Effects

Electromagnetic fields resulting from high-power transmitters can produce a variety of problems such as saturation or burnout of crystals or other circuit components as well as hazards to personnel, ordnance or fuels. EMC analysis techniques presented in this volume may be used to determine power density or field strength over an area as a result of a particular equipment environment. These levels may then be used to assess potential burnout or hazard problems. EMC analysis results may be used to identify areas in the vicinity of high-power systems where burnout or radiation hazard problems are likely to exist and to provide information on areas where radiation levels are above "safe" limits.

10.1.6 Development of Specifications and Standards

EMC analysis techniques described in this volume may be used to develop EMI specifications that are tailored to specific equipments or systems. By applying appropriate analysis procedures, it is possible to develop equipment or system specifications that are both "necessary" and "sufficient" to ensure compatibility. By considering both of these conditions, i.e., necessary and sufficient, in the development of EMI specifications, it is possible to optimize the requirements and avoid the wasteful expense associated with overengineering or the inadequacy and problems associated with underengineering the system.

The application of EMC analysis techniques can be used to assist in the development of EMI standards. Specifically, EMI prediction techniques can be used to define emission and susceptibility levels that may be tolerated without creating EMI problems and may be used to evaluate tradeoffs between emission and susceptibility requirements.

Additionally, EMC analysis techniques may be used to evaluate the adequacy of a specification or standard for a given equipment or system configuration, to assess the impact of conditions of noncompliance, and to define the amount of additional suppression or rejection required in the case of specific EMI problem areas. Analysis techniques can also be useful in identifying potential problem areas which should be examined carefully during acceptance testing.

10.1.7 Propagation and Coupling Loss Problems

Propagation and coupling loss problems are an important and necessary part of any EMC analysis. The primary requirement is to predict coupling loss for a system of emitters and susceptible devices which satisfy the input data and environmental restrictions imposed by the user. The prediction of coupling loss depends on system parameters such as frequency, polarization, orientation and geometry and on environmental parameters associated with the intervening transmission media. For example, in the case of a conducting sphere (such as the earth), it is necessary to specify conductivity and permittivity.

In general, two basic functions are performed by the propagation and coupling loss models for EMC analysis. First, based on the input data specified by the user, the appropriate mode or modes of coupling are selected. Second, propagation or coupling loss is calculated for the specific system and environmental parameters of interest.

Aside from the EMC analysis, there are many other systems engineering applications which require propagation and coupling loss predictions. If an EMC analysis process contains comprehensive propagation models, they may be used for calculating propagation and coupling loss for many of the various system applications. Because of the generally broad requirement for propagation calculations, propagation models are often the most widely used models in an EMC analysis process. The propagation models described in this volume and in the cited references may be used for path engineering and other applications in addition to EMC analysis.

10.1.8 Spectrum Signature Data Analysis

One of the primary sources of information for use in frequency management and EMC analysis is the data obtained from spectrum signature measurements performed under MIL-STD-449. In certain analysis problems, the information derived from spectrum signature measurements may be used directly, but in many cases the data must be subjected to analysis before it can be applied to a problem. The purpose of spectrum signature data analysis is to provide spectrum signature data in a reduced form that is readily applicable to analysis problems.

There are several basic analysis techniques that are extremely useful in reducing the spectrum signature data to a form that may easily be used in frequency management and EMC problems.

Three basic techniques that are widely used in analyzing spectrum signature data are: regression analysis, probability distribution function analysis and spurious response identification. The method of least squares presented in Chapter 3 is an application of regression analysis.

Regression analysis is used to derive functional relationships for the various transmitter and receiver characteristics from measured data. Probability distribution functions are used to evaluate the mean value, standard deviation and probability distributions associated with measured data. Spurious response identification is used to define the specific local oscillator and interference products that produce a particular measured response in a receiver.

10.2 Electromagnetic Compatibility Analysis Center (ECAC)

The Electromagnetic Compatibility Analysis Center (ECAC) is a Department of Defense facility established to provide advice and assistance on EMC matters to the Secretary of Defense, the Joint Chiefs of Staff, military departments and other DoD components. The center serves other government agencies and government-sponsored civilian activities as resources permit.[1,2]

ECAC provides users with analytical solutions of EMI problems or computer printouts from a comprehensive EMC data base containing topographic information, CE equipments, associative surroundings and equipment technical characteristics. ECAC has established an EMC analysis capability consisting of mathematical models and computer programs developed and applied by an experienced group of EMC engineers and analysts. Final conclusions and recommendations are summarized in a report to the agency that submitted the project. A briefing or oral presentation of results is provided if desired.

The ECAC data base consists of environmental information regarding deployed government and civilian CE equipment, selected technical characteristics of such equipment and topographical information. Portions of this data are stored on magnetic tape and random access storage services for computer retrieval; other portions are contained in documents available from the center's technical information services.

10.2.1 Services Available through ECAC

The following services, based on the use of ECAC analytical techniques, are typical of those available:

1. Assistance, from an EMC standpoint, to system developers on all aspects of frequency selection, equipment design and placing in operation of new CE systems
2. Guidance in selecting locations for all types of CE equipment
3. Determination of power densities as affected by distance and topography
4. Prediction of EMC degradation for various tactical missions
5. Technical support to frequency management, primarily on the potential effect of incorporating new electronic systems into present and future environments
6. Evaluation of potential equipment sites for electronic line-of-site coverage and for compatibility with surrounding electronic and topographic environment

Since each analytical task has its own special objectives and requirements, it is not practical to specify standard outputs or formats which ECAC would provide as a result of a study. Outputs have ranged from narrative discussions of interference effects and possible remedial techniques to tabulations of expected performance levels including graphs and curves suitable for application by the user in further analysis of his situation.

The figures that follow in this section illustrate representative ECAC outputs. Note the potential applicability of these outputs to research and development needs, to frequency management requirements and to situations encountered by operational field commanders.

Power-Density Analysis

Power-density analyses are studies of the potential effects of high-power emitters on electrical or electronic equipments. Such studies support assessment of biological or ordnance hazards. An example of power-density computations is shown in Fig. 10.2.

Figure 10.2 is a map overlay showing points of constant power density. The overlay is generated as a direct output of the computer using data from both the environmental and topographic files. The data in the legend allows interpretation of the letters and numbers on the overlay. If all points having the same level are connected, a contour of constant power density is obtained. Blank spaces enclosed by contours have the power density indicated by the contour.

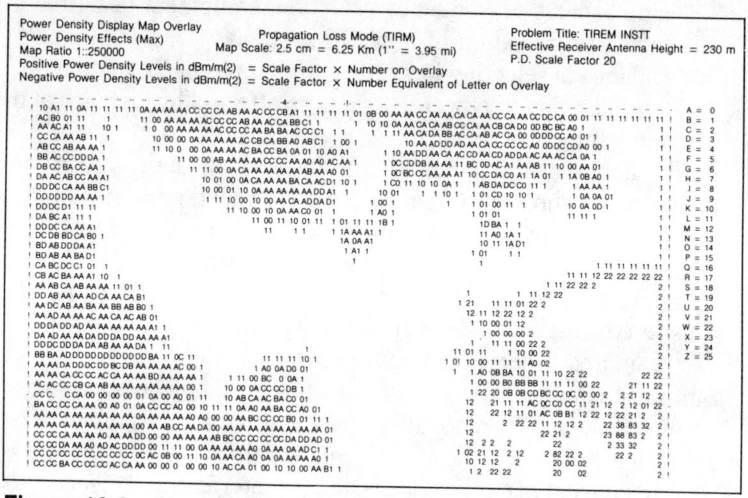
Power Density Display Map Overlay
Power Density Effects (Max)
Map Ratio 1::250000
Propagation Loss Mode (TIRM)
Map Scale: 2.5 cm = 6.25 Km (1" = 3.95 mi)
Problem Title: TIREM INSTT
Effective Receiver Antenna Height = 230 m
P.D. Scale Factor 20
Positive Power Density Levels in dBm/m(2) = Scale Factor × Number on Overlay
Negative Power Density Levels in dBm/m(2) = Scale Factor × Number Equivalent of Letter on Overlay
A = 0
B = 1
C = 2
D = 3
E = 4
F = 5
G = 6
H = 7
I = 8
J = 9
K = 10
L = 11
M = 12
N = 13
O = 14
P = 15
Q = 16
R = 17
S = 18
T = 19
U = 20
V = 21
W = 22
X = 23
Y = 24
Z = 25

Figure 10.2—Power-Density Display, Map Overlay

Spectrum Use

Many agencies want a description of the levels of signal intensities across a given frequency range when viewed from a specified location. The results of this type of analysis may have an effect on equipment design, site selection, frequency assignment and frequency allocation. Figure 10.3 illustrates the distribution of users over the channels available in the VHF band.

Much information can be gained from knowing the location of equipments that operate in a given frequency band. Although this information can be found through a straightforward listing, a computer can also be used to cosntruct a map overlay showing the locations of equipment in specified frequency bands. This type of display showing potential interfering sources for new equipment has proven valuable. Figure 10.4 is a map-type display of frequency occupancy.

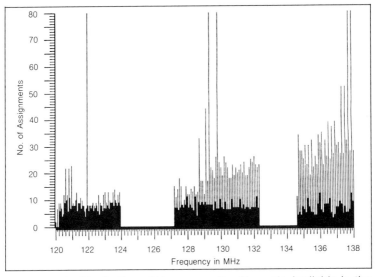

Figure 10.3—Distribution of Users over the Channels Available in the VHF Band

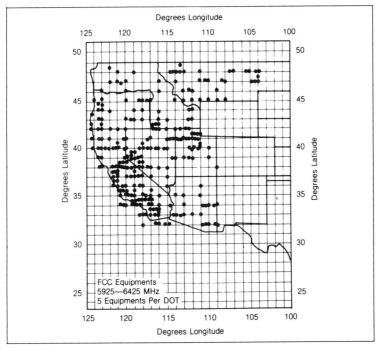

Figure 10.4—Geographic Display Depicting Equipment in a Frequency Band as a Function of Location

Site Analysis

Significant in the analysis of many EMC problems is the topographic shielding in the vicinity of a site. ECAC, together with the Army Topographic Command, has developed techniques for generating site analysis models by acquiring and storing topographic information in computer-usable form to account for site analysis. This data provides the capability to automatically introduce topographic shielding effects into analysis programs developed at ECAC.

Figure 10.5 shows an overlay which has been generated for a map using the site analysis model. This overlay shows the shielding characteristics for a site by printing an X on map areas that cannot be seen from the indicated site for the conditions specified in the overlay's legend.

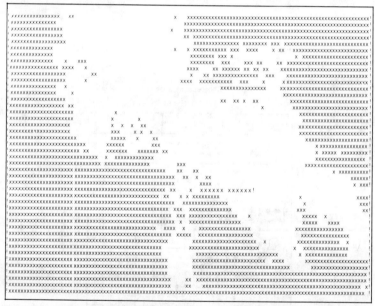

Figure 10.5—Site-Analysis Model Overlay Showing Masking Characteristics for One Site

Figure 10.6 shows a perspective plot of a user-specified area; Fig. 10.7 depcits the terrain profile of a propagation path 137 km (85 mi) long. Using appropriate geometry and physical phenomena, one can calculate the propagation loss over the path.

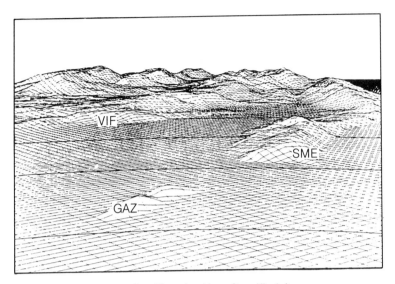

Figure 10.6—Perspective Plot of a User-Specified Area

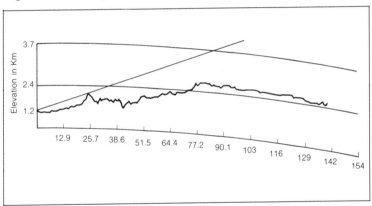

Figure 10.7—Sample Terrain Profile, 4/3 Earth Radius

10.2.2 Data Analysis from ECAC

A primary function of the ECAC is to establish and maintain the data base necessary for EMC analysis to support DoD components and, as approved by the managers of DoD EMC programs, for other government agencies. To this end, ECAC has compiled the most complete EMC-related data base in existence, which consists of numerous data files that fall into the following broad categories:

equipment characteristics, equipment complements, background environment, topographic data, space systems and hard-copy library.

Equipment Characteristics

The ECAC equipment characteristics file (ECF) consists of the nominal characteristics file (NCF), the future systems file (FSF), the foreign equipment characteristics file (FECF), the electronic warfare integrated reprogramming file (EWIR) and the equipment parameter file (EPF). The NCF contains basic technical characteristics of military and commercial transmitters, receivers and antennas. Data is manually extracted from all available data sources (technical orders, manuals and commercial documentation). The FSF contains general information on equipment planned for future development and deployment. Data is extracted primarily from published articles and frequency allocation applications. The extent of the data varies widely, but normally the nomenclature, frequency band and general description are available. This file also contains references and pointers to data sources for equipment planned for future deployment. The FECF contains basic technical data on foreign equipment. The EWIR file contains detailed technical characteristics of U.S. and foreign electronic warfare (EW) equipments. The EPF contains data required for specialized, detailed, EMC analyses and is developed at ECAC.

Equipment Complements

Equipment-complement information is composed of data files that describe the CE equipments on ships and aircraft and assigned to mobile ground tactical units. Nonautomated data is continually received and evaluated to determine its value and applicability to the ECAC mission. Some is extracted and entered into automated files. That which is too voluminous or would not be cost-effective to automate is retained in a hard-copy library. When possible, multiple sources are consulted to ensure that the best data is extracted for inclusion in the automated files.

Frequency Spectrum Use

The frequency resource record system (FRRS) data base contains worldwide DoD frequency-assignment records. Each record contains administrative and technical data concerning the type of assignment, organizational information, transmitter and receiver location and technical data. The data in the records is provided by all DoD components and is maintained in support of world-wide frequency management activities, and ECAC EMC analysis requirements.

The spectrum allocation and use file (SAUF) is a file of international allocations, U.S. national allocations, U.S. military spectrum usage policies, foreign national allocations, NATO-Europe national allocations and NATO military spectrum usage policies. Data for the SAUF is extracted from various source documents for entry into the file. The SAUF, therefore, is basically a simple low-cost library of allocation data that is conveniently retrievable. A library of spectrum allocation documents is also available for use by project engineers.

Background Environment

Background environmental data consists of many files, both automated and nonautomated, that contain digitized topographic data for world areas of U.S. interest and electromagnetic environmental information describing military and civil CE operations worldwide. Large-volume electromagnetic environmental files are processed into ECAC standard format(s) for compatibility with internal data management systems.

Electromagnetic environmental information in selected categories is automated by extraction of data from source documents and storage in an appropriate ECAC data management system. These categories have evolved through experience to be either critical to EMC analysis or required on a recurring basis. The quality of this data is largely a function of the validity of the source document. When possible, however, multiple sources are consulted to verify information.

ECAC also works with the military services to define tactical deployments that incorporate various threats. The tactical environment generation and analysis system (TEGAS) uses this information in assessing environmental effects.

Topographic Data

The ECAC topographic data file (TOPO) consists of digitized ground elevation information that is used to characterize a geographical region. The data is in an automated file in accordance with a spherical coordinate system with the spacing between elevations given in angular measure. Topographic data is a vital component in EMC analysis applications for propagation predictions, line-of-sight coverage, radar range predictions, etc.

Space Systems

Three types of satellite-system data are available: general system information (hard copy), orbital characteristics (automated) and detailed technical characteristics (hard copy).

The detailed technical characteristics needed for in-depth EMC analyses of space systems are taken from technical manuals, system description documents, technical reports and frequency-allocation applications. General system information includes international frequency registration board (IFRB) notifications, technical articles and bibliographies concerning each system. Data has been collected over many years from project engineers, conference records, government publications and other open literature. The accuracy of the information varies with the source and date of acquisition.

Orbital characteristics describe the motion of a payload in space. They are received from the North American Aerospace Defense Command (NORAD) on computer tape and are updated by AUTODIN messages. Accuracy and completeness of the data depends on the NORAD worldwide satellite tracking network. To meet future needs, ECAC is expanding its space systems information through development of a comprehensive automated data base.

10.3 Interference Prediction Process (IPP-1)

The Air Force at Rome Air Development Center (RADC) has developed an EMI prediction process that should be useful to system or equipment planners, designers and operational personnel.[3] The process, which may be used to analyze compatibility for both communication and radar systems, provides a basis for defining EMI problem areas, identifying potential solutions and making engineering decisions. The interference prediction process (IPP-1) contains a set of computer routines that may be used to analyze and predict potentially interfering situations among a proposed or existing deployment of transmitters and receivers.

The IPP-1 computer program provides an engineering tool that may be used in various phases of CE equipment development such as (1) the preliminary system or equipment requirements and specifications, (2) the preparation of specification compliance test plans, (3) the evaluation of test results, (4) the revision of either specifications or equipments for conditions of noncompliance and (5) the evaluation of systems in a specific operational environment.

Typical problems that may be handled by IPP-1 include the following:

1. Examine the EMC situation for a complex of equipments and identify problem areas
2. Examine the impact of changing the operating frequency of one or more equipments in the complex
3. Examine the impact of adding a transmitter to an existing complex of equipments
4. Examine the interference produced in a receiver when added to an existing complex
5. Determine which one of several possible locations for a receiver provides the least probable interference
6. Determine the source and cause of a known interference problem.
7. Determine the amount of suppression required to correct a specified interference situation
8. Obtain site survey or EMC environment type of information for a given location
9. Obtain site survey or EMC environment type of information for a given receiver or group of receivers
10. Determine propagation loss over a specified path
11. Obtain specific interference characteristic data on transmitters, receivers, or antennas contained on the equipment characteristic tape file
12. Provide information as to the adequacy of given specifications for an equipment
13. Provide information as to the best frequency band to use for a system which is being defined

The IPP-1 computer program consists of an executive program and the following major subroutines.

1. Problem Input
2. Data Acquisition
3. Equipment Catalog
4. Data Synthesis

5. Rapid Cull
6. Frequency Cull
7. Detailed Analysis
8. Propagation Loss
9. Power Density and Field Strength
10. Intermodulation Analysis
11. Frequency Band Analysis
12. Adjacent Signal Analysis
13. Frequency-Distance Separation Criteria

The major subroutines of IPP-1 are divided into preparatory and analysis subroutines. The preparatory subroutines include the problem input, data acquisition, equipment catalog and data synthesis subroutines, and the major purpose of these subroutines is to provide the data that is required to perform an analysis. The remaining subroutines are used to perform the various types of analysis that may be required.

The following problem illustrates how the IPP-1 could be used when installing a new transmitter into an existing equipment complex. An equipment complex of three radar receivers and one UHF receiver is assumed. The deployment of equipments within the site is shown in Fig. 10.8. The transmitter and the receivers are designated T-1 and R-1 through R-4 respectively and their characteristics are summarized in Table 10.2

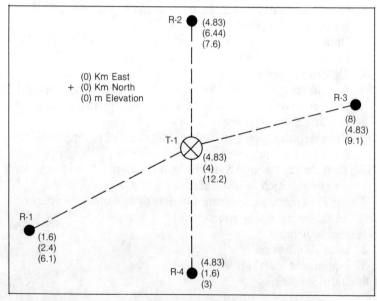

Figure 10.8—Coordinate System for Installing a Transmitter

Table 10.2—Equipment Characteristics

Characteristic	T-1	R-1	R-2	R-3	R-4
Frequency Band (MHz)	2,800	2,800-3,100	5,450-5,825	2,700-2,900	225-399
Tuned Frequency f_o (MHz)	2,800	2,830	5,600	2,740	275
Power or Sensitivity (dBm)	+ 97	– 100	– 100	– 102	– 92
Antenna Gain (dB)	35	39	33	32	7
Antenna Height (ft)	40	20	25	30	10
Antenna Bearing (°/North)	*	*	45	325	**
East Coordinate (Km)	4.83	1.6	4.83	8	4.83
North Coordinate (Km)	4	2.4	6.44	4.83	1.6
Spurious Characteristics $(f>f_o)$					
Slope (dB/Decade)	– 30	20	20	10	37
Intercept (dB above Nominal)	– 40	76	76	56	57
Standard Deviation (dB)	10	12	12	12	12

* Denotes Rotating Antenna
** Denotes Omnidirectional Antenna

Table 10.3 shows an example of the interference prediction results obtained from the computer for one of the transmitter-receiver pairs. For this sample problem, the potential sources of interference are summarized below. The fundamental output of the transmitter has the potential for interfering with the fundamental response of the R-1 receiver.[4]

10.4 Interference Prediction Model (IPM)

The interference prediction model (IPM) is used to perform an analysis and evaluation of EMC and the vulnerability of Army procedures, equipment and systems.[5] IPM consists of a set of inter-related computer routines programmed in FORTRAN IV for use at Fort Huachuca. Included in the IPM are data preparation, interference identification, scoring and output routines required to assess the EMC and vulnerability of CE systems or equipments in a large scale deployment. An overall block diagram of the major routines of IPM is presented in Fig. 10.9. Figure 10.9 indicates that IPM consists of five sections which are (1) IPM input, (2) data preparation, (3) interference identification, (4) scoring and (5) IPM output.

The input section of IPM consists of inputs for a specific problem as well as the various data catalogs and files that are required to perform an analysis. Included are: (1) propagation and terrain statistics, (2) antenna statistics, (3) spectrum signature data, (4) net value source file, (5) categories for system effectiveness, (6) equipment class file, (7) general antenna data and (8) scoring data.

The data preparation section provides a method for performing certain preliminary calculations on some of the input data to generate new data in a form that is acceptable and consistent with other sections of IPM. Additionally, samples of links and equipments to be evaluated are selected, and some of the data is restricted or eliminated.

Table 10.3—Computer Printout of Results

Transmitter Security Classification

Transmitter Nomenclature

Transmitting Antenna Security Classification

Transmitting Antenna Nomenclature

Transmitter Coordinates
Vertical (Km) 4.0225   Horizontal (Km) 4.8270

Transmitter Fundamental Frequency (MHz) — Data Source

Transmitter Mode

Power Output (dBm) — Data Source

Receiver Security Classification

Receiver Nomenclature

Receiving Antenna Security Classification

Receiving Antenna Nomenclature

Receiver Coordinates
Vertical (Km) 4.8270   Horizontal (Km) 8.0450

Receiver Tuned Frequency (MHz) — Data Source

Receiving Mode

Nominal Gain (dB)

Sensitivity (dBm) — Data Source

Nomenclatures
Transmitter T – 1   Receiver R – 3   Transmitter Harmonic Number 1

Frequency (MHz) 2,800,000

Separation Distance (Km) 3.218

Receiver Response 1.   – 1.

Antenna   Transmitter Rotating   Receiver Fixed

Distance Region Far Field

Nominal Gain (dB)

	Mainbeam to Mainbeam	Mainbeam Rec. to Side Lobe Transmission	Mainbeam Transmission to Side Lobe Rect.	Side Lobe Transmission To Side Lobe Rec.
Probability of Interference (Percent)	0.	0.	95.	0.
Median Interference Margin (dB)	0.	0.	23.	0.
Standard Deviation (dB) Time Dependent	0.	0.	15.	0.
Standard Deviation (dB)	0.	0.	0.	0.

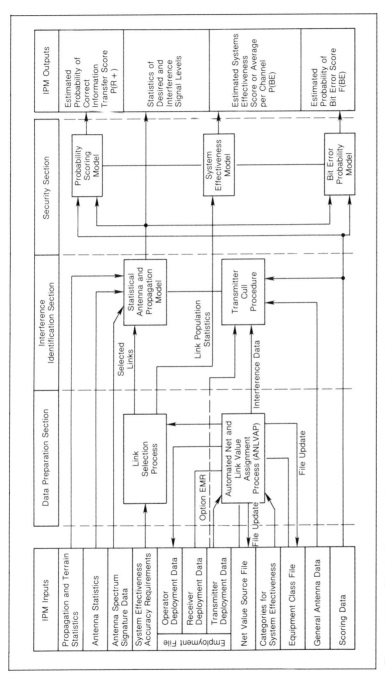

Figure 10.9—Block Diagram of Interference Prediction Model

The interference identification section analysis eliminates all transmitting equipments which cannot possibly cause interference with selected test links, and it calculates statistics of desired and interference signal levels for those transmitters that remain after the analysis. These statistical results can either be used as inputs to the scoring section or as direct outputs of IPM. The scoring section consists of the following: the probability scoring model which provides an estimated probability $P(R+)$ of correct information transfer, the bit error probability model which provides a capability for evaluating digital communication links and the system effectiveness model (which can either be used with the probability scoring model or the bit error probability model) to provide a system effectiveness score. The outputs of IPM include desired and interfering signal statistics, probability of correct information transfer, bit-error score and system effectiveness score.

10.5 IEMCAP

The Intrasystem Electromagnetic Compatibility Analysis Program (IEMCAP) is a system level, computerized analysis program which may be used in analyzing EMC for aircraft, spacecraft or ground stations on both present and future systems. The IEMCAP was developed for the Air Force Rome Air Development Center and it provides a needed tool for establishing and maintaining cost-effective interference control throughout the lifetime of a weapon system. IEMCAP is a link between equipment and subsystem EMC performance and total system EMC characteristics. It provides the means for tailoring EMC requirements to the specific system, whether it be a ground, air or space/missile system. This is accomplished in IEMCAP by detailed modeling of the system elements and the various mechanisms of electromagnetic transfer to perform the following tasks:

1. Provide a data base which can be continually maintained and updated to follow system design changes
2. Generate EMC specification limits tailored to the specific system
3. Evaluate the impact of granting waivers to the tailored specifications
4. Survey a system for imcompatibilities
5. Assess the effect of design changes on system EMC
6. Provide comparative analysis results on which to base EMC tradeoff decisions

IEMCAP is designed to predict interference in a population of receptors due to a population of emitters. The basic medium for modeling signals is the frequency domain. Each emitter's emission characteristics are represented by its power output, tuned frequency, emission spectrum in the vicinity of the tuned frequency and spurious emission levels and frequencies. The model assumes that harmonic spurious output levels can be approximated by one or more straight line segments. Spurious output frequencies are determined by the user as harmonics of the tuned frequency or, when applicable, are generated by the computer code.

The receptor representation is similar to that of the emitter; a receptor's characteristics are represented by its sensitivity, tuned frequency, selectivity curve, spurious response levels and spurious frequencies. It is assumed that spurious response levels can be approximated by one or more straight lines. Spurious response frequencies are either generated by the code or determined by the user external to the program using available techniques, e.g., the superheterodyne conversion process.

The gains of low-gain antennas are determined by pre-programmed equations. Medium- and high-gain antennas are represented by multilevel patterns in which each level is specified by a gain and associated azimuth and elevation beam width.

Various models of coupling or transfer functions are included in the program. Single-tuned, transformer-coupled, Butterworth-tuned, low-pass, high-pass, band-pass and band-reject filter models are used. The filter transfer models calculate the "insertion loss" (in dB) provided by a filter at a given frequency, i.e., the reduction in delivered power because of insertion of a filter.

Two antenna-to-antenna propagation models are available. For ground systems, the propagation model is a simplified theoretical ground-wave model that assumes a smooth earth surface and a 4/3 earth radius that accounts for atmospheric refraction. An intravehicular propagation model calculates the propagation loss associated with an electromagnetic coupling path when both emitter and receptor are located on the same system. Power received is related to power transmitted, free space transmission (Friis equation) and a shading factor due to the presence of the vehicle whose bulk may be interposed in the region between the emitter and receptor.

Environmental electromagnetic field interaction with the system wiring is determined by the program. External fields enter a vehicle through dielectric apertures in the system's skin and couple onto wires immediately adjacent. The coupled RF energy is a function of the aperture size and location. A lumped parameter transmission line model is used to compute the currents induced in the wire loads. Artificial apertures are required for ground systems to determine certain field-to-wire conditions.

Coupling between wires in a common bundle includes capacitive coupling (due to the interwire capacitance) and inductive coupling (due to the mutual inductances between the wires). Total coupling is approximated by summing the capacitive and inductive coupling (computed separately). Relatively complex wire configurations can be accommodated, e.g., shielded (single or double shield), unshielded, twisted pair, balanced or unbalanced.

The equipment case model treats each case as though it were a dipole. The source model assumes a falloff of $1/R^3$, where R equals the distance between cases for both the electric and magnetic fields.

10.6 Specification and EMC Analysis Program (SEMCAP)

TRW's SEMCAP computer program performs an EMC analysis between modeled generator and receptor circuits for various means of interference transfer. The program calculates the spectrum of generator circuits and transfers the energy via a transfer function to the receptor terminals. Received energy is compared with the receptor circuit threshold to determine compatibility. Contributions of each generator are added to determine whether the receptor is compatible with the sum of generator sources modeled. Generator types consist of single frequency (CW), trapezoidal pulse train, ramp step, trapezoidal single pulse and spectral density voltage or current generators. Filter types may be low-, high- or band-pass. Transfer functions may be mutual inductance, mutual capacitance, electric-field or magnetic-field coupling. Receptor field response types are E-field antenna and wire, H-field antenna and wire and wire only.[6]

In addition to performing EMC analysis, the program also can generate a set of specification limits for each type of interference transfer mechanism and perform a waiver analysis based on sub-system EMC test data. Only linear cases are considered and thus spurious responses, intermodulation, etc., are not specifically accounted for. The program performs a power analysis and is not necessarily applicable for determining degradation with modulated signals.

SEMCAP is similar in many respects to IEMCAP. Both programs divide the system into a generator or emitter of energy, a transfer or coupling function which alters the emitted energy spectrum to account for the transmission medium and a receptor response or susceptibility function. Although both SEMCAP and IEMCAP use similar models for emitters, transfer functions and receptors, the programs use different systems equations for describing the interaction of these basic elements. The SEMCAP systems' equations appear appropriate for transient or impulsive signals and threshold type devices, whereas the IEMCAP systems equations appear more suitable for continuous signals and devices that respond to average power.

10.7 Computer-Assisted Frequency Assignment[7]

Frequency congestion in the common carrier and operational fixed microwave bands has long been a fact of life that applicants for new authorizations have had to face. Several companies have developed extensive data bases and computer programs for selecting interference-free frequencies in these bands either for their own use, or for sale as a service to others. Until recently, however, little difficulty has been experienced in selecting frequencies in the television auxiliary broadcast bands because of their relative lack of congestion. There are four such bands at 1,990 to 2,110, 2,450 to 2,500, 7,875 to 7,125 and 12,700 to 13,250 MHz. They are used for television studio-to-transmitter links (STLs), television inter-city relays, television translator relays and mobile television pickups. The relative congestion in these bands and other microwave bands is compared in Table 10.4.

As is apparent from Table 10.4, the 6,875 to 7,125 MHz band is the most popular of the television auxiliary broadcast bands. The bandwidth permitted is greater than in the 1,990 to 2,110 MHz band, and it is affected less by precipitation attenuation than the

12,700 to 13,250 MHz band. However, this popularity has made it increasingly difficult to select interference-free frequencies for new systems in some areas of the United States, and the systematic EMI prediction approach may be used to perform what would otherwise be a tedious job of manually plotting and analyzing a large number of existing microwave stations for possible lack of compatibility with planned new facilities.

Table 10.4—Comparison of Microwave Channel Use

Band (MHz)	Service	Allowable Channel Bandwidth (MHz)	Number of Channels Derived[1]	Number of Authorizations[2]	Authorizations per Channel
6,875—7,125	TV Auxiliary Broadcast[3]	25	10	2,050	205
1,990—2,110	TV Auxiliary Broadcast[3]	17	7	510	73
12,700—13,250	TV Auxiliary Broadcast[3]	25	22	310	14
3,700—4,200	Common Carrier	30	17	16,620	978
5,925—6,425	Common Carrier	30	17	11,820	695
6,575—6,875	Operational Fixed[4]	10	30	7,310	244
12,200—12,700	Operational Fixed[4]	20	25	490	196

1　Maximum bandwidth, nonoverlapping
2　Estimated from FCC Frequency List dated 8/7/70
3　Includes TV Pickup, TV STL, TV Intercity Relay and TV Translator Relay
4　Includes Public Safety and Industrial Services

The approach taken in developing the EMC Analysis and Frequency Assignment Program is to first identify from the list of existing frequency assignments those transmitters and receivers that fall within certain criteria of frequency, antenna orientation and distance with respect to a proposed station. Each potentially interfering transmitter and its associated receiver are assumed to deny the use of a band of frequencies about their assigned frequency. Frequencies not denied are therefore available for assignment to proposed transmitter-receiver pairs.

The proposed transmitter-receiver pair which has the smallest number of available frequencies is the first to be considered in the frequency assignment routine. An assignment is made and the frequency is checked against the remaining proposed sites to determine compatibility. Available frequencies for remaining sites are updated using the same criteria used in evaluating the existing assignments. After the available frequencies are updated, an assignment is made for the remaining transmitter-receiver pair which has the smallest number of available frequencies, and the process is repeated.

10.8 Method of Moments Programs

The method of moments formulation (MOM) may be used to solve a number of complex electromagnetic radiation problems. Two well-known programs that make use of the MOM formulation are the generalized electromagnetic code for the analysis of complex systems (GEMACS) and the numerical electromagnetic code (NEC). The GEMACS code is described in the following paragraphs.

GEMACS supports all of the functions necessary for using a thin-wire MOM formulation. The GEMACS code uses a solution method for linear simultaneous equations called banded matrix iteration (BMI). The user must have a limited understanding of the solution method to ensure convergence and reasonable efficiency.

The GEMACS code includes a geometry processor to aid the user in reducing the physical problem to a thin-wire model. The user specifies the frequency, additional features (such as loading or the presence of a ground plane) and the excitation. Excitation options include plane or spherical waves, voltage sources for antennas or arbitrary excitations on specified individual wire segments. Load options currently include fixed (as a function of frequency) lumped parameter loads, series or parallel RLC networks and finite segment conductivity.

The code generates a set of linear simultaneous equations from the information provided. The user controls the process by which the equations are solved. If the total number of wire segments in the model is small enough, standard solution methods are applicable. Solution by full matrix triangular decomposition is one of the least expensive general methods and is supported by

GEMACS. For large problems this method is too expensive, and the BMI solution method should be specified by the user.

The user specifies other quantities to be computed from the wire currents such as impedances, coupling parameters and near fields or far fields. These are computed from currents regardless of the solution process specified. Regardless of the solution technique exercised, the user must be familiar with general results from the literature so that the computed solution using the model for the system is accurate enough for the intended purposes.

10.9 Geometric Theory of Diffraction Programs

The geometric theory of diffraction (GTD) is a procedure for including the effects of waves diffracted from edges or around curved surfaces in an electromagnetic scattering or radiation problem. Several computer programs have been developed, and the theory of GTD has been successfully applied to a wide variety of high-frequency radiation and scattering problems. The use of GTD is justified by the excellent agreement between GTD analyses and scale model experiments regarding radiation patterns of aircraft antennas.

The AAPG computer program is based on the GTD. The aircraft is represented by cylindrical, conical and planar surfaces as illustrated in Fig. 10.10, and the program uses interactive computer graphics to assist the engineer in the prediction and display of antenna-to-antenna-coupled EMI on an aircraft or missile. Such EMI is a function of two components. The first is governed by the electronic equipment characteristics. The second component, and the one on which AAPG concentrates, is given by the losses incurred along the coupling path between the transmitting and receiving antennas. AAPG is primarily an antenna-to-antenna-coupling model.

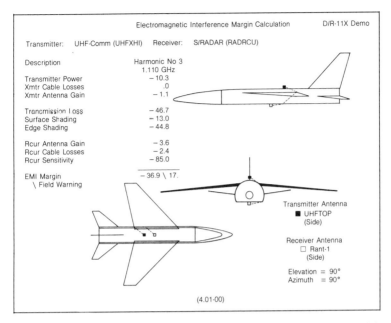

Figure 10.10—EMI Margin and Coupling Path as Generated by the AAPG Model

10.10 Propagation Programs

There are many radiowave propagation computer programs that may be used for EMC analysis. These models cover the electromagnetic spectrum from very low frequencies (VLF) to electro-optic frequencies and may be used to predict various link performance parameters such as basic transmission loss, power density and E-field strength. Several general-use tropospheric and ionospheric propagation models are available as well as a large number of special-purpose models. The reader is referred to the bibliography at the end of this book for references to specific propagation programs.

The general-use tropospheric models include both smooth-earth and irregular-terrain models. Smooth-earth models can be used to predict basic transmission loss over a smooth, spherical, imperfectly conducting earth. These models cover the frequency band from 10 kHz to 20 GHz. They consider groundwave, diffraction and tropospheric scatter modes of propagation and treat the effects of refraction in an exponential atmosphere. The rough earth mode can be used to predict path loss in the 40 MHz to 20 GHz band over specific terrain profiles. These terrain profiles may be entered manually or may be automatically extracted from a digitized topographic data base.

A number of models are available for predicting ionospheric propagation. VLF/LF models can be used to predict path loss in the 10 to 100 kHz band where the ionospheric D-region acts as a waveguide. Both groundwave and skywave modes are considered. The performance of HF skywave links can be predicted by the IONCAP model. These models can predict pertinent HF propagation parameters such as maximum usable frequency (MUF), lowest usable frequency (LUF), frequency of optimum traffic (FOT), signal-to-noise ratio (S/N), path reliability and service probability.

Special-purpose propagation models provide the capability to calculate earth-space coupling between terrestrial and earth-space microwave links, coupling between antennas on an aircraft, tropospheric ducting and foliage attenuation.

10.11 Nonlinear Circuit Analysis Program (NCAP)

The Nonlinear Circuit Analysis Program (NCAP) allows determination of the nonlinear transfer functions of an electronic circuit. NCAP uses standard circuit elements and can analyze interconnecting networks of these elements.

NCAP is written in FORTRAN IV, has been implemented on the Honeywell 6180 and can directly analyze networks containing up to 500 nodes. NCAP has a free-field format for input data to allow the user to build device models in addition to the several stored models in a user-oriented format.

NCAP solves the nonlinear network problem by forming both the nodal admittance matrix (Y matrix) for the entire network, and the first-order generator (current-source) excitation vector for all of the linear sources in the network. The generators can be located at any node in the network and can have any desired frequency, amplitude, and phase. The usual procedure of premultiplying the generator vector by the inverse Y-matrix results in the first-order nodal voltage vector for the network, the elements of which are the first-order transfer functions at all nodes in the network at the given excitation frequency. In the event that there is more than one generator at a given frequency, the first-order transfer function (which is linear) is the total transfer function because of the superposition of the generators. The higher-order transfer functions are solved iteratively.

10.12 References

1. "Analytical Services and Data Available from the Electromagnetic Compatibility Analysis Center (EMC Services)," ECAC-DAS-1-69, March 1969.
2. "ECAC, A Guide to Capabilities and Services," ECAC, 1985.
3. Duff, W.G.; Heisler, K.G.; and Hewitt, H.J., "An Automated EMC Analysis Process," 1969 IEEE International Conference on Communications, IEEE, 69C29-COM.
4. "Prediction Routine Studies Volume I—Sample Problems and Frequency Band Analysis," RADC-TR-68-345, December 1968.
5. Wall, R.A. and Hutchinson, G.K, "An Interference Prediction Model," *IEEE Transactions on EMC*, EMC-8, No. 3, September 1966, pp. 130-342.
6. Johnson, W.R. and Spagon, J.A., "Systems Approach to Achieving Intrasystem EMC Utilizing Computer Techniques," TRW Report No. 11176-E245-RO-OO. TRW Systems Group, September 1970.
7. Turnage, H.C. and Ferrante, F.E., "Computer Assisted Frequency Selection in the Auxiliary Broadcast Band," *IEEE Transactions on Broadcasting*, Volume BC-17, No. 4, December 1971.

10.13 Bibliography

1. Atlantic Research Corp., "Electromagnetic Compatibility Prediction and Analysis Computer Program Documentation," AF 30(602)-3858, 1967.

2. Dimarzio, A.W., "EMI Data Reduction, Prediction and Analysis Using Time-Shared Computers," *1968 IEEE International EMC Symposium Record*, p. 38 (New York: IEEE 1968).

3. Duff, W.G., et. al., "A Second Generation Intrasystem Analysis Program," *1979 IEEE EMC Symposium Record* (New York: IEEE, 1979).

4. Duff, W.G., et. al., "A System Data File and Handler for the Electromagnetic Compatibility/Intrasystem Analysis Program," *1979 IEEE EMC Symposium Record* (New York: IEEE, 1979).

5. Duff, W.G., and Hewitt, H.J., "An Automated Interference Analysis Process," *1969 International Communications Conference Record*, June 1969.

6. Duff, W.G., et. al., "Intrasystem Electromagnetic Compatibility Analysis Program," *1976 IEEE EMC Symposium Record* (New York: IEEE, 1976).

7. "Intrasystem Electromagnetic Compatibility Analysis Program (IEMCAP) F-15 Validation—Validation and Sensitivity Study," RADC-TR-77-290, Part I (of 2), Final Technical Report, September 1977.

8. "Intrasystem Electromagnetic Compatibility Analysis Program, Volumes I-IV," RADC-TR-74-342, December 1974.

9. Kimball, H.G., "EMC Engineering Analysis Modeling at ECAC, a Status Report," *1970 IEEE International EMC Symposium Record*, p. 154 (New York: IEEE, 1970).

10. Lustgarten, M.N., and Mayher, R.J., "ECAC Technique Computes EMC Performance of UHF AM Communications System," *Communications Designer's Digest*, IITRI Electromagnetic Compatibility Analysis Center, Vol. 3, No. 7, pp. 12-14, July 1969.

11. Morgan, G., "Interference Prediction Guidelines for VHF Non-Tactical FM Communications," Electromagnetic Compatibility Analysis Center, Annapolis, MD, ESD-TR-70-130, p. 47, May 1970.

12. Scott, P.O., "Computer Preparation of a Frequency Assignment Plan VHF Air-Ground Communication Channels," Royal Aircraft Establishment, Farmborough, England, RAE-TR-69064, April 1969, p. 57.

13. Scott, J.B., "A Computer Approach to the Interference Prediction Model of the Electromagnetic Environmental Test Facility," *Seventh Tri-Service Conference Record*, 1961, p. 833.

14. Siegel, M.D., "Aircraft Antenna-Coupled Interference Analysis," *1969 IEEE EMC Symposium Record*, pp. 85-90 (New York: IEEE, 1969).

15. Thomas, A.K., "Math Modeling Techniques for Computerized EMC Analysis," *1968 IEEE International EMC Symposium Record*, p. 236 (New York: IEEE, 1968).

16. Turnage, H.C., and Ferrante, F.E., "Computer-Associated Frequency Selection in the Auxiliary Broadcast Band," *IEEE Transactions on Broadcasting*, Vol. BC-17, No. 14, December 1971, pp. 99-105.

17. Williams, J., and Tremper, P., "Freavy-A Frequency Availability Computer Program," FCC, Washington, DC, FCC-6901, May 1969, p. 196.

Other Books Published by ICT

1. Carstensen, Russell V., *EMI Control in Boats and Ships*, 1979.
2. Denny, Hugh W., *Grounding for Control of EMI*, 1983.
3. Duff, Dr. William G., *A Handbook on Mobile Communications*, 1980.
4. Duff, Dr. William G. and White, Donald R.J., Volume 5, *Electromagnetic Interference Prediction & Analysis Techniques*, 1972.
5. Feher, Dr. Kamilo, *Digital Modulation Techniques in an Interference Environment*, 1977.
6. Gabrielson, Bruce C., *The Aerospace Engineer's Handbook of Lightning Protection*, 1987.
7. Gard, Michael F., *Electromagnetic Interference Control in Medical Electronics*, 1979.
8. Georgopoulos, Dr. Chris J., *Fiber Optics and Optical Isolators*, 1982.
9. Georgopoulos, Dr. Chris J., *Interference Control in Cable and Device Interfaces*, 1987.
10. Ghose, Rabindra N., *EMP Environment and System Hardness Design*, 1983.
11. Hart, William C. and Malone, Edgar W., *Lightning and Lightning Protection*, 1979.
12. Herman, John R., *Electromagnetic Ambients and Man-Made Noise*, 1979.
13. Hill, James S. and White, Donald R.J., Volume 6, *Electromagnetic Interference Specifications, Standards & Regulations*, 1975.
14. Jansky, Donald M., *Spectrum Management Techniques*, 1977.
15. Mardiguian, Michel, *Interference Control in Computers and Microprocessor-Based Equipment*, 1984.
16. Mardiguian, Michel, *Electrostatic Discharge—Understand, Simulate and Fix ESD Problems*, 1985.
17. Mardiguian, Michel, *How to Control Electrical Noise*, 1983.
18. Smith, Albert A., *Coupling of External Electromagnetic Fields to Transmission Lines*, 1986.
19. White, Donald R.J., *A Handbook on Electromagnetic Shielding Materials and Performance*, 1980.
20. White, Donald R.J., *Electrical Filters—Synthesis, Design & Applications*, 1980.
21. White, Donald R.J., *EMI Control in the Design of Printed Circuit Boards and Backplanes*, 1982. (Also available in French.)
22. White, Donald R.J. and Mardiguian, Michel, *EMI Control Methodology & Procedures*, 1982.
23. White, Donald R.J., Volume 1, *Electrical Noise and EMI Specifications*, 1971.
24. White, Donald R.J., Volume 2, *Electromagnetic Interference Test Methods and Procedures*, 1980.
25. White, Donald, R.J., Volume 3, *Electromagnetic Interference Control Methods & Techniques*, 1973.
26. White, Donald R.J., Volume 4, *Electromagnetic Interference Test Instrumentation Systems*, 1980.
27. Duff, William G., and White, Donald R.J., Volume 5, *Prediction and Analysis Techniques*, 1970.
28. White, Donald R.J., Volume 6, *EMI Specifications, Standards and Regulations*, 1973.
29. White, Donald R.J., *Shielding Design Methodology and Procedures*, 1986.
30. *EMC Technology 1982 Anthology*
31. *EMC EXPO Records 1986, 1987, 1988*

Index

I.1

Index

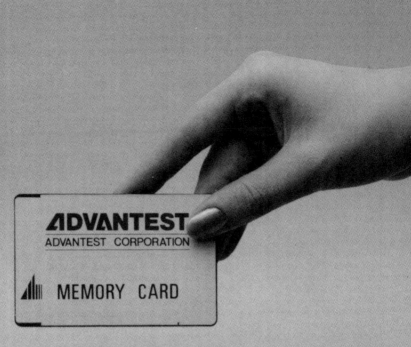

One Card for EMI Measurements

Photo : R2542B EMI Receiver System, connected to R3261/3361 Series Spectrum Analyzer with R3551 Preselector Antenna, and Plotter.

The R3261/3361 Series Spectrum Analyzers are ideally suited for RF signal analysis and offer superior functions and capabilities for EMI measurements.

Featuring the unique Advantest quasi-peak detection scheme, these analyzers offer a full 70dB dynamic range.

The IC memory card function simplifies operation and reduces the time required for routine measurements.

Difficult tasks are made easy by taking full advantage of the IC memory card and instrument controller. Using these two powerful features together allows the user to:

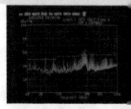

- ● Enter antenna correction factors
- ● Display measurements in a log/log format
- ● Display limit lines for FCC, VDE and VCCI standards
- ● Add the R3551 preselector f additional sensitivity, selectivity and protection from noise

/IDVANTEST®

Advantest America, Inc.	300 Knightsbridge Parkway, Lincolnshire, IL 60069, U.S.A.	Phone:(708)634-2552 Facsimile:(708)634-26
Advantest UK Limited	CI Tower, St. Georges Square, High Street, New Malden, Surrey, KT3 4HH, U.K.	Phone:(01)336-1606 Facsimile:(01)336-1657